The Birthday

Mrs Pápai arrived at the meeting right on time. The gentlemen were fifteen minutes late, for which they humbly and repeatedly apologized before greeting Mrs Pápai with a bouquet of flowers on the occasion of her sixtieth birthday. All of this occurred on Batthyány Square. The gentlemen were still apologizing when Mrs Pápai, with a flick of her hand, brushed aside any further protestation, and with a disarming smile, an unmistakable accent and a melodic voice, which together accentuated the charm of her pronouncement, said among the swirling snowflakes (which, by the way, the report neglected to mention): 'May this be the biggest problem, gentlemen.' True, she in fact addressed the gentlemen as 'comrades'. But in the interests of the solemnity this story merits, let us stick with 'gentlemen', which is, after all, more in keeping with the compliments the men extended alongside the lovely bouquet.

3

The formalities over, the little coterie, as agreed in advance, headed off along the edge of the square towards the patisserie situated beside or behind (depending on perspective) the twin-spired church and *below* the square, in the basement, evoking the time before the great floods, when the basement was at street-level. On hearing Mrs Pápai's tinkling laughter, even the river's grey spume seemed to cheer up momentarily – yes, even Hokusai might have envied the slanted curtain of huge snowflakes falling on the grey-silver water of the Danube. At that very moment, Tram 19 embarked on its journey along the river towards the Chain Bridge from its terminus behind the concrete cube of the subway station, its ear-piercing rattle drowning out Mrs Pápai's laughter.[1]

Not that Mrs Pápai cut such a strikingly elegant figure, with a colourful winter cap knitted from thick wool pulled down over her forehead and a rather plain-looking, beige winter coat – the product of the Red October Clothes Factory – that wasn't quite the latest model either. She wore a simple pair of flat-bottomed shoes; her sole item of jewellery consisted of her glittering emerald-green eyes, twinkling

---

[1] I report that on 3 December 1982 I met at the Angelika Patisserie with SC CN MRS PÁPAI. Also participating at the meeting were Police Lt. Col. János Szakadáti and Comrade Police Lt. Col. Miklós Beider.

We arrived at the meeting ten minutes late. MRS PÁPAI was waiting for us on Batthyány Square. After introducing myself I heartily congratulated her on the occasion of her 60th birthday, and then I accompanied our good wishes with our gift, a folk-embroidered tablecloth, which she liked very much, and a bouquet of flowers.

with speckles of grey and blue. As if she deliberately hadn't bothered with her looks. 'Ach! It's not how you look, gentlemen, not what you wear that makes a man!' she would have said, had she been asked. In fact, her unobtrusive appearance was well suited to the occasion. Certainly, Mrs Pápai hadn't told the gentlemen that today was her birthday, taking pains to let everyone around her know 'not to make a fuss': she didn't care for ceremonies, for needless celebrations. 'Oh dear, there are much, much more important things than this in the world! People starving, people without shoes, people dropping dead all over in diseases and wars.'

And yet a bit of uncertainty did float around Mrs Pápai's date of birth, though the three gentlemen couldn't have known this. From time to time her birthday fell on the first day of a famous moveable feast, and in her childhood, her family – which back then was still at times strictly observant – celebrated Mrs Pápai's birthday on this *double* holiday, sometimes for days on end, depending on the mood at home, for the lighting of candles, as is well known, lasts for eight days, and Mrs Pápai's parents, yielding to their bohemian, artistic inclinations, sometimes departed from the original, prosaic date; for the little girl's arrival, which in fact fell on 3 December, brought them just as much joy as the famous holiday itself. And it was because of the moveable feast that Mrs Pápai's mother – whose memory was by no means infallible, and who was famously coquettish and of a passionate nature – sometimes gave the wrong date when asked for it in colonial and other offices, of which, because of the dual administration, there were irksomely many, needlessly rendering the lives of immigrants that much more difficult. Yes, on the spur of the moment all she could recall was that her daughter's birthday was at the time of Hanukkah, and this presumably explains why, in various documents, Mrs Pápai's birthday is listed by turns as one of several days – 1 December, 2 December, 3 December, and, in one instance, even 6 December! This was enough to justify, for Mrs Pápai, given her professed nonreligious frame of mind, the indifference, even antipathy, she felt towards her own birthday.

But the gentlemen could have known none of this.

So Mrs Pápai descended the short but steep flight of steps to the Angelika Patisserie, escorted by the three gentlemen, Police Lieutenant Colonel Miklós Beider (renderer) and Police Lieutenant Dr József Dóra (receiver), not to mention Police Lieutenant Colonel János Szakadáti (sub-department head).[2]

---

[2] DECISION

I have hereby rendered dossier no. 2959, B-1, M-1, under code-name MRS PÁPAI and the handling of the agent thereof named (place of birth, birthdate, mother's name) for further review of employment as a network individual to Comrade József DÓRA (precise authorizing agency: III/I-3), and received said assets from Comrade Rudolf Rónai.

Budapest, on this . . . day of October 1982.

Rudolf Rónai
renderer

József Dóra
receiver

That this did not resemble a prima donna's entry onto the stage was thanks solely to the fact that two of them, Dóra and Szakadáti, in accordance with the rules of a conspiracy, lagged discreetly behind. But the surprises were not over yet. Having descended the steps, they were now sitting in a comfortable booth, though not before the three gentlemen had vied for the honour of helping Mrs Pápai to remove her winter coat, Miklós proving the most deft. As soon as the coat came off Mrs Pápai's shoulders the three gentlemen took in for a moment the bygone beauty of the no longer young, not so tall woman before them. It was conjured up by the shapely hips and full bosom whose loveliness had been revealed in its entirety by seaside photos – photos that, by the way, were unknown to these gentlemen – especially in those taken in the after-glow of sunset, which only enhanced her magnificent twilight silhouette and the profile of her radiant face, whose beauty stemmed as much from its exquisite proportions as from Mrs Pápai's unconditional love of life and cheerful character.

That these exotic pictures had been taken in the course of conspiratorial rendezvous of a different sort would surely have piqued the three gentlemen's imaginations, had their provenance come up, but the conversation did not touch on what had happened in those bays hidden in the shadows of the cedars of Lebanon, where ladies and gentlemen of diverse nationalities and religions had swum and flirted;

had had their pictures taken in the company of donkeys, waterfalls and the Mediterranean Sea; and had discussed the most important tasks of the local Party organization while the world war raged to their north.

So, once all four had gathered in the Angelika on this day, taken their seats in the booth, and had a chance to look over the menu, the three gentlemen said 'espresso' to the server in unison, while Mrs Pápai ordered an Earl Grey tea, which back then counted as the height of luxury. However, citing her full waist, she declined a pastry, despite the encouragement of the senior of the gentlemen, Miklós, in his warm baritone voice: 'The French cream-cake here is simply exceptional, sensational,' he declared. 'My grandson can eat two in one sitting, and that's not to mention the poppy-seed-filled—'

'*Flodni*, ah … That's some sort of Jewish thing, right?' Comrade Szakadáti blurted out before falling silent on noticing Miklós's and József's disapproving stares. Miklós, who had known Mrs Pápai the longest, continued to praise the pastry wonders of the Angelika – which, he insisted, were famous in distant lands – until Mrs Pápai, after prolonged hesitation, finally let herself be talked into consuming a cream puff. The resulting war between the tiny fork and the cream puff left fine dabs of cream at the edges of Mrs Pápai's lips, which she licked off while laughing heartily, occasioning numerous droll remarks from the gentlemen.

As for the gentlemen, even if they did desire something sweet, they were acutely aware of the meeting's budgetary implications,[3] and while the office had granted them free rein, they knew that a bit of self-control never hurt. Before the cream puff even arrived, József, who was about to cause Mrs Pápai immense delight, chose a moment of silence – a moment of the sort that often occurs in such cosy settings, when everyone senses, after the meaningless generalities are done with, that it is now high time to get down to business – to produce from his suitcase a splendid folk-embroidered tablecloth[4] wrapped in tissue paper and tied with a pink ribbon. In unison all three gentlemen – Miklós, János and József – once again wished Mrs Pápai a happy sixtieth birthday, for, as previously noted, this day of rendering and receiving was, it so happened, precisely that.

And yet the conversation, to the great dismay of the three gentlemen, did not go according to plan. This was due not

---

[3]   The meeting cost 386 forints.

[4]   RECOMMENDATION
Budapest, 1 December 1982

Secret colleague MRS PÁPAI celebrates her 60th birthday on 3 December 1982.

Since 1976 she has been in an operative relationship with the III/I Directorate, and during this time has in multiple instances provided valuable information about the Israeli agent and operative situation, as well as the endeavours of the Zionist movement. She brought us original materials concerning the 29th World Zionist Congress, and we plan to send her with operative purpose to the 30th World Zionist Congress.

In light of her work to date, on the occasion of her 60th birthday I recommend conferring on MRS PÁPAI a gift in the value of 1,000 forints.

Dr József Dóra, Police Lt.

9

only to the somersaulting of the upper part of the cream puff over the marble table and the smear of cream on the edge of Mrs Pápai's lip, to which József (in his capacity as the receiver), after a moment's hesitation, boldly called the comradina's attention. No, it had more to do with something Mrs Pápai blurted out after her interlocutors had detailed the rather complex tasks she was to be assigned; after she had repeated them word for word, reassuringly, like a star pupil,[5] having taken no notes, thus proving her exceptional memory, which the torrent of rich detail in her earlier reports also bore witness to; after Miklós had 'rendered' Mrs Pápai to József; and after Miklós, being the ranking officer, had waved to the waitress to bring the bill and had even produced his fat wallet. At that moment Mrs Pápai, in a sharp, piercing voice resembling the call to prayer sung by a muezzin from a minaret, and at which all three comrades pricked up their ears, suddenly announced, 'I think it not worth me doing this longer. No, no longer must I do this.' The air around the table froze as Mrs Pápai added, more quietly but in the same sharp falsetto, 'And not at all because I do not agree with our common goals.'

[5] We continued the conversation with the matter of the trip to Jerusalem.

MRS PÁPAI said her relatives are urging her to visit and have said they will cover her expenses while there. But one problem arose: they would like her to stay at least two months.

Comrade Szakadáti asked MRS PÁPAI to try shortening the duration of her stay, because we would need relatively fresh materials. He recommended that she call her relatives by telephone and re-confirm their willingness to host her. To cover the expense of the call I gave MRS PÁPAI 500 forints in return for a receipt.

The three gentlemen sat there stone-faced. As the waitress approached with a cheerful smile and a not so modest bill in her hand, Miklós, police lieutenant colonel that he was, raised his right index finger into the air, stopping her in her tracks. At first he thought he'd ask the waitress to return shortly, but then, perceiving the turn the situation had taken with exquisitely honed instinct, he realized that doing so would simply draw attention to them, violating the unwritten rules of a conspiracy. So far, in the half-full Angelika on this early afternoon, the merry gang had fortunately raised no eyebrows. The neighbourhood's office workers, who were fond of dropping by for a coffee or a beer at midday or after a tiring day of work, were engrossed in their own conversations; and of course, in the corner, the requisite lovers were cuddling, busy staring into the deep reflections in each other's eyes.

Just then Comrade Beider, with the intuition of a much-decorated general, signalled to Mrs Pápai – with the single word 'Later!' hissed through clenched teeth – that having risked this advance she would now be well advised to retreat. It has to be said that Mrs Pápai got cold feet on seeing Miklós's hardened face, whose convivial glaze had melted away in an instant, and she could have sworn she heard the grinding of his teeth, too. As a good communist she understood at once that she mustn't say so much as a word, even if the bitter disquiet that had been whirling inside her, suffocating her since 1975,[6] was ready to erupt.

When the waitress finally left, Miklós looked at Mrs Pápai, as did János and József, with no little apprehension. 'I,' said Mrs Pápai, 'have so far fulfilled your not so easy at all requests more times than I can count in the service of People's Democracy. In doing so I have cast aside serious personal problems – and more than once I also made specific recommendations to you. And even when you replied to my recommendations with words like "wonderful", "thank you", "remarkable", "exquisite", "splendid", "superb", "*yofi*", no, not even then did anything happen, not a thing. And despite these words of yours praising recommendations of mine, or maybe because of them, these days you do not even look me up, as if I am gone from this world. Well, why should I think this work important if, when I say or recommend something, no one is interested in me? When they only pretend? But when they need something, why then, like that – *poof* – you expect me to get up and go. Among comrades I don't think this is, how to say, comradely. In conditions like this I don't see the meaning of my work, and the only reason I keep

[6] SUMMARY REPORT
Budapest, 1 November 1982

The SC CN MRS PÁPAI was recruited in 1975 by colleagues of the former Department III/I-4. In fact she had inherited the position from her husband, who had been in contact with the service since the 1950s but who presently has serious depression and has become unsuitable for carrying out his duty.

MRS PÁPAI was recruited on the basis of convictions and patriotism. Her political foundations are firm and she is a professed believer in our social system.

THE ACTS OF MY MOTHER

doing it anyway is because I trust that the change will bring an upswing in our common endeavours.'

When Mrs Pápai's outburst had ended, the three gentlemen sat there for a moment like scolded schoolboys. They weren't prepared for this sort of thing: recruited agents were not in the habit of telling off their handlers. Miklós, though, who'd seen a lot in his time, rose to the occasion. 'Dear Comrade Mrs Pápai,' he began diplomatically, 'lately in particular we've had a great deal to take care of, and if you've read the news carefully you'll be able to imagine how many problems and difficulties we face, and at a time like this it must be understandable that there are certain priorities—'

Mrs Pápai was not so easily appeased, however, and brazenly interrupted: 'When you ask me to translate articles I disagree with deeply – filthy reactionary articles that bring suffering to me when reading and that I then disagree with even more deeply – sometimes word-for-word translations that make my stomach sick, even more because my Hungarian is not so good, so I need help, but I get no help from no one except maybe my son only, but I can't rob his time all the time, and I don't want for him be dragged into this . . .'

The longer she talked and the angrier she became, the more it was that charming grammatical errors began to pepper her meandering speech, that consonants were misplaced and suffixes enjoyed unintended lives of their own.

13

For their part, the gentlemen were greatly entertained, and when Mrs Pápai apologized, explaining that drafting her reports at night by hand was sheer torture for her, Miklós interrupted: 'These grammatical errors, these minor stylistic missteps, dear Mrs Pápai, make your reports all the more credible. I can tell you that they make a refreshing change from the headache-inducing grey sea of words I have to wade through every day. I remember how exceptional your very first report was – a debut performance, so to speak – six years ago, when you travelled with your son to visit your family. It was a virtuoso performance, a beautiful piece of prose, a little gem, when you described how you returned to the port of Jaffa for your bags.[7] It wasn't me you wrote the report for, but Comrade Mercz made a point of coming to my office and reading it aloud, and even back then I noticed what a brilliant observer had written it, and, well, I haven't forgotten how touching it was when you wrote that the dock workers "flopped down on the bags in the ship's *stomach*" – not the

---

[7] Interesting that even with strict police checks the police did not oppose me bringing down my own bags myself after most people wait in line for the customs inspection for long time, but wait in vain for their bags to arrive. The dock workers, after bringing just small portion of bags, at 9 o'clock flopped down on the bags in the ship's stomach and began breakfasting. No one could get them to hurry loading out and to eat only after. I left the big hall on the quay and easily asked to return to the ship, and then brought my suitcases down myself. Others waited hours for the customs inspection to finish. The inspection was strict with some American young people who before did volunteer work at a Kibbutz and now returned for same purpose. Probably the police were looking for heroin, because the American young people were very thoroughly inspected, inside-out, yes, they needed to turn over everything they had. The customs inspection for me was quite supercifial, both entering and leaving the country. They did not even open my suitcases. Customs form is customary.

ship's belly, comrade, but its stomach! – and that "American young people were very thoroughly inspected, *inside-out*" – "inside-out"! – and that the inspection was "quite super*cifi*al". Well, I burst out laughing. It made my day.'

Mrs Pápai, knitting her brows, interrupted Miklós once more: 'But I, no matter how hard I do so, do what you ask, write the reports, translate the articles. And I do so urgently, putting all other things aside, and then I am a good comrade. But if I ask something, why then I'm a little mouse, the lowest *jook*, crawling in dust.'

'A *jook*?' Comrade Beider asked, perplexed.

'Cockroach,' Mrs Pápai snapped in reply. 'Now you want me to shorten my trip. Even if I do, for what gratitude? My warnings, you toss those in the rubbish. My ideas aren't worth damn.'

Police Lieutenant Colonel Miklós Beider now looked conspicuously at Police Lieutenant József Dóra, renderer to receiver – yes, here was his chance to prove that he was up to the task, that he possessed the requisite psychological sensitivity to handle, if not in fact guide, Mrs Pápai, whom in these moments all three men secretly admired all the more, for her passionate outburst had made her young again.

'Dear Comrade Mrs Pápai,' József said in a warm voice, 'my goal, and perhaps at this meeting of ours I have proved this with a thousand signs, is that trust be established between us once again. Trust that endures despite the occasional hitch. For our goal – the struggle for justice – we share in common.' Tactfully he alluded to the folk-embroidered tablecloth, which, even if he hadn't bought it using his own money, had not been an obligatory means of greasing the palm of a so-called 'secret colleague'. Comrade Dóra did not suspect for a moment that Mrs Pápai would in turn give the tablecloth away as a gift, while she was already thinking that it would be perfect for her relatives in Tel Aviv, whom she would see on this trip to be paid for by her employers, a trip whose objectives – and Mrs Pápai was well aware of this – were completely beyond her; for though she would do all she could, she hardly stood a chance of gaining admittance to the World Zionist Congress.

Truth be told, she was secretly happy about this, for every fibre of her being recoiled at the 'nationalist ranting' she would have to listen to there, and she would at least get to spend time with her loved ones, to whom the embroidered floral motifs from eastern Hungary's Great Plain would bring much pleasure. For her part, Mrs Pápai had no affinity for objects whatsoever, and at the first available opportunity would get rid of them; or if not – she wasn't one to throw things away – they would vanish into some nook or cranny. As far back as her childhood she'd learned from her mother that objects mustn't be fetishized – her mother who, even though the family was by no means rich, regularly invited children from the street into their home and made them hot cocoa with whipped cream, and more than once, on a whim, gave them something that belonged to her daughters, a pair of shoes perhaps or a dress. And if she noticed her children's faces sink into despair, she would give them an impromptu lecture on communism, which, she insisted, would before long shine its light upon humanity, and which they must be exemplars of. No, Mrs Pápai did not care for objects: her eyes had glimmered at the sight of that birthday gift, yes, but – *etiquette shmetiquette* – they did so only as she contemplated what a fine gift this gift would soon make.

Comrade Szakadáti had been squirming in his seat for a while now, wanting to make a contribution of his own. When Comrade Beider discreetly pressed his colleague's knee under the table, Comrade Szakadáti unwittingly misinterpreted it as a gesture of encouragement, whereas Comrade Beider had meant to signal that this drawn-out meeting should come to a close. But Szakadáti, perhaps because he'd kept what he had to say bottled up for too long as his colleagues conversed with Mrs Pápai by turns jovially and then like grim professors giving a student a viva, now burst like a balloon. With the vehemence born of blind devotion to a cause, he reminded Mrs Pápai of the warm, intimate atmosphere that had characterized their first meetings.

Here it should be noted that, at those early meetings, this then forty-two-year-old divorced man, who lived a solitary existence (notwithstanding the occasional, rather wretched fling), had been decidedly pleased when Mrs Pápai had begged his pardon, explaining that when possible she addressed everyone with the informal 'you'. True, Szakadáti had to prohibit this, whereupon the two of them returned to addressing each other in more formal terms, though that, too, had its own erotic edge; for back then, and for a while yet to come, Comrade Szakadáti, an aficionado of older women – notwithstanding that every regulation strictly prohibited such liaisons – playfully held out hope of a somewhat more intimate relationship.

Now, aware that their meetings would be rarer or else end completely – for Comrade Dóra was to assume the handling of Mrs Pápai from Comrade Beider, and the processing of her materials would be solely in the purview of Comrade Dóra – Szakadáti was forlorn. Not that he could complain that he didn't have enough work: he was responsible for the whole of the Middle East, after all, even though he knew neither Arabic nor Hebrew, and his knowledge of English was pretty scant, too, even if he had passed the language test before an obviously good-natured committee. In short, his professional burdens were many, especially in these troubled times. And yet the same yearning trembled through his voice, even now, barely stifled, as he reminded Mrs Pápai of her ability to bewitch, of how adept she was at insinuating herself into the favour of others; and as he reminded her, moreover, of those perspectives which their common labour – the struggle against international Zionism – would open up before them in the not too distant future. What is more, and exaggerating somewhat, he added that Mrs Pápai's work was of inestimable worth to the People's Democracy, in light of her rare fluency in foreign languages and her adventurous spirit. Why, he even let slip that high-ranking Soviet comrades had praised the materials he and his colleagues had prepared from Mrs Pápai's summaries – but by now Beider didn't stop at a tactful bit of pressure on his comrade's knee but (while smiling at Mrs Pápai) kicked Szakadáti square on the ankle.

'*Rabota* calls!' Miklós announced apologetically, glancing pointedly at his watch as he got up. But it wasn't because of the *rabota*, the work, they had to do that he rose from the table so suddenly. In fact, he'd been struck with terror at that very moment on noticing that a notoriously opposition-oriented writer who'd achieved distinction even in the West had just stepped into the Angelika with a beautiful young woman. And, as he knew from the reports that regularly crossed his desk – reports that concerned Mrs Pápai's trustworthiness, not exactly questioning it but, let's say, keeping an eye on it – Mrs Pápai's children were on very friendly terms with certain circles of Budapest's intelligentsia. Miklós was terrified that Mrs Pápai, too, would recognize the writer in question. He had to keep them from greeting each other at any cost. He cursed himself for having chosen the Angelika, which, as he'd also read in no few reports, was among this writer's favoured venues for romantic rendezvous, since his flat was close by. And so Miklós sprang up from the table like a soldier standing to attention, gazing fixedly at his watch. What an entertaining spectacle these three beaux made, rising from the table at precisely the same instant, like robots, glancing at their watches. It was ten past four.[8]

Mrs Pápai – having tied her silk scarf around her neck and buttoned her coat all the way up as she stepped out into the gently falling snow, her knitted cap pulled down tight over her forehead – went off on foot up the slight ascent of Batthyány Street towards Moscow Square, and from there towards the Ferenc Rózsa Veterans' Home, where, in their tiny living room, her crazed husband, the one-time Pápai, awaited her, a crooked, trembling figure standing in the doorway, tormented by premonitions, frantic with worry.

[8] We concluded the meeting at 16:10, agreeing to meet next at 15:00 on the 6th in the snack bar near the front desk of Kútvölgyi Hospital.

The Attempt

By then the two boys had been sitting in the hallway for a good half an hour. They'd taken the elevator to the third floor. The sound of fingers diligently tapping away at type-writers could be heard beyond the padded doors. The office was clearly busy: secretaries in apparently obligatory stil-etto heels, documents awaiting signatures in their hands, whisked past between the hallway's veneer walls; now and then a pot-bellied gentleman in a cheap wrinkled suit and tie trotted past, a thick dossier under his arm; and from time to time a figure in a military uniform appeared, holster at his side. They came and went, going about their business as if not even noticing the two boys.

No one else besides them was waiting in this hallway with its veneer walls, which perhaps had not been designed for waiting at all – no one else, and that was pretty odd, though despite it all they had the sense, possibly unfounded, that they were being watched, that all the hubbub had been staged for their amusement, and that the prolonged waiting was nothing more than an opportunity to observe them, even if they sought to dispel the thought, to laugh it off, saying to themselves that, here, waiting was nothing unusual: an office is an office is an office.

And yet the hint of suspicion arose in them again when a balding young man walked past for a second time, and even as they made as if they were outside and above it all, that uncanny, *unheimlich* feeling took root in them all the same, that haunting feeling that the entire building was watching them. Or perhaps they weren't being watched, but instead were being *made to feel* as if they were being watched? They'd arrived right on time, after all, even if they had come separately, and though an office worker saddled with lots of work can't be expected to drop everything to receive just anyone who steps in off the street – if indeed this was an office, and it certainly looked like one, and if indeed this was where they'd been summoned for an appointment – why the long wait?

An unspeakable disquiet had taken hold of them earlier, even as they approached the greyish building on the corner – grey more from neglect than from being plastered grey – and as they arrived at the porter's booth by the main entrance, where a uniformed man had asked for their IDs and made a record in a huge logbook, the porter's book, and as that man called some number to signal their arrival. Just outside the entrance, gold letters on a black glass board told them they had arrived at the Interior Ministry's passport department, 45 László Rudas Street, a bleak house whose proportions invariably inspired a momentary impression of beauty nonetheless. As for the boys, they hadn't noticed the strange asymmetry – no, they had seen nothing much of the building while approaching on foot moments earlier from Lenin Boulevard, only its greyness or, more precisely, steel-greyness.

And perhaps that sums up just what happened as these two boys approached, and then arrived at, their destination one not particularly sweltering summer's day in June 1978.

It was a pre-war building, that much was certain from its proportions, its windows and the two rosette inlays in the façade above the main entrance, which were partly obscured by a wrought-iron glass-encased structure extending above the door. Touched though it was with the same paltriness that characterized all the neighbourhood's buildings, if the two boys could have seen it in its entirety, perhaps they would have noticed that it looked as if a church had been turned into an office: to the left of the entrance, columns and arched windows composed a surprising ornamentation on the bay of the façade; a tympanum up above hinted at the multi-faceted nature of the spaces inside; and, rendering the bay even more mysterious, a smaller tympanum was visible under the larger one. As for the stone-faced sphinx lounging on the roof, there was no seeing that – for who would have thought to approach the building from the other side of László Rudas Street? Just to peruse the Interior Ministry's façade?

From a distance, from the fifth floor of some building beyond the tracks of the nearby train station, perhaps the ministry building could have been seen in all its beauty. Most significant, though, and beyond the notice of those not approaching from László Rudas Street, was the year MDCCCLXXXXVI inscribed in the tympanum, proudly announcing that the building had been built not one war earlier, but two, in the glorious year of 1896, that annus mirabilis that had marked the thousandth anniversary of the Hungarian state. The hermae of half-naked women that had projected from the rustic keystones of the ground floor had been dismantled by careful hands – or by bombs or a well-aimed round of machine-gun fire – to make way for austere rhombuses. Other omissions were attributable to the crafty architect himself: that corner of the building where László Rudas Street met Vörösmarty Street seemed to have been lopped off with a cake knife, leaving the building without a corner at all, as if with this small surface the building sought to address all the city's residents; its second storey held a statueless niche, above which, as if above an orator's lectern, was some unexpected decoration in the form of a lace-like

baldachin; and above that a coat of arms perhaps intention-
ally left empty; for all of this had been stripped away in the
whirl of the Second World War. Yes, it had vanished, with
nothing left to reveal that on this Friday morning in June
the boys had stepped – timidly, from the sun's blinding
glare – into the former Symbolic Grand Lodge of Hungary,
the one-time palace of the Freemasons.

It was a classic communist office building, though perhaps more elegant than most, with its veneer walls and a
few surviving pieces of the original, custom-made furniture
in its offices. The building's architect had been asked to
include three sanctuaries and two workshops. This was in
accordance with the Masonic custom of the time, because,
in contrast to earlier practice whereby individual lodges
had their own premises, here several lodges operated in one
building, at set times and in their own reserved spaces. The
building also had a refectory in which jovial conversations
unfolded after the work was done, a restaurant available for
lease, a library, a reception room, a recreation room, and, yes,
offices.

The key symbols of Freemasonry could be found in less
conspicuous spots, in keeping with the Freemasons' tendency to shy away from revealing too much of themselves to
the world. Bouquets were set in the small tympanum below
the larger one above the main entrance; and rocailles ornamented the aedicules of the second-floor windows. But the

stucco decorations spotting the wall had no symbolic import. Only the most observant pedestrian would have noticed the ornaments on the roof, behind the parapets decorated with urns and balustrades. Along with the sphinx leaning against a globe, the building's other crowning ornament comprised four owls holding up a celestial sphere marked with the signs of the zodiac. Its pedestal bore the most important Masonic symbol, a square and a set of compasses joined together, the crowning triangle symbolizing God.

It was an irregularly shaped office with a rather low ceiling into which the younger of the two boys, his stomach softly churning, now entered. An enormous desk stood in the centre of the room, and the short, double-chinned man in a lieutenant colonel's uniform and gold-framed glasses who stood and genially offered him a seat seemed to vanish momentarily behind the desk as he, too, sat down. Owing to its irregular shape, the office, which seemed to have been spliced together from several spaces, at once seemed unusually spacious and, in its narrowness, also rather cramped. A small recess could be seen on the left, by the rear wall, whose depth could not be determined – it may have been a passageway to another space. If someone wanted to eavesdrop on the conversation in the office, he could hide away quite happily in that recess, for anyone entering from the hall, even if he took several steps into the room, still could not see him.

Both because of the low suspended ceiling and especially because of the clumsily half-covered arched windows – which had evidently been made to serve a much larger space – the office lamp had to be kept on during the day, and so at certain moments the room, in harmony with the emotional state of those inside, seemed minuscule and dark. Yet another oddity: owing to some technical constraint or less fathomable consideration, a one-and-a-half-metre span of floor in front of the arched windows was a few inches lower than the rest, so that anyone walking back and forth there would have to constantly take one step down, and one step up, as if limping. For this reason, the room's current occupant probably stayed put on the near side of the room, while the colossal desk – in fact two pieces of furniture of different sizes pushed together – stood in the middle and swallowed up nearly all the space. The room resembled a jail cell. Was this that 'dark room' where a Freemason candidate, before being led into a sanctuary to be subjected to various rites of passage, could undertake solitary reflection and write his spiritual will? Whatever the case, anyone passing his days in here would feel simultaneously diminutive and gigantic: a weary, enervated bureaucrat on the one hand, an omnipotent éminence grise wielding power over the fates of his fellow man on the other. To the right stood two large safes painted a revolting brown, keys hanging out of their shiny locks; and beside them was a piece of rococo period furniture with a glass door – a sort of document cabinet, conspicuously empty. To the left was a round marble table with two bentwood chairs that would have better suited a café; on the table was a doily, on top of which was a lead crystal ashtray and a sparkling mocha pot resting on a hotplate, from which a black cord led to a plug hanging clumsily from a socket on the wall. The air held the aroma of freshly ground coffee beans.

After politely introducing himself, the lieutenant colonel stared in silence for some time at his well-manicured hands. Before him was a brand-new passport, the smell of which seemed to linger in the air. Scrutinizing the nails of his left hand, the lieutenant colonel placed his right hand gently on the passport as his eyes fell upon the boy with a distant stare, like a predator deciding what to do with its victim: kill it immediately or first play with it?

Both boys had been surprised when the secretary – a fiftyish matron with dyed hair, a long grey dress and a white blouse with baggy sleeves – called the younger of them in first. Jacob and Esau, that immortal story of the privileges of the firstborn.[1]

The lieutenant colonel had two approaches to choose from. He'd honed his skills for long years now, so he could effortlessly put either one into practice – the words were right there at his disposal, in his desk drawer so to speak, and all he had

---

[1] MRS PÁPAI called our attention also to her sons, who would likewise wish to travel in the near future to Israel to visit relatives. (We are processing their case also.)

to do was pull them out: one version was foreboding, the other enticing; one was strewn with storm clouds and, more to the point, indirect threats, such as the blocking of a career, the other promised undreamed-of opportunities, security and pink sunrises. Like a virtuoso, the lieutenant colonel had the script at his fingertips, and it was this moment of recruitment that he considered one of the most exciting and inspiring of all his duties. This is what he savoured the most, that most resembled that which he'd dreamed of as a boy – the theatre. It was a role he gladly played even if he knew – he was no fool, after all – how ludicrously petty it was, the prospect he was now preparing to unveil before the kid sitting across from him, who could not guess what awaited him.

As with all suspects, including those accused of crimes they surely hadn't committed, the boy's entire being was delicately vibrating. Perhaps he was scared, too, without being entirely conscious of it. All this was evident in the way his lips parted, ready for a breath; on his faintly flushed skin; in his sparkling eyes; and in other signs an amateur would not notice – signs the individual himself wasn't even aware of. And while he wasn't actually a suspect – why *would* he have been? – this moment of opportunity had to be exploited. Yes, he, the lieutenant colonel, had to suggest, delicately of course, that the balance of power here was unequal. But he had to do so without scaring off or even alarming his prey, but, rather, luring it into his trap. It was often enough – even in the case of those with intellects sharper than this kid's – to subtly allude to the twists and turns, and the accidents, that can befall one's chosen career.

During a professional development course in Moscow, the lieutenant colonel, by some miracle, had got hold of a dog-eared volume of Talleyrand during political history class. Noticing his lingering stare, Lieutenant Colonel Volkov, a brilliant mind, had pressed the book into his hand with a manly slap on the shoulder, and after the young man managed with no little difficulty to acquire a French–Hungarian dictionary, he was finally able to read the book. Of course he'd lied when he said that he knew French. Lying was – what else? – a professional affliction, or so his supervisor had once declared as he filled him in on his affair with some woman. 'But let us not call this lying,' his supervisor had observed. 'It is diplomacy!'

Without a doubt the future lieutenant colonel had, in Moscow, fallen in love for life with that French bishop-turned-revolutionary, Charles-Maurice de Talleyrand-Périgord. He was in the habit of repeating his finest aphorisms by heart. Was it not Talleyrand who'd said, 'A married man with a family will do anything for money'? Of course, at the *firm*, money did not grow on trees – though it wasn't all about money – but sometimes it was necessary to pay blood money or a reward or drop-in-the-bucket disbursements – trivial sums, but enough to further ensnare delinquents, with a guilty conscience if nothing else. This came with the territory. And was it not Talleyrand who'd also said, 'Speech was given to man to conceal his thoughts'? *Brilliant!* thought the lieutenant colonel as he began to rack his brain for an apt little saying with which to impress this young man who worked in the theatre, who was said to be – which it took only a look to confirm – highly cultivated and clever.[2] But nothing came to mind. Perhaps during the conversation it would.

The point was, in any case, that the subject must not have even the faintest suspicion that they were being coerced. Of

---

[2] sc cn MRS PÁPAI, whom we have fruitfully employed for a long time, mentioned at our last meeting that both her sons have submitted passport applications to the Interior Ministry's competent office. According to MRS PÁPAI, the foremost goal of her sons' trip is to take part in their grandfather Avi-Shaul's birthday celebration. Avi-Shaul is a noted Israeli writer and peace activist, and vice-president of the [Israeli] League for Human [and Civil] Rights.

[. . .]

The sons of sc cn MRS PÁPAI: Péter Forgách (DOB: 1950. IX. 10), a research fellow at the Institute for Public Education. András Forgách (DOB: 1953. VII. 18), dramaturge, at present still a member of the National Theatre in Kecskemét. He studied the history of philosophy at Loránd Eötvös University and is preparing to be a film director. He is a member of the Federation of Communist Youth. He professes himself to be a communist but cannot accept the responsibilities that accompany party membership. He is a highly talented individual who knows how to keep quiet but at the same time travels the world with open eyes.

Based on our knowledge it seems expedient that prior to his departure to Israel, citing his passport application as an excuse, we engage him in a conversation in the offices of the Passport Department.

In the course of the conversation we would call his attention to the pitfalls he might expect in the course of his travels, by pointing out the sorts of difficulties the lack of diplomatic relations could mean for him.

We would have him clarify the main purpose of his trip – besides the visit to his relatives – and with what notions and expectations he is travelling to Israel.

If in the course of the conversation it is our impression that he is inclined to co-operate with us, we would look him up after his return.

The conversation will be undertaken by Police Lt. Col. Comrade Miklós Beider with the participation of Police Capt. Comrade György Ocskó.

31

course, in Mrs Pápai's case coercion was unnecessary. True, they had not told her that they had long since re-classified her,[3] but she didn't need to know this – after three years of trouble-free co-operation she must have come to suspect that this certainly wasn't child's play, and, besides, what was the difference between a 'secret associate' and a 'secret colleague'? A question of nuance, really, but an individual's moral sensitivity had to be considered. No one is eager to snitch voluntarily; or, rather, those who are eager represent the dregs of humanity, though of course one must do business with such people too. Though it became clear early on that Mrs Pápai was an avowed Party member (there were such odd birds in the world), she undertook her increasingly frequent trips, which were not without risk – Shin Bet was, after all, no doubt the world's most formidable intelligence service – above all so that she could visit the father she so adored. And then she had her crazy husband around her neck; a husband who, previously – the lieutenant colonel had conscientiously pored over his three thick dossiers when the matter of employing Mrs Pápai was first considered – had operated pretty erratically until, one fine day, he went mad. A man of many talents, that much was beyond question – he spoke seven languages fluently – but he was too careless

---

[3] With her local knowledge of Israel and wide circle of social contacts there, MRS PÁPAI helped our work with most useful tip-off research activity, besides still being the only Hebrew-language translator we can count on. Since her official classification as a secret colleague is only a formality, we would not inform her of this in particular.

and unpredictable. Most of his reports might just as well have gone in the rubbish bin had it not been necessary to bind them into his work dossier. What's more, despite being a practising journalist, he told them hardly a thing, and his handler's repeated observation was that in the conspiratorial flat where they met, words had to be pulled out of him like teeth, and when the words did come, he'd recount the same story differently on every occasion. And when Mrs Pápai let them in on her husband's well-developed paranoia, the telling phrase, à la Talleyrand, nearly slipped from the lieutenant colonel's mouth: that at least in this case it can be determined that the objective circumstances validate the subjective state of mind, that the base determines the superstructure, as old Marx said.

Of course, the point wasn't that the reports should always be useful, but that they had to be manufactured nonetheless, and the lieutenant colonel wasn't so fond of this, the industrial aspect of his work. But if the factory kept churning out its wares, something nice came off the production line every now and then. And of course an informant had to be kept busy, could not be neglected, and had to feel watched. But Pápai, despite the seven languages he spoke and his apparent enthusiasm for the work, was, in his babbling way, an atrocious spy, descending easily into arguments with anyone and unable to co-operate with those who didn't share his political convictions.

Unfortunately, the same was partly the case with Mrs Pápai, which rendered her no more reliable than a 'lottery ticket' as well, as Comrade István Berényi cynically observed at a meeting. She had to be weaned off the habit, if at all possible, of placing her convictions above her work.[4] She made no attempt to hide her antipathy towards the Jewish state – on the contrary, that is essentially what motivated her – and so had to be patiently guided to separate her personal convictions from her service to the cause, the opinions of the network individual from the interests of the socialist movement.

More than once the lieutenant colonel had taken her to task about this, but naturally without questioning her entrenched worldview, which was itself a matter of anthropological interest – he had rarely met a Jew who loathed the Jewish state – her homeland no less – with a vehemence that was almost a caricature of itself.[5] Mrs Pápai always took care to correct him when the lieutenant colonel suggested that she'd been born in Israel – 'Not in Israel, but in Palestine,' she'd nervously interrupt, at which he couldn't help breaking into a smile. This hurt Mrs Pápai, but the lieutenant colonel did not

[4] MRS PÁPAI is a resolute, 'headstrong' individual who works single-mindedly and diligently. Her age (60), her secondary education, her scatterbrained nature due to family tragedy, and her insufficient degree of training, do not allow us to maximize her potential.

[5] Throughout our conversation it was evident that the experiences MRS PÁPAI has acquired concerning the Israeli situation have deeply upset her, and her passion very nearly prevents her from a clear-headed and objective assessment of political issues. At every step she emphasizes the indefensibility of Israeli policies.

regard what he saw as a rigid and childish distinction as all that significant. On one occasion, he spent some ten minutes slapping his knee and laughing over a sentence in one of Mrs Pápai's reports,[6] but he decided not to press the issue; not even to satisfy his own curiosity would he call the secret colleague's attention to her logical stumble. But he would have been quite keen to know how Mrs Pápai would have replied to his not entirely innocent query: 'What on earth led you, comrade, to conclude that "there *probably* is such a feeling"?' It was not that he couldn't sympathize with Mrs Pápai. Even he had doubts and obsessions that were contrary to his work, but he would have been unable to perform his duties satisfactorily were he to heed these Siren calls. Still, even with all her contradictions and her excessive toeing of the line, Mrs Pápai was an ideal 'client', one who had been inexorably thrust into their arms by her rather topsy-turvy financial affairs, her children's muddled and deviant worldviews, and the need to ease the entry into Hungary of her many relatives in Israel. Of course the lieutenant colonel spoke with Mrs Pápai about these things only in passing, and he never asked her about her family affairs; as needed, he adjudicated on this or that visa application. But when Mrs Pápai gushed forth with complaints,[7] he commiserated wholeheartedly with all she

---

[6] *Jews, if they feel themselves to be Jewish (for there probably is such a feeling, true or false, but there is).*

[7] MRS PÁPAI is a reliable, conscientious, and above-board partner. Already she has pulled her weight of information-gathering work. But her activity is influenced

had to say, all the while racking his brain to figure out how the hell he could encapsulate this useless and marginal information into a necessarily compound but nonetheless succinct phrase in the report he would have to write. Was there any valuable fact or titbit to be gleaned from the heap of information that came his way? 'Trifles have gigantic consequences,' Lieutenant Colonel Volkov had said in Moscow, but that might have been said by Talleyrand as well. All the same, such forays into personal matters occurred rarely in the course of the lieutenant colonel and Mrs Pápai's meetings, which focused mostly on her duties as a network individual, duties she carried out with the utmost zeal.

A black-and-white picture from 1951 bears witness to the fact that the building at 45 Podmaniczky Street – no doubt to welcome the celebrating throng marching towards Heroes' Square on May Day – was decorated, between two large and two smaller red flags, and above the inscription THE PEOPLE'S PARADE FIGHTING FOR PEACE, with portraits of Lenin, Rákosi and Stalin, though Rákosi's was somewhat smaller than those of his Russian and Georgian colleagues.

by her husband's condition, by its reverberations. Even aside from this, her family situation is exceptionally complicated and disordered. (She has three adult children – two sons and a daughter.) Her life is not easy to begin with, and with the exception of the latter, each of her children burdens it all the more with serious problems. During a family visit to the USA in the past year, her daughter – who, by the way, had been under surveillance by internal intelligence – got married and remained abroad. Intelligence deems it expedient to prevent her entry [to Hungary]. The daughter's departure and especially the blocking of her visits home have caused MRS PÁPAI serious conflicts.

By 1978 the building had been the headquarters of the Interior Ministry for more than a quarter of a century – initially the State Protection Authority (ÁVÓ) had been based here, and in 1951, when the Interior Ministry moved here once and for all, the name of the street was for a time changed from Podmaniczky to Rudas. But on that June morning in 1978, at any rate, neither the lieutenant colonel nor the boy knew it had been in this very room – in which their own intimate conversation would unfold[8] – that the

---

[8] On the basis of an approved recommendation, on 1978. VI. 23 I had a conversation in the competent office of the Passport Department with András Forgách.

In the course of the conversation I politely called his attention to the anticipated pitfalls of his Israeli trip, to the difficulties the lack of diplomatic relations might pose him. I told him that at their own request we are permitting a few young people whose personal and political bearing we hold in high esteem to visit Israel, but we are devoting attention to their travels, for we are concerned that on account of the lack of diplomatic relations they may be subject to provocation or other, unanticipated, difficulties. During the conversation I mentioned one or two specific incidents, too, involving Hungarian citizens in Israel. The fact that he was aware of a good number of these risks strengthened his confidence in me.

After this I asked him with what notions and expectations he would be travelling to Israel.

András Forgách said he is travelling there at the invitation of his grandfather, Avi-Shaul, the noted Israeli writer and public figure, to help organize his literary estate, in light of Avi-Shaul's advanced age.

After this we had a short but in-depth conversation about Israel, about the situation that has developed there today. Wishing him a good trip, I then said farewell, adding that I'd be happy to see him after his return, too, for the experiences and impressions he comes home with would interest me. But I emphasized that he should see me only of his own accord, if he feels he could thus do us a useful service and if that doesn't give cause for self-conflict. I asked him to keep our conversation confidential, that he not even tell his older brother, who was present on this occasion, and with whom I would speak separately on this subject, except that I would not ask him to report after his return.

I told András Forgách that I asked him to report after his return only because, as a reasonably good judge of people, I feel he is someone I can turn to if the goal is noble.

András Forgách thanked me for my confidence in him and promised that after his return he will by all means present himself at the Passport Department, where I left my telephone number. After this conversation András Forgách's mother contacted far-right politician Gyula Gömbös's secretary, who bore a striking resemblance to the lieutenant colonel's secretary, had typed up the speeches her boss – Admiral Horthy's sometime ally and a future prime minister – gave from 1920 to 1928 as president of the Hungarian National Defence Association (Hungarian acronym: MOVE). For back then, that narrow passageway in the back of the room had led to a closed-off, still-domed area of the great hall, which the Freemasons had abandoned along with the rest of the building with the communist takeover in 1919.

So it was into this spacious space that Gömbös settled, which became his office, his young henchmen passing the time by mocking the hall's Egyptian-style frescoes, which were, as they put it, 'spittingly Jewish'. But for some odd reason, Gömbös – years before he was obliged to rein in his radical anti-Semitism as a condition of his ascendancy to the throne of government in 1932 – would not allow the frescoes to be either covered or removed. More than once his secretary caught him, deep in thought, staring at the art

me. She said that after the meeting András contacted her and spoke in the most positive terms of the conversation in the Passport Department and said he firmly intends to prepare a report on his Israeli trip and what he experienced there.

András Forgách, who is a research fellow at the Institute for Public Education, is a dramaturge, studied the history of philosophy at university, and is preparing to be a film-maker. He is a colourful, winsome personality. He possesses above-average erudition and has a strong command of English.

When András Forgách presents himself after his trip I will endeavour to exploit that for the purpose of deepening our relationship, because in my assessment he could become a valuable contact for us.

Miklós Beider, Police Lt. Col.

nouveau-style Egyptian reeds on his office wall, as if touched by some metaphysical force radiating from those ancient images.

The Freemasons had in fact been sent packing from the building on 19 March 1919, two days before the Hungarian Soviet Republic's hundred-day reign began and well before the White Terror that followed. And then – just two days later, on 21 March – the Hungarian Soviet Republic seized the whole of the Grand Lodge. Gömbös's far-right organization, MOVE, took over the building on 14 May 1920, and on 18 May (by which time communist leader Béla Kun had escaped to Moscow) Interior Minister Mihály Dömötör outlawed the Freemasons. In September 1923, Interior Minister Rakovszky – who, ironically, was the son of a previous grandmaster of the Hungarian Freemasons – ordered the registry of deeds to transfer ownership of the building to the Civil Servants' National Medical Benefits Fund. (Hungary's real estate mafia was alive and well even back then.) In the late Twenties Gömbös left the organization he had cofounded, but his men, a number of whom later emerged as prominent members of the fascist Arrow Cross Party, remained in the building, which became their base for raids against Jews, and the Freemasons' former cellar an ideal storeroom for their loot.

The siege of Budapest was still underway in February 1945 when those Freemasons who emerged from air-raid shelters all around Budapest requested that the Provisional National Government return their Grand Lodge to them. In the euphoria of freedom following the war the request was granted. But the new government recommended that the Freemasons reach an agreement with the National Peasant Party under which the latter, which had earlier moved into the building, could remain.

The Freemasons' extensive network of contacts had paid off splendidly. Renovation of the building began in September 1946 thanks to both local donations and American funding. As the work started, the Freemasons insisted that the building be vacated; the National Peasant Party begged to differ. Reluctant to admit defeat the Freemasons went so far as to apply for recognition of the Grand Lodge as a national monument – in order, that is, to reacquire the right to do with the building as they pleased. These were financially trying times, but nonetheless the work progressed smoothly. One of the biggest problems was flooding from groundwater, the solution being to treat the symptom: the basement was filled with rubble. On 15 March 1948 – the centennial of the 1848 Hungarian Revolution – a formal ceremony was held to mark the opening of the newly renovated first-floor workshop.

This idyllic state of affairs did not last long. In early June 1950, József Révai – one of the founders of the Hungarian Communist Party – issued a fierce diatribe against the

Freemasons, and on the 12th the ÁVÓ raided the Grand Lodge, seizing the premises. With that, the building's fate was sealed.

* * *

From the deafening and quite unexpected silence that descended, perhaps even plummeted upon their conversation right from the start – a silence that was in fact his own – the lieutenant colonel sensed that the young man seated across from him would be a tougher nut than most to crack. An air of inviolability and invulnerability enveloped him, radiating from his compliant smile, and there was an aura of profound solitude, which the lieutenant colonel – he couldn't do otherwise – began to respect. Because of this, in the course of their conversation his sentences became – he found he couldn't help it – less certain of themselves, and his words of caution – intended to sound unrelenting, steely and menacing – softened like butter in his mouth before he spoke them.

The time allotted for the meeting was soon up, but the lieutenant colonel was still racking his brain for something from Talleyrand with which to impress the kid. He has no family of his own. Perhaps he never will have one, the lieutenant colonel thought dryly as he noticed that the lad's eyes bore a striking resemblance to Mrs Pápai's. This filled him with a sort of hope, and yet he still could not penetrate the silence. The lieutenant colonel had already stood from behind the table, passport in hand – he didn't seem much taller than when sitting – and was proffering the passport towards the boy when he looked up, straight into the boy's grey-blue eyes, and said, with a fervency that surprised even him, 'Coffee should be black as the devil, hot as hell, pure as an angel, sweet as love.' When he finished, his face was red. 'Talleyrand,' he added. 'Would you like a cup of coffee?' In that moment it struck him that he'd made a colossal mistake. 'Ah, Talleyrand,' said the kid with a wide grin. 'This is the beginning of the end.' To which, as in a game of chess, the lieutenant colonel replied immediately with another quote: 'It is worse than a crime, it is a mistake.' 'That's actually Fouché,' the lad responded nonchalantly while taking the passport from the lieutenant colonel's hand. 'He was Napoleon's Minister of Police.' 'Who?' 'Stefan Zweig wrote a book about him. It's a must-read.' '*Who* wrote a book about him?' The lieutenant colonel was utterly confused. 'Thanks, but I don't want any. My brother is waiting outside.'

The lieutenant colonel, reeling slightly, as if waiting only for this magic word, now gathered himself. 'Please ...' he began to say, surprised at the almost pleading tone seeping into his voice. Meanwhile he thought (and he would have gladly sunk into the earth with shame), *We're just like two lovers in a French film, at a train station* – his eyes were misty, his breathing laboured. But he quickly pulled himself together. 'Please,' he said resolutely, 'don't mention the subject of our conversation to your brother. Will you do this for me?' 'Of course,' said the boy, who looked back once more before stepping through the doorway.

The lieutenant colonel stood there, already half turned away, as if with one eye on a person in the rear of the room whom only he could see, before vanishing from the boy's view as he closed the door behind him.

'What do you say, Gyuri?' he asked Captain György Ocskó, who now emerged from the passageway. Ocskó, who was in civilian clothes, lit a cigarette. 'Dunno,' he said. 'I think you could have been harder on him.' 'Harder?' asked the lieutenant colonel, casting Ocskó a perplexed stare, 'I'm glad I managed to make any sense at all.' 'Was he really so mesmerizing?' The lieutenant colonel paused before asking, 'Think he'll check in after his trip?' 'I have no idea,' said Ocskó, who then shouted for the secretary: 'Marika, coffee!'

Marika entered the room from the opposite side; from between the safes, that is, through a hidden door that opened noiselessly. 'Shall I make it now?' she asked. 'Wait a sec, comrade,' came the lieutenant colonel's throaty reply, at which Marika's eyes opened wide. That the lieutenant colonel had called her 'comrade' was a very bad omen.

London, 1962

Pápai was nervous.

A little boy, his nine-year-old son, was firmly in his grip as they walked down Finchley Road in Hampstead, if it could have been called walking: the boy trying to keep up with the rhythm of the long and unpredictable strides of his dad as they passed small shops and a crowd waiting in line at a bus stop. The smell of fish and chips enveloped them, and then they were walking past the dark throat of an Underground station, which seemed to be gobbling up and spitting out so many people at once. Approaching their destination, the man held his son's hand so tightly that the little fingertips were crimson, as if blood might spurt out from under the nails at any moment. Despite the pain, the boy didn't dare utter a word. Immersed in thought, not even noticing the passers-by, Pápai rushed along the pavement with long, nervous steps, dragging his son.

And he was singing.

Catching the eye of other pedestrians, the boy kept his silence, knowing very well that it was not always advisable to speak and that at times it was best to remain silent. At their crowded home in Buda, and here in Hampstead, in the long hallway of the cosy flat in Elm Tree House, Pápai's children had become used to jumping like grasshoppers out of his path whenever Pápai – gnashing his teeth, clenching his fist, hitting the air, mumbling indecipherable words – fought with his invisible enemies.

He had many enemies.

Wherever Pápai looked he saw people intent on destroying him. Perhaps it began with losing his father when he was four. Those tall men in the room, all in black, looking at him. The heavy, jaundiced, ice-cold hand of his dad on Pápai's head. But Pápai was no egotist. What bothered him more was that the great cause he was fighting for was in constant danger of being defeated. The great cause of mankind. And he was alone, terribly alone.

And he was singing.

'Dad,' said the boy almost inaudibly. 'If you sing, they'll think you're an idiot.'

He wanted to bite off his tongue; he immediately regretted it – why had he said it? The huge man – his overweight father, whom the boy adored, and whom he dreamed of becoming just like, just as disorderly, capricious and funny, and who only a moment ago had been singing a happy little song – froze instantly in the middle of the street, his left leg mid-step. His face contorted, and squeezing his son's hand ferociously, he shouted at him, causing some people to stop, turning their heads left and right, to discover where that raucous cry came from.

'How dare you call your father an idiot?'

His face livid, his lips trembling, Pápai left his son alone in the middle of the traffic on Finchley Road and never turned back. Tears started to well in the boy's eyes as, unable to move, he stared at his dad's crumpled, windblown mackintosh slowly vanishing in the distance among the nameless people of the early afternoon, all those big grown-ups living in Hampstead and doing their shopping before going home to watch *Coronation Street*.

Yes, Pápai was nervous.

* * *

He had every reason to be nervous. That morning he had risen at five o'clock to get to the tiny Fleet Street office of MTI, the Hungarian News Agency, on time. He had to read all the newspapers at breakneck speed to be able to type a short report for his colleagues in Budapest by seven. He couldn't get there early enough: his colleagues were liable to call at impossible hours and they always made outrageous demands; for they wanted to stab him in the back, they wanted to annihilate him, they wanted to prove that he was lazy, incompetent and unprofessional. He'd show them who was lazy, incompetent and unprofessional! He typed with two fingers as fast as he could, never looking at the keys, like a virtuoso pianist. He savoured the physicality of it: putting the typewriter down anywhere and conjuring up the perfect expression at a furious pace. And he did not lack the phrases and idioms a credible journalist needed in his new homeland at this time. His ideological pedigree was impeccable. Who was better than him? *Who?* He'd built up his life from scratch for the third time – no, for the fifth time – from scratch, like a phoenix rising from the ashes, from the ruins of a terrible war he'd watched from the sidelines with all the cunning in the world – with every advantage that a solitary, charming fellow with good looks and a fast tongue could muster.

But it was all in vain. Everything seemed to crumble again, exactly at the moment when he'd started to understand the tricks of the trade, his mission; when he'd made the necessary connections, built up his network, and was ready to apply the 'dark art' of information-gathering, getting closer to people who trusted him sufficiently and had valuable information to unwittingly share. The dream job he'd begun two years ago was a kind of reward for his exemplary behaviour after '56. He was a communist. He had known right away whose side he was on in those heated, happy, exasperated, dangerous, treacherous, murderous days of October six years earlier, and he was proud of it. Indeed, he boasted of it right to the face of a society that learned – after a few days of exuberant freedom – fear and silence again. And now the grand prize: four years in London. Why, he'd even bowed before the Queen! The envy and disbelief in all those eyes he met on the street gave him a sort of bitter satisfaction amid the whispering behind his back at work, where, when his colleagues did talk to him directly, they did so as if he were a piece of shit. Yes, once again he felt that he could turn his life around, revive all his hopes, and at long last take up his true vocation; he could correct his mistakes, eradicate the failures of his past, which had happened only because he was an alien, blown to Budapest by the wind, someone not born there, *not born anywhere*. He had never again set foot in his birthplace, never crossed the border to see what had become of the world of his youth, where everyone he'd loved had been murdered.

He had never been an insider – no, he'd only impersonated one with his mellifluous words, the raw logic of the new ideology he'd made his own, Bolshevism. He'd jumped blindly into the unknown, having no intimate knowledge of the finely woven web of friendships built up over generations. He had no family in the true sense of the word – it had vanished in the Nazi extermination camps – and he had no human network to sustain him. All he had was his unshakeable faith in an ideology, a religion in the true sense of the word, that could explain the world in a second. And those diligently scribbled notes he'd addressed to Party comrades certainly hadn't helped – sometimes he'd bombarded them with endlessly complaining letters begging their attention, letters filled with malicious remarks about his colleagues, letters that had given him the unenviable reputation of a denouncer even before he'd become one. A denouncer. The worst thing that could be said of anyone. Even those who helped him were mistrustful and cautious around him. A living Jew who hated Zionism. What an oxymoron. He was the perfect stranger.

But in the face of these vicissitudes he constructed his life from nothing with a rigorous rationality. After the war, in which he lost everything, he was given a second chance, the greatest gift life would offer him: the most beautiful woman on earth, who, moreover, had faith in the same things as him; who believed, as he did, in the bright future of mankind. Before the eyes of his incredulous rivals, he had won her as a wife and companion. 'You are a second Ingrid Bergman,' he used to say in his arduous, rational way, as if wooing her with convincing arguments. Yes, he'd hunted her down, he'd clutched her to him, knowing that his incurable love was not reciprocated, and she kept her feelings for someone else. It was a price he was ready to pay. His marriage was built on the same beliefs as his life. He was a twenty-six-year-old who'd survived the darkest night to roar at the world, his passionate words all the more convincing and disciplined because they came from a dithering and disorderly young man. They were almost hypnotic, his faith in them absolute despite their own absurdity.

This is how the letter read, exactly, word for word, *in English*, because the girl of his dreams – born of Hungarian parents but already in the promised land, her mother tongue the ever-changing new Hebrew – did not yet speak Hungarian:

12th of February, Jerusalem, 1946

My dear Bruria!

Your letter, dated the 24/10, is still my latest source of information about you. I could not guess what are (or I hope were) the reasons of your silence. I don't want to make any precipitated conclusions, I am only stressing the necessity of a more frequent exchange of views, considering my very complicated position.

You know, Bruria, I have decided in a certain way. This was the easiest part of the job, you will agree with me I am sure. What comes now is to rid myself of all the unnecessary burdens barring the road leading towards the realization.

It is difficult like hell to drop the great majority of my tasks in the movement, when I don't see who will do the job, at least as well as I was trying to do. But I must drop them or otherwise my plans with chemistry will remain empty promises.

I have seen Helmut to-day. He told me that you received my letters and that you have been glad about the news. On my questions why Bruria is so silent lately, meaning the letters, he told me that you are too busy for that. I have swallowed this quietly since there is nothing Helmut can do about it. However I must confess that this can be only a secondary reason.

Is it too much to ask somebody, who is as close to me as I believe it to be, to tell me frankly if anything has changed?

'Bruria will not change her heart' – you wrote to me – 'I shall not give a spark of hope if I would not be sure' – you wrote. Still, it can happen, what then? Will you keep quiet for a while and ponder about the smoothest way of conveying me the news?

You did not write to me and you must have had a reason. Suppose I would have chosen the way I proposed in my previous letters: Humanities and all that. What was to be your attitude towards our relation in a case like that? Can it be true that you would have dropped the whole affair, including writing?

I wish this would not be true. I am asking myself and

*that's why I am asking you about it. The weeks have passed
'somewhat nervously', to quote you again. I have been
Friday evening in Tel Aviv and slept at your home. I met
your brother but until now we could not find a way for
a closer understanding, although I was trying hard. He
was somewhat reserved. His wife is a wonderful person, I
started to like her from the first moment and she was very
communicative. I had a chat with your father, he could not
attend the celebration of '7 November' because of a cold. He
is getting nearer to me every time I meet him. I must make
a headway towards his personality – to grasp more of him.
It is quite difficult because our conversation is limited to
questions from his side and answers from my side, and all
this concerning me alone.*

*I must stop now it is very late in the night and I am so
tired that my eyes are aching. So good night to you Bruria
and don't forget to write to me whatever you may deem
necessary. I am taking my chances.*

*Your Marcell, who is incurably in love with you and only
you.*

* * *

Some dozen years later he had to sign a little sheet of paper
in a windowless room before taking up the most lucrative of
missions. No, lucrative not in material terms – he had four

children, and so his salary was just enough to make ends meet – but in a spiritual sense. In the Sixties, in the middle of the Cold War, his was a job in which people like him, with a rigid ideological creed and a supple mind, could thrive. Signing that sheet of paper and learning some essentials about secret codes and espionage – the tricks of a spy at the lowest grade of the hierarchy – seemed to be a small price to pay to be transported to the dream city called London, the centre of the world. He signed it without blinking – all journalists who worked abroad had to do the same – out of 'patriotic conviction', which they ascribed to those collaborators who weren't blackmailed or badly beaten or otherwise physically coerced into signing, because in those days being a Party member was identical to being patriotic – yes, it was a synonym for patriotism. At a stroke he became not only MTI's first post-war correspondent in London but also a secret agent with the code name Pápai at the II/3 Intelligence Bureau of the Political Investigation Department at the Interior Ministry.

Why did he choose the name Pápai? Meaning 'from Pápa', it was the sort of name one might expect of someone whose ancestry reached back to the sleepy baroque town of Pápa (i.e. Pope) in the Bakony Hills some way west of Budapest. But Pápai had never been to Pápa or had any connection with the head of the Catholic Church. There was nothing 'papal' about him; he was simply a faithless

Jew. It was a strange decision, but he seemed to be ready for such whimsical changes of identity. *Nomen est omen?* Was this name an omen, as the Latin proverb had it? The thought did not cross his mind. The willingness with which he, only a few years before, had thrown away the name he'd grown up with, Friedmann ('man of peace'), and put on a grey and characterless costume, keeping only the initial 'F' for Forgács (which meant 'woodchip', but which no few blue-blooded families had been proud to bear), testified to this. At the request of his boss in 1948, Marcell Friedmann had gone out into the corridor at the press department of the prime minister's office, where he had a prestigious job, and come back a minute later, introducing himself as 'Comrade Forgács'. Comrade Woodchip: the name was an invitation to become fragmentary, to a forlorn existence, as a piece torn off from a living thing.

Sir Woodchip. A character from a Shakespeare play? That's what it sounded like. He couldn't have cared less. The point was not to sound Jewish when the Party was so full of Jews that even the bureaucrats in Moscow shook their heads in disbelief and wagged their fingers menacingly. One had to be cautious. One had to hide one's true identity. An old identity. Someone more or less already left behind, anyway, in the chaos of the Second World War – at least this is what he must have said to himself. And what's more: a Jewish name didn't have such a good ring to it at a time when a group of doctors, mostly Jews, were accused of conspiring to poison the Big Brother himself in the Kremlin.

It was an officer of the Interior Ministry who had helped him out.

Pen in hand, Lieutenant Takács looked bemusedly at Not-Yet-Pápai's childishly round face, at the almost comical, thick black horn-rimmed spectacles Not-Yet-Pápai had bought for himself through the SZTK, the Social Security Centre of the Trade Unions – at those unutterably cheap, clumsy, rigid black rectangles which, apart from his very bald head and double chin, defined his face as they sat ponderously on his nose. At first the lieutenant wanted to call him Pápaszem ('Pope-eye', meaning 'spectacles', a word of a bygone age, harking back to when the gold-rimmed spectacles of Pope Leo X, who had lousy eyesight, had amazed the Hungarian delegates to the Vatican – and Raphael, too, who painstakingly painted him). But Takács found Pápaszem too funny – it sounded like Hawkeye, the name of an Indian – so he cut it in half. Let it be Pápai. Papal.

Another method of hiding a Jew: paint him in Catholic colours! A masterstroke! The officer was extremely pleased with himself. Pápai nodded. Yes, Pápai he would be, and he signed his new name in his usual, energetic hand on the document put before him.

Shedding one's identity step by step.

Even Friedmann was not his original name, thanks to

the otherwise liberal Kaiser Joseph's strict decree of 1787, when all Jews had had to change their names to the German equivalent. But that original name was lost. Almost two hundred years later Comrade Woodchip stepped onto the stage briskly, with a firm handshake, leaving Comrade Friedmann behind, and now here was Pápai, the secret collaborator, scribbled furtively on a piece of paper.

In the Sixties, still in search of an identity, one that was to be found nowhere, he invented an alter ego, a grotesque figure he called Ugo Kac (pronounced *Katz*). Someone with whom he could, at long last, identify. Ugo hated music. That was his peculiarity. His trademark. Music made him nervous. Music. Just a silly noise. Music. The only thing that made his wife, the mother of his four children, happy. Schubert, Mozart, Bach. It was all crap.

This was the last dark hole into which – before everything got darker – Ugo Kac crawled. His last stand.

But back to the courtship, to their love affair. After a period during which Pápai suppressed his instinct to sleep with any other girl, and on realizing that even this would not help, and still having had no response from the beautiful would-be bride, the young and desperate lover returned to the fray with another long letter.

This letter concerns those existential decisions that are the preconditions of a good marriage. After proving that he has become a serious man – one who has begun his studies at the prestigious Hebrew University of Jerusalem – he confesses that his little knowledge is not nearly enough for the demands of his chosen profession (he never did finish his studies), and has also got a decent – well, half-decent – job. True, his job description hardly inspires confidence, but to take on such a menial job could itself appear to be a courageous step. Like a hunter, he is getting closer and closer to his prey. He promises – and it is hard for him to resist the temptation to be a glorious revolutionary – to withdraw from all Party activities, where he is a leading light, a future star, someone absolutely indispensable and so very important. He is ready to delay such a career for her sake. And, yes, he has found a place where they can stay together as a young married couple, a students' home. In the same breath, however, he admits that there will be no real privacy there, so it is in fact inadequate and inconvenient for a honeymoon. Every plan that seems at first sight to be built on solid ground is undermined the next moment by harsh reality. But such is Youth. Run into the wind. Follow your dreams. Such is Fate. The *idea* itself is important. The ideal. Does it have to be realistic? Not at all. The less realistic it is, in fact, the more it deserves to become reality. And already he has another brilliant idea. A rabbit pulled from a hat. A race against time. How to make the unreal real: let's marry during Hanukkah! Hanukkah exists, Hanukkah is important, Hanukkah is the thing! Hanukkah and marriage fit together like two halves of a riddle. An irresistible offer, because he *'can't see when next there will be such an occasion'*. Isn't this in itself an irrefutable argument? All built on drifting sand. But, a miracle!

Yes, she would be his partner, jumping with him blindly into the abyss.

21st of February, Jerusalem, 1946

Bruria my Darling.

So I have started both things: the laboratory and the job in the morning. I can't tell which of them is the worst. In the lab I am sometimes wondering how can somebody with so little knowledge, as I have got, start chemistry. It is like an adventure. Still I will have to complete all my deficiencies, if you will be here, the study will go easier. I am taking off the rust from my brains, so my heart can send some fresh blood into it.

The job is not so bad only I have to sleep somewhere in town otherwise I won't be able to be there in time. There are about 14–16 machines to be washed. When the night is dry the job is easy, but when wetness covers the machines, I am having a hell of a time. Not only it takes double time, but it is never nice enough for the customers who don't spare their voices and vocabulary to tell me what they think.

The party takes the heaviest toll. There is no excuse for me. We are approaching the X Congress. I shall try NOT to be a delegate so I can quietly study at least during those three days without being chased from one 'extraordinarily important session' to some other action where I am 'indispensable'. Slowly I am convincing the Secretary about me being a student also for studies and not only for political activities in the University.

I was looking for a room in the neighbourhood of my working place but I couldn't find anything good for us. Still I hope that in the worst case we can stay in the students home. I demanded permission for this from the Students organization and in principle there is no opposition. The trouble is that there is not much privacy in such students homes and I don't see why should I share those very few moments I can have with you with two dozen strangers.

Say Bruri, what's your opinion about getting married in the course of Hanuka! There is a whole week, when the University is closed and outside study I can have a spell of time to be with you more than five minutes a day. We can have a couple of days in Tel Aviv or Haifa too. If not in Hanuka I can't see when next there will be such an occasion.

Don't forget to convey my greetings to Naama, and don't forget that I love you more than ever. If your eyes are getting tired, go to an eye specialist at once, the glasses won't spoil your beauty. I shall be in Tel Aviv on the 6th in the afternoon.

Marcell

How flattering to read these words, like red-hot embers that scorched the paper they were written on; to feel the torrent of unconditional love, the exaggerations of one who loved blindly. But, alas, for him, in the end this was too easy a victory. Only three months into their marriage he observes, *'It is overwhelming and therefore confusing.'* The young husband, the poetic yet at first sight so rational thinker, was compelled to note – arming himself with the arguments at he had learned from Marx, Engels, Lenin and Stalin, those thinker-giants who wielded the sword of an irrefutable logic and conquered the world – that facts are sometimes stronger than words. He is not afraid of bitter truths. *'Because there is no solid ground under our feet and I already lost the touch with my previous life.'* Not giving up in his case meant that he had to run headfirst into a thick wall of silence. *'It is true I loved you even in my being isolated from all hope of meeting you.'* And as he himself so perfectly put it at the end of his letter, he wanted to reach *'the tenderness of your feelings locked somewhere in the depth of your shell'*.

19th of March, 1947

Bruria Darling!
    There are three months since we married. It is time to make some observations although I do not dare to pretend

to know more about the future of our relation than my own hopes for its perpetuity.

To begin with, it is something we both know: all marriages are, or better, have got their difficulties at the start, still our case being a special one, we made the mistake of underestimating the dangers. I have taken too lightly the fact that you were not in love with me; you have been too daring in expecting from yourself to be able to cope with all the demands and possible complications of marriage in case of marrying anybody (anybody from the point of view of the sentimental attachment).

We both were mistaken and we both did not give up. This is the 'deus ex machina', the surprise for me and for the sceptics as well.

We did not give up because this would have been a mechanistic attitude.

We did not give up because there is not guarantee that something better or at least as good as that and not worse, waits around the corner.

We did not give up because we BOTH need love, and both of us genuinely hope that there is a possibility for changes, for a development to put it better.

The trouble was and partly goes on to be, that we had such a different attitude towards love, owing to our diametrically opposed background and practical differences, that we were unable to compromise on the sentimental ground although logical decisions have been taken in this respect.

The question remains if only the form is divergent or the content of love is so altered in each case that no development, say no compromise will be able to patch it up?

I think this view is mistaken: love is a natural neccessity common to all normal and healthy people, those then, whose soul has not been crippled under the existing social conditions.

That much for what I think is common ground. Now for me alone:

I must confess to-night that I became too strongly involved in this affair. Too strongly because there is no solid ground under our feet and I already lost the touch with my previous life. It is true I loved you even in my being isolated from all hope of meeting you, but this love never obliged my thinking, planning and carrying out – my full self; it only affected my sentimental half or quarter.

To-day it is overwhelming and therefore confusing.

Please don't take this for blackmailing you with my sentiments. It hurt me terribly when you asked in Ben Shemen last Thursday if I shall commit suicide in case you will leave me. The amount of love is not weighed by desperate deeds. I am sure that I am strong enough to stand any blow may this bring the greatest pain and the longest suffering.

In the past I experienced this in a very concentrated form, you know the fate of my beloved ones, this has shaken me out of my track for some time, but I got back and carried on.

Now this must be clear to you: I don't want you Bruria because I cannot imagine life without you, I want you because life is nicer, better, fuller, nearer to perfection with you than without you.

More about this: you can make, and in some respects you already made a better man out of me, this of course only if you will find the right approach, and believe me dearest one, I can help you in bringing about the changes you wish to see in yourself, if you will open yourself to me not only with logical decisions, but with the tenderness of your feelings locked somewhere in the depth of your shell.

There is never too much love if we are ready to take it, not for its own sake but for the sake of our belief in an ever blooming, glorious march of the human race towards that to-morrow that sings in our hearts.

There is nothing more I can say that you don't know already, I shall not use the word your name conveys me its content: My Bruria, Your Marcell

'I have taken too lightly the fact that you were not in love with me,' says the young and desperate husband almost casually, and in the turmoil of a brewing civil war and in the wake of the war of independence, during the birth pangs of the state of Israel, these young people are wondering if they have both made a mistake.

Her feelings were *'locked somewhere in the depth of your shell'*, he wrote, but otherwise the two of them were wonderfully happy together. The cornerstone of their shared faith was a certain person, still alive, one Iosif Vissarionovich Dzhugashvili. As Bruria wrote in a letter dated 11 January 1946, not to her husband but to her comrades in Beirut:

I was discussing with a boy of nineteen about current problems. Whenever I mentioned the word 'Democracy' he made a wry face and murmured: 'Again an empty, common-place word' – He is a student in the university, took up mathematics. His world was shaken during the last few years and every expression which for us is full of meanings, because there is action behind it, for him is an empty phrase. So was it when I mentioned a book by Stalin. Here he retorted: 'You too are contaminated with this blind adoration of a man?' You see, he is an intelligent boy. Not a Zionist. Not narrow-minded. But altogether detached from the life of the simple people, the majority of humanity, from whose lap he himself grew. He is afraid to see meanings behind expressions. He is afraid to decide where to take a place. He is a typical petty-bourgeois intellectual.

Thus she writes in a letter to her comrades in Beirut, where she spent a number of years and where she took the first steps of her adult life – at the American University, studying to be a nurse. Alongside people of different nationalities, in the middle of an incredible, Levantine landscape she later simply called 'Paradise'. People of many backgrounds – Armenians, Iraqis, Syrians, Americans and Jews – studied and socialized there, enjoying an amazing degree of freedom during the war, in the 'Paris of the Middle East', living life to the fullest. When she went back home to Jerusalem and started working as a nurse in a hospital, she felt as if she had been exiled in her own hometown, and this feeling of exile, like that of her suitor, never left her. She felt like an alien in her birthplace, where every day she witnessed both British colonial oppression and the terror wrought by right-wing Zionist extremists. She imagined a multinational country in place of a single, nationalist state. All her life. She knew it was a utopian vision, and yet it was a utopia she wanted to believe in:

To day it is a wonderful springday. Those who know Jerusalem, can imagine the clearness and freshness and charms of this city. When one looks at the city from the mountains, he forgets that it is reality which is in front, because it is so easy to fall into a dreamy state and see all like in a fairy-tale. I know what is wishful thinking, all of

us do fight such thoughts but they come up nevertheless.
To day my thoughts were concentrated on a truly dream –
like subject: Palestine free and democratic. On the
mountains hundreds of people picking flowers and dancing.
Amphitheatres for thousands of people are surging with
people who visit the best plays there. At night, to the full
moon, the best music is played and the ballet dancers give
the most fantastic and beautiful dance, which thousands of
people enjoy and understand!

Well, I think it is more than enough to bother you with
my dreams.

Although they shared a worldview, young Pápai knew he
was walking a fine line. In the letter written three months
after they married, he had talked of blackmail:

Please don't take this for blackmailing you with my
sentiments. It hurt me terribly when you asked in Ben
Shemen last Thursday if I shall commit suicide in case
you will leave me. The amount of love is not weighed by
desperate deeds.

What a prophecy! Two years before their London adventure, in 1958, in Budapest, he was standing on a chair in the
bathroom with a rope around his neck when she stormed

into their home, which only a few weeks before she had been ready to leave for ever. She was tortured by premonitions. And there she found him, a farewell note on the floor. That morning she'd phoned him every ten minutes, and when he didn't answer, she ran to him, faster than she'd ever run. She would never again try to escape.

Shall we dance or shall you accompany me home? was the question asked by Bruria, a beautiful, wild creature from whom the young Romeo could not tear his gaze – yes, the glowing fire of love at first sight had been lit. She was standing there, outside the room, in the candlelight, Jerusalem's cool evening breeze moving her dark hair around her face – Bruria, her jasmine eyes beaming from her suntanned face, in a simple white dress embroidered with colourful flowers, like a fairy in a folktale, a fruit ripe for plucking.

She stood, momentarily alone, among the happily dancing, red-faced communist youth of Palestine – at this ball where the band, between foxtrots and tangos and sambas, played the 'Marseillaise', the 'Internationale', and a Russian folk song. The dance floor was packed with young men in the uniform of the British army, most of them immigrant Jews who wanted to fight the Nazis in Europe but were instead stranded in North Africa or Egypt or Palestine because the Brits didn't trust them. And there were young men dressed very casually, or in their work clothes, in simple sandals or even barefoot, who represented the new type of Jew, and all were ready to build the brave new world of which they had a clear vision. The girls, often dressed too in men's clothes, were among the most beautiful daughters of Poland, Germany and Hungary – the children of those who'd escaped fascism and the war. A brand-new breed of Jewish youth who were already tasting both the hardships of cultivating a new land and the pleasures of a life in a free world to come, a world they partly owned even now and would own fully before long. The war was over, the sun was sinking behind a hill against a crystal-clear sky, and the music was loud and joyful.

Shall we dance or shall you accompany me home? was the question, the bait thrown to the fish still blithely swimming in clear waters, and the fish bit. The young man loved rash decisions, mistaking them for courage; and she too was swift and sometimes rash – yes, she could act decisively at difficult times, and he was already in a trap. He accompanied her home: far, far away from the lights of this great communist ball, through dark alleys where anything could happen, where someone might rob them, where the military police might arrest them or simply intimidate them, where they might be killed. Stabbings, as in the days of Flavius, happened all the time in Jerusalem in those feverish days of 1946. And after a long, seemingly endless walk through the streets – during which they agreed on many points, giving false hope to the boy in British uniform – on arriving at her room, where they had to whisper, because the whole house was sleeping, she, instead of kissing him, asked for a favour. Could he deliver a letter to an English soldier, a certain Thomas Rogers, who coincidentally served in the same town in Egypt as him? She didn't trust the post office in those turbulent, dangerous times. Yes, he was ready to be the postman. And it would change nothing if the letter he had to deliver was a letter of farewell. Maybe it was, maybe it wasn't.

* * *

Folding the signed sheet of paper and putting it away, Lieutenant Takács beamed a satisfied smile at Pápai. They seemed to have reached an understanding, and Pápai had a good sense of humour, seemed very well informed, and, not least, the Party was behind him.

'Don't worry, we shan't bother you for a long time, Comrade Pápai.'

'I am not worried,' said Pápai. 'I can't wait to serve my country as best I can.'

'That may not be enough,' said Takács sombrely. A cloud passed over Pápai's face. But Lieutenant Takács, whose change of tone was calculated, went on: 'I'm only joking, of course.'

The familiar game of cat and mouse began. The invisible thread of dependence had to be stretched between them, the distance measured, the connection assured, the subordination clarified, the discipline practised. All this in a casual way, so the subject wouldn't feel constrained in the least, all this being quite voluntary, a service to the homeland and the Party, and to the great common cause of humanity.

'To whom can I turn at the embassy in times of emergency?'

'Nobody,' said Takács. 'Wait until you get instructions from us. I see no reason for any emergencies. What counts is this: we are trying to change the image of our country on an international level. To show that we are independent actors, not what they call a satellite state. The counter-revolutionaries who escaped in '56 are all over Europe. They denigrate, smear, blacken and slander their own motherland, our socialist system, unashamedly. All you have to do for now, until you get new instructions, is to befriend as many people as you can. And it wouldn't hurt if they are high-level state functionaries, secretaries in a ministry, MPs of any – I repeat any – party, right or left, or the editors of influential newspapers – no matter how reactionary. The more reactionary, the better. As far as I'm concerned, they can be capitalist pigs. Just befriend them. Win their confidence.'

'I am not worried about that,' said Pápai, and Takács took note of the reappearance of the little word Pápai had introduced into the conversation five minutes earlier. He knew that denials are affirmations of sorts.

'But you should be,' said Takács theatrically. 'I warn you to be alert *all the time*. Do your job as best you can. We will not interfere, but please be alert. And here are the instructions.'

He handed Pápai an envelope.

'Read them carefully, learn them by heart and burn them. Today.'

A stupid little ritual, he thought, *to make the agent feel more important*.

'We shall have a little conversation in order to go over the details in a week or so. But this is not a spy novel, comrade, and you are not a dog on a leash.'

He wondered why he had said that. What had made him think of a dog? He stood up quickly, his hand in the air between them. Pápai wasn't sure if it was an invitation for a handshake. It wasn't.

'Good luck, comrade!'

Apart from the dull code name, they did leave him alone. As promised, they allowed him a little breathing room in the first days, weeks, months and even year. No one bothered him for any favours, either in London or in Budapest; he received no burdensome tasks, was ordered to no secret meetings. Instead he was on his own for a while, for the learning period, and he was a quick learner. He was handled by the Hungarian embassy as a kind of sleeper agent, a resident spy. He had no idea who the others were. Perhaps everybody at the embassy – every worker and every secretary, from the chauffeur to the gardener up to the ambassador himself. Perhaps even the wives. In critical situations it was of inestimable value if the wives were in the know, as all the manuals emphasized. But he had to watch his words, and that wasn't easy, because his tongue was quick and his convictions strong.

* * *

Moments before Pápai left his son alone on Finchley Road that early spring afternoon, the two of them had stepped out of a nearby bakery. Pápai loved sweets. He ate all the time, this and that, here and there, spending most of his money on food. He was a gourmand. Maybe this partly explained why he was so overweight: the huge belly, the childish round face, the double chin. True, his wife also loved sweets, not only the figs and dates and halva of her native land, Palestine, but also (lots of) marzipan – made from her cabalistic fruit, the almond – as well as Cadbury chocolates filled with nuts and raisins, which she bought and consumed in formidable quantities after her long years of poverty and deprivation in Hungary.

But who doesn't love sweets?

Popping into that little bakery in Canfield Gardens, near the Underground, had been one of the day's more pleasant errands. Pápai had cooked up the plan knowing it would be an opportunity for a bit of chit-chat with the ladies who worked there, a chance to reinforce his son's admiration for his father's capacity to befriend strangers – especially women, women of any age. How he made them laugh! How he made them blush! He was a master of the dashing compliment. Now, back on the street, passing a single muffin between them as they munched away, Pápai was in the middle of regaling his son with the story of a prostitute in a brothel in Alexandria, where he'd been as a soldier. The two of them, the big man and the little boy, had paused in front of a branch of Marks and Spencer – loitering here, looking at the displays in the windows, was one of the boy's favourite pastimes – when a stranger, an elderly gentleman, approached. Well, not quite a true gentleman, but more the caricature of one, as if clipped from a 1930s magazine, a Clark Gable moustache above his colourless lips and comically formal manners.

'I heard you speaking Hungarian,' he said, raising his little green hunting hat. 'Excuse me for interrupting.' He was talking Hungarian, but his Hungarian sounded funny in the young boy's ears: he recognized the words, but the man's cheerful tone, forced mirth and manners were odd, an echo of some ancient tune on a crackling vinyl record. 'And how do you like life here in London, in the free world?' he asked Pápai, adding, 'Will you stay?' But this ersatz gentleman had chosen the wrong man, because instead of an affirmation, he received a mighty slap in the face, metaphorically at least.

But before his angry tirade could begin, Pápai had to crack a joke: 'In a country where they can't make decent coffee? Never!' And then came the lesson he had to deliver to this grotesque old man who'd appeared from out of nowhere. Pápai lectured him in ready-made journalistic lingo about the exploitation of the English working class, the imminent fall of the British Empire, the inevitable decline of capitalism, the West German army training on English soil, the atomic bomb, the Common Market, and, yes, the United States of America and the military-industrial complex. Pápai knew how to deal with such people, how to hold them at bay. At least he was convinced he knew how to, and in this instance it seemed to work, for the man with the funny moustache withdrew abruptly. Tipping his green feathered hat, he very nearly ran away. When the man had vanished, Pápai, looking after him, muttered under his breath: 'I know who sent you.'

Grabbing his son's hand, he now headed towards the chemist's on Finchley Road to get medication for his wife, and for the boy, who had had a minor accident the other day. And this was the moment when he began to sing. But, before that, he still had something to say, father to son.

'These types don't just pop up accidentally,' he told his son in a serious tone. 'I tell you, my son, and don't forget this, that was an *agent provocateur.*'

Strange: he was talking to the little boy as an equal, and he didn't care if the kid understood him or not. When they were by themselves he suddenly changed, treating his son as an alter ego, no matter that the boy didn't understand half of what he said. He didn't mince his words, he spoke from the heart, he confessed, he let on, he owned up, he avowed all the dirty little secrets of his life; he spoke freely, and he didn't care a bit if his dear son understood it all or not. He treated him as an heir who will need to know where the family treasure is hidden – how many steps and in what direction from the old tree – when the time arrives.

But when they sat down as a family – he and his wife and all the children – he invariably switched back to normal, if it could be called normal: a funny, menacing, anxious figure who had no real authority over his children. His wife ran the business that was their household – keeping the flat in order and dealing with their landlord, talking to the milkman, chatting to the neighbours, arranging for an electrician to come, painting the rooms, buying the furniture, cooking the meals, deciding how to spend every penny. Pápai, despite his formidable intellect, his wit, his quick mind and his fluency in many tongues, was a strangely absent presence at home. There he became one of the children himself, the biggest of them all – sometimes the entertainer, sometimes the bully, sometimes the boss. His portly frame may have taken up a huge space in the flat, but this space was more or less empty. True, he used his scathing words and fast hands to discipline his children, and thought nothing of it, having himself been reared with the lightning-quick slaps that occasionally rained down on him from his loving but temperamental mother, Margit, a widow, whose only son he was. But he'd grown up without a father, and never truly learned what it was to be one.

'The black girl in that dark room, you know ...' he said, continuing his tale of the Alexandria prostitute as his little boy stared longingly through the shop window at a painted, pug-nosed wooden Pinocchio with yellow hair and a little blue bonnet from which hung a tiny copper bell. How he yearned to get this puppet as a birthday present! 'A woman from Nubia – know where Nubia is? Under Egypt, but they say it's *above* Egypt, yes, over there everything is upside down, and the blackest people on earth live there, and they are so black you can't see them at night. And did I tell you this?' – Pápai suddenly cut short his own story, for he loved digressions – 'The beautiful slender girl standing by our train in the desert, there was a bet about whether she was a he or a she, and someone threw a coin to her – or him? – and shouted that she should raise her rags to show us what was below them. Oh yes, we were betting on it, we were, and she saw the money flying her way through the air, and then she raised her rags as the train slowly moved on, and, wouldn't you know it, that beautiful girl was indeed a boy, and how. He had quite an instrument, my son. But back to the Nubian girl in that dark room, that room which reeked of the unmistakable stench of Arab brothels in Egypt, so unpleasant at first, so enticing later. Well, she took that majestic gown of hers off her panther-like body and, wouldn't you know it, she was shaved all over, not a single hair anywhere, know what I mean?'

It was at this moment that the Hungarian with the Clark Gable moustache had interrupted them. A little intermezzo that Pápai handled briskly and efficiently.

'Where was I? Did I tell you about the soldier in the training camp who did nothing all day but pick up dry leaves in the courtyard? While picking them up he muttered to himself, "This is not it. This is not it" – and he threw the dry leaves away. He was sent to a doctor, and after three weeks he came out with a slip of paper in his hand, beaming, "This is it!" It was his discharge paper, and he left us for ever. And then there was a chap in the habit of helping himself to other people's beer and then leaving the bottles lying about. He'd begin by asking, "Can I?" But, not waiting for a reply, he'd take a good long guzzle. Until one day another soldier, fed up with this brazen behaviour, prepared a special treat for him: after drinking a bottle of beer he pissed in it. He then sat down on top of a hill and set his bottle down. Well, the other chap came by and asked "Can I?", and as usual he took a good long guzzle without waiting for an answer. But never again. Oh, that face!' Pápai laughed, still amused by this scene he'd either heard of or had really seen. 'I myself never drank beer and never smoked a single cigarette, no, I always gave my ration to others – for money, you know. So I was rich then, I could travel to see your mother. And, by the way, did I tell you about that girl I took in my lap, a very sweet girl? We were kissing, and suddenly she farted, and that fart rolled all the way down my trousers, like a marble, all the way to my shoes. I could never kiss that girl again. Why? I don't know. Anyhow, this black Nubian girl, what breasts she had, full breasts, and rosy lips, and the blackest of eyes. Well, when I saw that she was shaved, you know, I couldn't do a thing – yes, that was it for me. What a shame! She was the queen of the brothel, but I could do nothing, you understand? We used to go to the brothel after school back in Hungary. I had a special price, you know: the madam loved my rosy cheeks, pinching me whenever she saw me. She was an old lady with huge gold earrings, painted like an old doll. One day she led me into a room that had a hole in the wall behind a painting. Yes, she took me in there at half price just to take a peep and see what the others were doing. And a sister of a classmate worked there, too, and we all tried her, we did, just for fun.'

Pinocchio in his short blue trousers and red shirt was still smiling at the little boy.

But then Pápai grabbed his son's hand, pulling the boy away from the shop window as he headed off and began to sing to himself – of all songs, 'It's a Long Way to Tipperary'. He didn't have time to think about a puppet – he had other worries. Chaotic plans filled his head, irresolvable decisions to be made, moments of clarity and confusion furiously following one another.

And then his son, his favourite, told him that he was an idiot.

* * *

That morning Pápai had arrived at 6.30, after only three hours' sleep – sweating and out of breath, having taken a taxi to get there on time – at MTI's Fleet Street office. There, to his great astonishment, he found his colleague, the old guy, 'the old reactionary', as Pápai not very affectionately used to call him during confidential conversations with his wife in the marital bed after midnight. Well, the old reactionary was already sitting by the telex machine, busily typing away, not even looking up at Pápai but only murmuring something that could be taken as a greeting. But of course it wasn't a greeting. It was a curse. Things had unmistakably deteriorated in the past month.

A few months earlier Pápai's boss himself, the president of the Hungarian News Agency, Comrade Barcs – originally Bartsch, but Hungarianizing the German was not a bad idea after the Second World War – had come to London to set Pápai straight on what the problem was with the news Pápai was sending home from London, and why it mostly landed in the wastepaper basket after emerging from the telex machine in Budapest, in MTI's grey building on Naphegy, a leafy residential hill beside the block of flats within which was the permanent residence of Pápai's family. Yes, Pápai had seen MTI headquarters every day, under the Buda Castle, even after being chased out of the Agency.

The explanation was in fact more like an execution. Pápai felt as if he were standing before a firing squad.

From that day on, the old reactionary – that seventy-six-year-old man with perfect English manners who'd lived in London since the Twenties and had done all he could to make it his home– used a different tone with Pápai. Dr Rácz was performing a careful balancing act: the Hungarian embassy had recruited him once again during the post-1956 years of consolidation to demonstrate to the world that Hungary was 'opening up', and his neutral and 'progressive' attitude was highly valued. Ever since the boss had visited, Dr Rácz knew exactly the fate of this 'fat guy', this 'obstinate, obtuse and obsolete figure' as he used to call him, with a fine sense of irony, adding, rolling his eyes, 'And that is an understatement.' Yes, Rácz knew that the days of this colleague, whom he never considered a real colleague, were numbered. He was rude to him, and could not forgive Pápai for forcing him to be rude.

It was a rather complex and sophisticated manoeuvre on the part of Comrade Barcs, who wasn't a Party member, but was naturally on intimate terms with the regime's intelligence service. A puppet-member of the Hungarian parliament, he had sat on the jury of the most infamous show trial in Eastern Europe, the Rajk trial. He must have known perfectly well that Forgács was Pápai. He had to tread carefully. Before acting, he had to prove to the Intelligence Bureau – because even a matter such as the appointment of a common-or-garden foreign correspondent was approved at the highest levels of the Party – that parachuting Pápai into the serpent's nest of the Hungarian News Agency had been a big mistake. He also had to defend his staff. Having been successful in his previous role, as president of the Hungarian Football Association, Comrade Barcs was acutely aware of the importance of gaining the confidence of his staff, and at MTI it was of course made up mainly of Party members, along with some non-members who were all affiliated with, and tested and trusted by, the regime. To appease them, Comrade Barcs had to undo Pápai, but to do so he had to prove to the intelligence service why he was unsuited for the job. The painstakingly precise letters he'd written preceding the boss's visit, which we shall not quote in detail, contain a shrewd observation deserving of our attention. This was apart from Barcs's efforts to provide cover for MTI's grumbling staff, who from the beginning had sought to hinder Pápai's efforts to become a foreign correspondent, and who, failing in this, had sought to annihilate him altogether once he had been nominated as chief of the London bureau. Pápai was an intruder, a virus, an alien body put there by the Party and the intelligence service; he was the hated 'parachutist'. He had to be undermined. Destroyed. But it was not as simple as that. Barcs had to have connections to do so. And here he found Pápai's weak point.

Barcs had detected in Pápai's reports a paranoid tendency to see conspiracy even where there was none: a cabal, a plot of international news organizations, of seemingly opposed parties. Pápai was constantly trying to make news out of news-making itself; that is, of nothing, or rather, of something that had no real substance. As Barcs saw it, Pápai was neglecting a genuine correspondent's real investigative work. And so Barcs accused him of filling some of his reports with suppositions, guesses and obscure references to unnamed sources. As for Pápai, he honestly admitted some of his mistakes – he wasn't stupid, after all. He knew what he was doing: he had remained a fighter, a revolutionary, all his life. Some stuff even seemed to have been made up, invented on the spur of the moment within a narrow ideological framework. As a result, Pápai's stories were, on more than one occasion, about the world-wide conspiracy of Manichean powers to destroy the forces of good – better known as the Soviet Union, the Socialist Camp, the Sacred Aim of Global Communism. This attitude of Pápai's, who was otherwise a professional, was doubtless reinforced by the new, secret role he had to play, even if it was theoretical in the beginning.

Leading the double life of an intelligence agent – the paranoia a secret agent had to cultivate! – had become a sort of spiritual burden on Pápai, exacerbating the constant tension within him. Not that every Hungarian journalist who became a secret collaborator of the notorious II/3 – Department II/3 of the Interior Ministry, that is, which from 1963 was re-dubbed III/1 – was destined to wind up in a lunatic asylum. And yet it is not wholly unreasonable to assume that this double life of his heightened his tendency for paranoid thinking. He arrived at his Fleet Street office like some animal being chased by a predator – sweating, breathing heavily – and here was Dr Dezső Károly Rácz, sitting at the telex machine, busily typing up his report. Pápai was exasperated.

'When can I use the telex?'

'How should I know? Come back later.'

There stood Pápai, in the middle of an awakening London, on busy Fleet Street early one morning, thrown out of his own office, not knowing where to go, where to turn. In a few hours he had to be in Parliament, where an important session would be underway; he had to do his job, he had to go on, as a man with an amputated leg forgets what has happened to him, continues as if everything were normal, feeling the intolerable phantom pain in the missing limb. Pápai was losing touch again with the world, losing the solid ground under his feet.

Call my wife and ask her? This thought flashed through his mind, but, shivering in the early-morning breeze, he refrained from acting on it. He had to eat something quickly, anything, just to calm his nerves.

And he had one more very good reason to be nervous.

A scandal had erupted in his own household a few days earlier, and it was approaching its climax. It had started when his perhaps over-inquisitive wife had opened an envelope and read a letter her niece – a guest in their home, living with them for a few weeks as an au pair in London to perfect her English – had written, but not yet sent, to her parents back in Hungary. She was a lucky girl. After an almost year-long fight among the relatives about who would send their daughter to stay with them, she was the chosen one. She had won, and now her presence made the Pápais' almost comfortable, idyllic home in Hampstead just as crowded and disorderly as their flat in Budapest had been, where one could not move about without bumping into someone. It was not easy to keep four children in a three-room London flat. Conflicts invariably erupted: the bigger kids needed space of their own, and nobody could have any privacy without some sacrifice or other. Neither Pápai nor his wife had a room of their own. Yes, they were used to it. But the kids were everywhere, and hysterical arguments flared up every day. And of course the children brought friends home, and there were always guests from different parts of the world. In short, the London flat was full to the brim, and the food in the fridge invariably ran out sooner than expected, along with the money. Now, with the niece living there, things were even more of a squeeze, and the parents' nerves were fraying.

And then the scandal. Pápai's wife happened upon the letter, which her niece had left lying around, and which she – perhaps not so inadvertently – had then read. The contents scandalized her. Yes, the childish complaining about the circumstances of her home was like salt rubbed into her wounds. The fact that there was at least a grain of truth in the vicious caricature the niece had written to satisfy her parents – who already had a bad opinion of Pápai and company – made it hurt all the more. Now, the niece's parents had always made a good show at family gatherings back in Hungary of being diplomatic: they had never been the ones, for example, to start a shouting match about what and how a decent Jew should do and think about Israel. But Pápai's wife felt, not without cause, that this letter was an act of treason. After all, feeling obliged to swallow the bitter pill and take in the noisy girl, who in any case wasn't her favourite relative, she had sacrificed much. Pápai's wife was aware that she might have been overreacting, but she was on edge, knowing perfectly well her husband's precarious situation at the Hungarian News Agency, and trying to soothe him every night at home. No, there was no other solution: the girl had to go, she must be sent home. It wasn't an easy decision, but Pápai's wife was adamant.

Well, it could happen in any family. But the story had a twist. And this was Pápai's secret – a secret he didn't even dare share with his wife. Checkmate.

Where am I again? thought Pápai, on Finchley Road, before singing a song:

> *It's a long way to Tipperary,*
> *It's a long way to go.*
> *It's a long way to Tipperary*
> *To the sweetest girl I know!*
> *Goodbye, Piccadilly,*
> *Farewell, Leicester Square!*
> *It's a long, long way to Tipperary,*
> *But my heart's right there.*

I am at the starting point again. Nowhere. I am a nobody once more.

Now, the niece – the one who'd written that malevolent letter describing in rather rude terms the Pápais' family life in London – had not quite accidentally befriended the future wife of an up-and-coming young English historian. It so happened. And it so happened, too, that the latter had just published a rather successful book, *The Appeasers*. And this historian, since visiting Budapest a year earlier, had been, it so happened, in the crosshairs of Hungarian intelligence. He was, after all, something of a leftist –a communist almost. In this respect he was not unlike many young scholars at Cambridge and Oxford. But, belonging as he did to an upper-class family, it so happened that he also had good connections with the British Conservative government. Hence he had access to government archives. He was, then, ideal material for a spy. During his Budapest visit, therefore, Hungarian intelligence had 'befriended' him, by way of agents masquerading as historians or historians who were in fact agents. These contacts had subsequent rendezvous with the young man in Vienna and Paris and had sent him friendly postcards which he'd answered warmly. Indeed, he seemed to understand exactly what was at stake, and all seemed to be working out quite well. He was candid in his critiquing of the British political system. He enjoyed his stay in Budapest a great deal. He had many friends there, at least he thought so. And he already had a code name in the dossiers: 'Carrel'.

Pápai – and this was to be his first real job – had to furnish information about 'Carrel', and he had to somehow manipulate the niece's movements in London. A perfect task for a new spy to prove he is up to the job. Alas, it fell to him in the moment of his effective dismissal from the Hungarian News Agency, where his days were cruelly numbered. What a mess! Still, he had to make an effort, or show that he was making an effort, and he hoped, perhaps not without reason, that if he succeeded somehow, he would be kept on as a correspondent as well. The comrades would talk to Barcs on his behalf. He could gain time. A glimmer of hope, and now this thunderbolt: the insolent little niece – the ideal bait for a big, big catch – had to be sent back to Budapest, back to her parents on the first plane. There was no way out of it. She couldn't stay a day longer. How could he explain his fix to his wife when he could not tell her the plain truth? Madness.

She looked at him in disbelief. 'You want her to stay?' He tried to convince her, but she cut him short. 'No!' she shouted. 'Never!'

She was a wild one. She could disappear in an instant. She was not afraid of scandal. She was not a frightened little thing. She was a wild cat when she wanted to be. One Friday evening when she was sixteen, a young communist, she'd gone home, into her room, and turned on the radio. Her father appeared at once in her room, turned off the radio and reminded her that it was Sabbath, the time of silence and reflection, and the loud music would certainly disturb the religious feelings of their neighbours. He was once a believing Jew but not any more – a cautious atheist perhaps – and, like a schoolmaster, gave a pedantic lesson to his disobedient daughter about the respect they owed to other people's feelings. They had a heated discussion. She, a revolutionary, shouted into his face, 'All religion is a lie, a remnant of the old system, opium for the people!' And she turned on the

radio again. She wanted to listen to Beethoven. And then
the unbelievable happened. Her father slapped her face. The
classic Makarenko slap. He'd never done this before and he
would never do it again. He regretted it instantly, this gentle
man, this teacher who had never hit any of his pupils, had
never lost his temper, or only once, and that one time just
had to be with his beloved, wildcat daughter. And then she
ran, a gazelle, through Tel Aviv. She jumped onto a military
truck and vanished in the north of the country. She was a
runner too, an athlete. The fastest in her school. She wasn't
very studious, but was a dreamy, book-devouring idealist.
And she ran away to become a tutor in an orphanage-camp
somewhere in the north, close to the Golan. And it didn't
take long for her to fall in love with a boy who was, in her
eyes, as beautiful as Michelangelo's David. A real prince.
And he was a Christian. She had a thing for lovers who were
out of the ordinary. A Christian Arab. Who came to fetch
her one evening on a black horse. She jumped onto the back
of the horse behind him and they vanished in the darkness.
She was not to be blackmailed, no, she was not to be tamed
by anyone.

* * *

Lieutenant Takács was not satisfied. The conversation in the
secret flat in Budapest had not been pleasant. Lieutenant
Takács didn't give a damn about Pápai's personal problems or

his official problems. What he needed was his co-operation. Pápai didn't even write anything down, as he'd promised. Takács had to question him slowly, methodically, and, what was more, he would have to write the report himself, and that didn't make him happy. Sensing Pápai's distractedness, he simply thought that Pápai was a lazy man, and he told him so. The business involving 'Carrel' was too important to be thwarted by a lazy, superficial agent like Pápai.

Little did he know that every little thing Pápai told him about his wife's niece – and Takács practically had to use pliers to tear out each one – was spiritual torture for him.

Failure again. Again failure.

An old family feud bound Pápai's tongue more strongly than any Sicilian code of silence. His wife's family was, at least theoretically, also *his* family: 'my phantom family', as he put it. And yet this family was only the phantom pain of his own, for ever lost family. It was little more than the shadow of a family, a family in effigy, a prosthetic limb of a family, one which never gave him the respect and sympathy he so craved. No, instead he suffered their contempt, opposition, denigration: he was never, never accepted by them.

And here was an opportunity for revenge – but in a strange way Pápai felt utterly debilitated, unable to speak a word. Lieutenant Takács did not understand why this otherwise loquacious journalist, this communist with such a healthy sense of humour and broad knowledge of the world, was behaving like a child keeping mum, or, rather, a stuttering, muttering child who contradicted himself with every word painfully drawn out of him.

But Takács, the able lieutenant of Department II/3, didn't know that he was talking to a heap of ash, a shadow of a man who'd lost all faith in the world and in himself. He was not a Jew, and he was not not a Jew either. He was both. And nothing.

All his wife's aunts and uncles had followed her father and mother to Palestine in the Twenties, but some of them, like the parents of the insolent niece, had gone back to Hungary or thereabouts at the worst possible moment, between the two wars, not having found life attractive enough in the Palestinian Mandate of the British Empire, or simply having been thrown out by the colonial powers for subversive activities. The Brits were in a precarious position, caught between the Arab and Jewish populations, and when they encountered illegal immigrants who happened to be communists, they were unmerciful.

The family's strangely contrary travels, the opposing directions they took, crossed and mirrored each other. When Pápai, as a young man, first escaped the approaching apocalypse in 1939, stepping onto the train in Gara de Nord, Bucharest, his mother, who had furnished him with a passport and money and all the goods she could heap on her beloved son for his daring journey to the Middle East, told him, to explain why she was staying behind, 'They won't hurt women.' No, she had no idea of the horrors that would engulf her. Even as Pápai went one way, half of his future wife's family had done the opposite, returning only to suffer the horrors of the fascist regime. But, in a strange twist of events, they all miraculously survived. During which time, as they said later, he was living a happy life in sunlit Palestine. This, then, became a reproach and an accusation: how could he oppose Zionism if he had never himself experienced on his body and in his soul the atrocities of the war? To him, this was the cruellest argument. Why would he come back with his young wife *after* the war? Why would he demand the support of a family if he was being so irrational? Why did they come back? Why didn't they stay there?

But, when they were still in Palestine, his newlywed wife had written in English to a friend, describing it as *hell*, nothing but *hell*:

Tonight I write to you with a fresh feeling of resistance, with a stronger will to struggle and with a clear knowledge of our difficult task here! You know that Palestine today is a hell. With all its smallness it contains all the ingredients necessary to make it a great camp of suffering. This is what the English wanted and this is how they succeeded in their aims. There is no use to write more about the present situation, what you know, with some exaggeration, from other papers is enough. You have only to interpret it, to read in between the lines. So we live here and sometimes a flash of thought demands from us to run away from here. It is easy to hide in a mountaineous village, where no paper ever reach, or to go to Ethiopia and work there in a small village. It is all too easy. But we must face it. *Without facing it we shall agree to the foreign rule, to the ruthless crazy imperialism. And you know: we don't want to run away, because it is against our class-consciousness. Not because it is easier to fight but because we want to live with a clear conscience.*

I am sorry for the long sentences, but you understand me, dear friend.

I work in the hospital for a long day ... It is so far from the town. But it is good, I have work and earn my living. My husband studies, but unfortunately much of his time is exhausted in other things than chemistry ... You know the constant need for people ... and it is too sad that it is not realized that he must finish his studies well. Science is not a joke! It cannot be done superficially.

Strange words. But this is how they felt, two young communists with ideals in their obstinate heads. She was a good girl, Bruria, a young woman of conviction who could write a clear political analysis of the situation, who did in fact write a letter about the *'burning problems of Palestine'* – on 26

December 1946, exactly one week after her marriage – that is striking for matching the tone of some of the reports Mrs Pápai would submit to Department III/1 thirty years later:

Now I am in Jerusalem, living in a curious suspension. I can start to work next week in a job that will give me many opportunities to develop and teach. It is in a Child-Welfare-Centre, in the old city of Jerusalem. It is the poorest and dirtiest section of Jerusalem and may be of Palestine. The only objection to start the work is the extremely low salary. It is 9 pounds monthly, with the additional pay for high cost of living it will be about 17–19 Palestinian pounds. It is less than minimum for us. My husband is a student of chemistry and he does not earn except occasionally by working after his studies. It is truly a problem. It seems that I'll have to continue a hospital job, where I'll earn more, but where I shall not get any satisfaction. Anyhow all is quite pale in comparison with the burning problems of Palestine. The X. congress of the P.C.P. [Palestine Communist Party] *has formulated its decisions in a small pamphlet. I'll send it to my sister. Please ask her to translate especially those parts which concern the Jewish and Arab relationship. I hope that soon the Party will send an English translation. It will be good to translate it to French.*

You will notice that the question of Immigration is formulated in a very tactical manner. The party under

*the present circumstance cannot find a way to bring the
question in a more direct and open manner. I cannot agree,
but at the same time my only place is with the C.P. I'll work
in the Y.C.L.* [Young Communist League]

*As you know probably from the newspapers, the Zionist
congress in Basel completed its session without reaching
any final decisions. The main discussions were around the
question: 'What imperialism should the Zionist movement
choose for its protector? The British or American?' The
American sector in the congress is the most reactionary
section of this jingoistic movement, and they had a
majority. Now the Zionist activity will be operated on
'American Orientation'. The 'progressive' parties, those
who call themselves Marxists–Zionists, decided to move for
Weizmann, who is for 'British Orientation'. The end results
are: Weizmann's proposals to go to London's sponsored
'round-table' for Palestine was defeated. The new 'higher
Zionist committee' prepares new proposals for Zionist
activities in the future. Most of the delegates in the congress
are for continuation of the 'illegal' immigration into Palestine,
and for new 'settlement-movement' which actually means
new Zionist strongholds in different places in Palestine.*

In all this political games the C.P. stands as the only
*anti-imperialistic factor, and is confronted by very difficult
tasks. We are very weak in Jerusalem. We have not entered
at all into the working-class circle. Our comrades have not*

developed yet the spirit of public, social worker. I think that
Jerusalem is particularly difficult for our party work. It is
a town with 'comportments', with a strange individualistic
stamp on its people.
    Nevertheless I'll work hard and do my best.

It was the summer of 1947 when Pápai and his beautiful
wife – his prey, who made men turn their heads in disbelief –
got off the train that arrived from Prague at Keleti railway
station. Leaving everything behind, they had escaped from
war-torn Palestine, where they felt it was impossible for
them to stay. For Pápai, this meant burning his bridges for
the second time in his life. And so they arrived in Budapest,
the land of hope, the 'furnace of the future', not knowing
how they would thrive. They had jumped into the void. Her
family had to take care of them, finding money for them and
handing down furniture, but they were treated by some of
her relatives as traitors. Traitors of Israel. It was a strange
family, his wife's. Pápai was an alien in their midst and
remained so, a double traitor to the cause of world Jewry in
their eyes. He struggled hard to prove that he was a man, a
capable man, but all he had to show for himself after long
years of struggle were his four children and a beautiful wife.
Everything else was a sham, a fake. That is how he felt.

* * *

When, holding the hand of his son, he stepped out of 13 Netherhall Gardens, the famous Elm Tree House, and started down the hill in the pleasant breeze of a late spring afternoon, Pápai started to talk, and his son, although he'd heard some of these stories before, was happy to hear them again.

'You know your grandma kicked me in the arse once? Did you know that, and why she did it?'

'She kicked you in the arse?'

'She did. She also broke an umbrella over my head when I brought shame on her on account of how I did in a school exam before all the other parents. As we stepped out the front door she began hitting my head with it. And it broke. And then she cried. And then we laughed. And then we returned home to find two ladies sitting in the living room, two boring old ladies who were collecting money for the Keren Kayemeth.'

The boy didn't understand what Keren Kayemeth meant, but he adored words he didn't understand. He played with them when he was alone, throwing them up into the air and watching them fall.

'They were collecting money to buy land in the Promised Land. "A land without people for people without land," as Mr Balfour so famously put it.'

The boy didn't ask who this Mr Balfour was, but all was still well. It was good not to understand things.

'Or maybe it wasn't him who said it, maybe everyone

was saying it back then, 1936, I remember the day, yes, they were having tea and talking about building a homeland for the Jews, and they said to my mum: "But there is nobody there. It is empty, it is a desert" – and when I heard this and I saw my mother opening her purse and giving them quite a lot of money, I simply asked, "But aren't there any Arabs there?" And my mum had a fit of anger – she jumped up and kicked me right in the arse so hard that I flew out of the room like a ball. I was sixteen. *Bang*, right in the arse, she could have played for any football team with a kick like that, I can tell you. I was laughing, I enjoyed having a mum like her. Anyway, when the two old ladies left she was still a bit angry, though I wasn't. She was baffled by what she'd done and already regretted it. She just couldn't control herself, you know. So then she kissed me and gave me some money and said, "You idiot. They were my best clients, silly boy" – because the ladies came regularly to buy carpets from us, and my mum was the best business-woman in the world, you know, after my dad died, and we were robbed of the little shop, Friedmann and Company, we were robbed by the Company, and my father always dreamed of renaming it Friedmann and Son, he told me, like in the Dickens novel *Dombey and Son*. And now my mother was left there, without a penny, and with me, and she started this business with a little peasant girl sent by her family to help her, yes, they started weaving carpets,

carpets so beautiful that in the end she sold them even to the royal family in Bucharest, and we were quite rich, I was really spoiled, and the two ladies with their collection tin for the Keren Kayemeth bought from her regularly. And I remember that we had to visit my father's tomb every year, on Rosh Hashanah.'

As Pápai and his son arrived at the foot of the hill where Netherhall Gardens meets Finchley Road, the boy started to muse over the words 'Rosh Hashanah'. He didn't ask what they meant. Distracted, he had meanwhile missed a few words his father had spoken.

'Aren't you listening?'

'I am.'

'So what is Rosh Hashanah?'

'I don't know.'

'You are right not to let it trouble you – it could be any day in the calendar. But all the same, it was at Rosh Hashanah, every year ... in autumn, and it was usually quite cold already ... it was at Rosh Hashanah, in the kitchen, which was huge, because we had two big flats on the first floor, one being the workshop, where the girls wove the carpets, beautiful girls I liked to chat to and who were always singing. Anyway, it was at Rosh Hashanah every year, in the huge kitchen, that my mum told the maid ... we had three maids, actually, one specially for me, who took me to school every morning ... it was in that kitchen that she told the maid to bake ten crescent rolls. Know why it had to be ten?'

'No, I don't.'

'Well, you know, the ten righteous men of the Bible, the Tzadikim. And we also went to the cemetery.'

They were already standing in front of the bakery in Canfield Gardens, but Pápai wanted to finish his story before going in. They should have gone to see the doctor first, because the son had had a little accident two days earlier: he'd fainted at the embassy after sipping from his mother's cognac, and his father had carried him through the crowd on his shoulders. How good the boy had felt riding on the huge shoulders of his father among those lit-up faces all turned towards them, all the ladies looking at him. How proud he'd been of his father! And how proud of himself for fainting – yes, it was so nice to faint, everybody asking, 'What happened with the little boy?'

'And there were always beggars standing there in the cold, waiting for the rich folks to give them money, and my mum gave them the warm rolls, and they followed us to my father's grave to pray with us, to that black marble grave which was so cold, you know, and I had to kiss it, every year I had to, and I hated kissing it – I was scared that my lips would freeze – but my mother insisted. Perhaps the only ritual she insisted on. Yes, in fact, the only ritual she ever insisted on.'

Silence fell upon them, Pápai and the boy. Pápai took a

deep breath and started for the bakery's entrance, almost forgetting that he was not alone. He looked back at his son for a moment.

'You know,' he said, 'I shall never forget it. The silence of all those tall, black men in the room. My father's yellow face in the bed. Chrome yellow. A path opened up for me, a path made by the people standing on each side. I was only four, you know, and it was such a long way to his bed. And he was yellow, chrome yellow. I remember thinking, why is he so yellow? You know, when the big war broke out, he was already twenty-eight, and he didn't want to go to the war. It was the First World War, you know, so he smoked two hundred cigarettes and swam through the icy Szamos River and almost died of fever, and ten years later he – you know, his family didn't want him to marry my mother, because her family was so poor, it was a mésalliance in their eyes, a mésalliance. You know what that means?'

He didn't wait for an answer or offer an explanation. But that didn't matter. The word flittered before the eyes of the boy, like a butterfly. It was beautiful.

'My mother's family didn't want the marriage. They said, "This Friedmann is a sick man. He has tuberculosis, besides which, he'll never have offspring." *Offspring.* Yes, they liked this word, because to make things worse, he was beaten up once in a brawl in a pub and lost one of his balls – luckily not the one that produces semen, but the other ball, the one that stores semen, you know, the one that's always a bit colder than the other one. Did you know that? Otherwise you wouldn't be standing here and looking at me with your blue eyes, my dear little son. And you know, I remember my dad: I had to go right up to his deathbed, and I was terribly afraid, especially of the silence – yes, I shall never forget that terrible silence. And then my dad put his hand on my head, and his hand was so heavy, my son, so heavy, I never thought a hand could be so heavy. Never.'

Under the Buda Castle

She must speak to them.

When she finally reached the second floor, which, counting the mezzanine, was actually the third – after climbing the steep spiral staircase, where it was advisable to stay close to the wall, because the steps became dangerously narrow towards the centre – Mrs Pápai, gasping for breath, found the door open. For a moment it seemed closed, swinging back and forth almost imperceptibly in the breeze. The door had three windows of frosted glass: the uppermost of which could be locked from the inside with a small latch, but it was open now. As Mrs Pápai peered through that little window, a draught blew the flat's musty odour right into her face. Not wanting to press the buzzer, with the tip of her shoe she nudged the door, which, creaking and groaning, opened slowly before her. An elegant black plate above the letterbox still held, in gold letters, the name Marcell Forgács. As if on a gravestone. The lukewarm air generated by the flat's central heating, several days of mustiness and the sour scent of spoiled food struck her at once, and no one answered her sharp, loud, impatient cry. When she now gave the door a good kick, a fire engine, siren blaring, whizzed over the parquet floor. She had to sneeze. She took two uncertain steps forward and, with a big sigh, picked up the little red toy and put it on the table. She opened a window. Judging from the objects scattered about, the inhabitants must have been home not long before – yes, maybe they just popped out somewhere for a little while, whether to the shops, the chemist's, the post office, or the playground. Through the wide-open window the heat from the radiator streamed out into the cold autumn afternoon.

A mother yearns for the manifestations of love. When her grown-up children receive her with cigarette butts, unwashed dishes, unmade beds, dirty laundry strewn on beds, on chairs, on the floor, rotten and withered food in the fridge, spoiled milk in the plastic bags it came in, a dirty floor, strands of hair all over the place, a toilet bowl spotted with desiccated faeces, the smell of unflushed urine, and books thrown about everywhere, and not the love and filial warmth she yearns for, the manifestations of love and care

she so longs for – well, something sinks in the vicinity of her
heart. Or in her head? For she has just arrived home (her
home?) from work or a visit to the hospital (which she's been
doing for four years almost without interruption), and how
good it would have felt to be greeted by signs of care and
love, and not with a [sic] dirty, smelly, mucky, messy rooms.
How much good it would have done her, a clean, made bed,
a good cup of hot tea, a few warm words. The absence of the
tenderness or the selfless goodwill a mother yearns for from
her grown-up children can't help but raise the question:
where did she go so wrong that this desire for love yields
only a knot of pain in the vicinity of her heart or in her head?
Is she being served the dish she cooked? She cooked and
concocted poison? And fed it to her young children, and now,
twenty years later, this is the result? The poison? I lied! I
denied my depression. It seems I should have stripped myself
totally bare, opened myself up, revealed myself howling away,
so 'mum's depression and its cause' would have slashed its
way into my poor children's souls. Would this 'honesty' have
brought more understanding kids into the world? Would the
yearned-for love have then been given?

A petty (!)

mother.

The boys' room looked out on Buda Castle, the royal palace,
whose grey rear façade belonged to the flat every bit as much

as the furniture gifted or lent by friends and relatives but never given back, one piece so different from the next and yet, over time, starting to resemble each other in a strange way. The three-part castle wall, which faced Naphegy, that leafy residential hill, comprised a row of projections, balustrades, loggias, black gaping windows and walled-up arches, and in the middle of the grey façade six Corinthian columns supported a huge terrace, with six blackened statues, half-dressed female figures, swimming in the air above it. The elegant dome that crowned the castle had been blasted away: the royal palace had been more ornament than a fortress to be defended and had taken on its final form exactly at a time when royalty had for all practical purposes lost its historical significance. The Austrian emperor had sometimes slept there when he happened to be in town, and then later so had Horthy, the regent, who likewise was no king. Roaring lions' heads looked down from the pointed arches of burnt-out lancet windows; the façade was pockmarked with chafes and holes, compliments of machine-gun and mortar fire; and here and there along the foot of the castle wall were enormous shattered crossbeams and heaps of rubble a storey high.

The whole of this monumental grey pile, this colossal structure swimming in the moonlight, was like a faded postcard on a wall or an impossible-to-open closet in the corner of a room. It towered there above the buildings, empty and fit for nothing. The green horse. On a platform, above the scraggly bushes and thin trees sprawling forth from the cracks in the supporting brick wall, right across from the boys' room, stood a prancing green horse – though it seemed more to be floating there, who knows since when. The horse was every bit as green as the castle's caved-in dome. A fairy-tale horse that had thrown off its rider. Truth be told, it had not thrown off its rider – though it was not as if the boys could have known this. In fact, on the far side of the beast – the side the boys could not see from their window – was not a horseman but, instead, a mere horseherd, a kind of Hungarian cowboy, the sort who wears pantaloons. Yes, there he was, trying to tame that unruly green horse in front of the former Royal Riding School. Now, the boys had never seen this nameless horseherd – they didn't even know he existed, even though he was none other than the *Horse Tamer* who'd wound up there in 1901 after appearing at the Exposition Universelle in Paris, and had later survived both world wars. Ladies strolling up or descending from Castle Hill were partial to having their pictures taken next to the pedestal of the frisky horse, which must have been a sensitive spot in the castle-hill, because in the winter of '44 the square had been guarded by a scared and sulky SS armoured division. From the boys' window, however, nothing could be seen except a heap of rubble – entering the grounds of the castle was strictly prohibited. There, in a wooden booth, sat a security guard whose job it was to keep people away from the shut-up building, and whenever he spied children, he'd emerge, flailing his arms and shouting and scaring them away, and as the children ran off, only the green horse remained there, standing steadfastly in its place.

Even as she got off the tram she was full of grim foreboding. With a careworn expression she approached the block of flats, and had no desire to encounter acquaintances.[1] Hurriedly she passed a snow-white cluster of statues: a peasant leader, who

---

[1] DATA SHEET
on the case-filed individual
(to be filled out by an operative employee)

1. First and last name: ... *MRS MARCELL FORGÁCH*

2. Former name (maiden name): ... *BRURIA AVI-SHAUL*

3. Birthplace, year, month, day: ... *Jerusalem, 1922 December 3*

4. Mother's name: ... *Yedidya Lea*

5. Education: ... *college of health care*

6. Social class origin: ... *intelligentsia*

7. Citizenship: ... *Hungarian*

8. Nationality: ... *Palestinian*

9. Occupation: ... *housewife*

10. Employer (according to the actual situation): ...

11. Monthly wage (according to the actual situation): ...

12. Address (according to the actual situation): ... Budapest, District III, 22 Kerék Street

13. Code name (indicate if changed): ... MRS PÁPAI

14. Basis of recruitment: ... *patriotism*

15. Date of recruitment: ... *March 1975*

16. Recruitment officer: ... *József Stökl, Police Capt.*

17. Classification (indicate if changed): ...

18. Line of employment (indicate if changed): ... *Zionist organizations, as well as Hebrew–English translator*

had been burned on a fiery throne, stood there alone, in the centre, with colossal muscles, a corselet of chainmail draping his trunk, mace in hand, and – as seen from the pavement – looking at least a head higher than the castle façade. Behind him, a serpentine road led up to the castle. Here, up until the late Fifties, before a low and humble wall, as if carved from the stones of that wall, stood the monument to the artillery-men of the First World War: six horses in two rows, their heads bent, with all their might dragging a heavy cannon stuck in the mud, a helmeted artilleryman seated on three of the horses, and inscribed on the wall of the memorial, among other things, were the names of the cities torn from Hungary by the Treaty of Trianon. The regent, Horthy, who had a penchant for erecting monuments, had inaugurated it himself in '37: a wreath for every city, twenty-nine of them hung all about like lifejackets on an ocean liner, but then this ocean liner had sunk, and after the war children played hide and seek by the feet of horses that had had their heads torn off, horsemen whose heads were blown away – the children saw these harnessed beasts as lions, not horses. And, further back, a relic of the palace of the great Renaissance king, Matthias, stood a single, time-gnawed granite column, like the denuded trunk of a tree.

The tram no longer passed by their building, rattling like a toolbox being shaken, rousing the residents from their deepest dreams at dawn. The stop had been moved a hundred metres to the far side of what had once been a fountain and was now a meadow of flowers – closer to Naphegy, full of the bones of fallen soldiers, unexploded mines, the remains of unfired cartridges and magazines, and mysterious caves reeking of piss and shit. There had been a time when one of the rougher kids from their building would step from the front door, leap right onto the steps of the moving tram's rear platform, not even bothering to unlatch the iron railing, wave exultantly at those he'd left behind, and then, after a bumpy little ride to the top of the slope, jump off the steps right in front of the little neighbourhood cinema and buy tickets to the evening show. The whole thing had the atmosphere of a village. In summer the ice-man came, fine shards flying in the sunlight every which way as the garrulous chap chopped away at the blocks with a hatchet, using a cramp iron to pull them from his wagon down into the buckets of the locals who'd quickly gathered around it. Coal arrived on lorries, the coal-dust scintillating and its smell wafting through the air as soot-faced musclemen shovelled the briquettes or coke into large woven baskets which they carried inside on their backs or else poured right into the coal chute beside the furnace, so that once a week, on Saturdays, there would be hot water in the building. An army of freshly painted blue-red tin soldiers, smelling sharply of acetone, were drying outside on the windowsill of a basement flat.

The painter, the wife of the deputy concierge, doled out fried dough dabbed with sour cream through the window railings to the kids crouching there. It was the concierge's job to keep the furnace burning: through the peephole of a grey, armoured basement door, one could catch a glimpse of his shiny, sweating face, lit up by the flames. As if the entire building were a great big ship. And there came the hawker and, yes, the knife-grinder. Old nags from a fairy tale standing in front of a rickety wagon scratched at the bumpy road with their roughly shod hooves, and the sweet aroma of honey cakes emanating from the ancient honey-cake shop pervaded the air. The window was full of large glass jars filled to the brim with honey cakes; the door jingled as one entered and was greeted by two kindhearted, smiling, white-haired old ladies.

Ani lo yoda'at. I don't know. No, I don't even know if they're home.

She recoiled for a moment as she stepped into the building's deep, box-like lobby. She prepared her face in case she should bump into an acquaintance. Ever since she had moved away a couple of years ago, coming back had not been easy. They knew her as a person who only smiled, and though she played this role day and night, even now, she was always aware that she was only pretending to be a person who only smiled. She wore her cheerful mask in vain, for at every moment she could see herself, and she knew that it was a lie. And now she was in no mood to smile. The memory was too strong.

It was exactly from here that she had stepped out one summer's day at dawn in 1958 when she'd run off with Tom, the English soldier she'd fallen in love with back in Palestine, who'd come to visit her along with his wife and two children, traversing half a continent, and she'd run off with him to Lake Balaton. She'd had to go. Fate could not be denied.

And it was here, too, where Pápai had stood, holding his red-haired little girl, listening to the radio broadcast that could be heard through the wide-open windows, in October '56, when some insurrectionists, cockades pinned to their chests, wanted to hang him on the first lamppost they could find.[2] And here, too, it had happened that Pápai, agitated,

[2] It was no longer bearable in the flat. I can hear the radio out in the courtyard, on the street, because the broadcaster's voice blares through the open windows of several flats at the same time.

I take the two older children, Péter and Vera, with me down to the courtyard, and we sit out in front of the building's entrance. From the concierge's basement flat we can hear a speech by Imre Nagy: '... the vital interests of the People's Democracy demand that Soviet forces be called in ...'. A young man wearing dusty shoes and wrinkled clothes walks over to us. He too is listening to the radio.

'From Pest?' I ask.

'Yes,' he replies.

'What's the situation? Are the counter-revolutionaries still resisting?'

'On Kálvin Square the counter ... revolutionaries ... are still fighting,' he says, continuing hastily, 'There's blood on the streets.'

Four or five young people who are well dressed notwithstanding their wrinkled clothes, cockades on their chests, now come over and shout away:

'That's not how it is! Half the university students are still out there fighting on the streets!'

pressed for time as ever, left home late one day with his older son and daughter, and, stepping out of the building, looking neither right nor left, wanted to rush across the street, pulling his kids behind him, when a Csepel lorry screeched to a halt in front of the building, nearly running them over. Pápai let loose a volley of invective at the driver, who simply hopped from his cab and slapped Pápai hard across the face, sending his spectacles flying right off his nose. But Mrs Pápai never heard of this slap. It was only in the memory of the older son that the image of Pápai's defenceless, speechless, stunned face burned itself inexorably.

It was presumably around the same time that an inscription

'They have to put down their arms, until then the fighting won't stop.'

'Who are you? Who takes orders from you?'

'Imre Nagy said that, you heard it yourselves.'

'Imre Nagy can go to hell.'

'Yesterday you were demanding that he be prime minister.'

'He's not a Hungarian prime minister any more, because he called on the Russians for help. As for you – see that lamppost over there? Well, we'll hang you up there soon enough.'

I hold Péter and Vera's hands tighter as one of the youths adds, 'What are you doing out here with kids, anyway?'

It's relatively quiet in our Buda neighbourhood, Krisztinatown. The walls alone speak, smeared with that vile chauvinist graffiti. The voice of anti-communism, a vulgar voice reminiscent of the days of the Arrow Cross, has spoken. The first piece of graffiti could only have been written by someone who was a fascist himself in the fascist days. But lots of them seem to have been written by the unsteady hands of children. Pre-adolescents have taken up the slogans of the fascists and are passing them assiduously on. The building's thirteen- and fourteen-year-old children gather at the entrance to excitedly discuss the events. One of them was in the city centre on the 23rd. He speaks enthusiastically about how he saw the fighting, and how he and others got into a confectionery warehouse and feasted on the sweets there. It's obvious that he thinks of himself as a hero and that the others in this building listen to him in awe and with envy.

115

appeared on the building – who had written it? The insurrectionists or those who'd later locked them up? – in green paint, all in capital letters. PEOPLE'S IRON RULE! The letters had by now faded away; only those who had once seen them could make them out. Still, that inscription had become the building's lucky charm. When Mrs Pápai's younger son came home from school, making his way down the steep steps of Naphegy, he always read it, without fail, and never understood a word of it, and never asked a soul what it meant.

SCHMITZ, SCHMITZ, LITTLE SCHMITZ, YOU WON'T EVEN GET TO AUSCHWITZ. There was an inscription of this sort, too, somewhere. Mrs Pápai had come face to face with it in those revolutionary days, what a slap that had been, too, and she knew she must leave this land, and yet she had stayed.

What has passed, has passed.

Looking neither right nor left, she headed inside with determined steps, into the building's cool lobby with its ashlar floor. One dark stairwell opened to the right and another to the left, and in front of her a glass wall shone brightly onto the castle and the building's inner courtyard with its abundant flowers. The concierge's booth seemed abandoned, its curtain drawn to. Ever since the residents had been given their own keys to the front door, the concierge-couple had been mostly holed up in their basement flat, to which steps led down from the glass booth. And yet the woman was standing there now, besom in hand. She swept once, twice, the sound alarming Mrs Pápai, who looked her way.

'How is your dear husband, Mrs Forgács?'

Mrs Pápai mumbled something in lieu of a proper answer, and then, once the question had been repeated, broke into a wide smile and, in her melodic voice, repeated, louder now, what she'd mumbled before: 'Getting better, doing his best, Mrs Lénárt!' But Mrs Lénárt took no pity on her, no, and did not let her pass. 'Poor Comrade Forgács,' she said, 'this really isn't the fate he deserved.' She made a couple of strokes with her broom, sending dust up into the air. 'I saw him not long ago, and that man is in horrible shape. Like someone broken in two. No, this really isn't the fate the comrade deserved.'

Mrs Pápai felt as if she'd been stabbed. Was Mrs Lénárt mocking her or did she mean to console her? More likely the former. She was about to move on when Mrs Lénárt's harsh voice blared loudly, like a warning shot, again stopping her.

'Just sayin', but yesterday the police was here. Not that I heard a thing, but someone was making a commotion in there, there was a racket, and even after some other tenants called out five or six times and the neighbours knocked on the ceiling, pounded on the walls, the noise went right on.

You should have a word with your children, Mrs Forgács. I haven't the faintest idea who called the police, but if I'd heard what was heard then, I'd do the same, I would. After ten at night some female, maybe your daughter, was shrieking out the window, and on my life they were still coming after midnight, lots of folks, slamming the front door all the time, they were, yes, the whole building rocked, believe me, I was scared out of my wits that the glass in the door would shatter. Oh, I understand young people, I do. I was young once, but this sort of behaviour really shouldn't be allowed after ten at night, ain't I right? Working people live in this building, Mrs Forgács, as you know full well.'

'Working people.' Mrs Lénárt had taken care to pronounce the word as befitted the 1950s. Memories of bygone words bubbled up inside her, including 'gendarme' – in fact, she had almost said 'ÁVÓ', but caught herself just in time.

'And it's not good for anyone if the gendarme comes out here so often. That ain't proper, is it?'

Her tone suggested that she might be gloating: finally she could rub Mrs Forgács's nose in what she herself had feared under the communists. Perhaps that was why these strange words now came to her lips. Because these Forgácses were *that sort* too. No, not bad people, exactly, but *commies*, and for some mysterious reason one had to be scared of them – even of that big buffoon, the potbellied Comrade Forgács, who'd never passed by her without blurting out some stupid compliment or giving her a tickle. A spry plump man, he was, Comrade Forgács! He didn't drink and he didn't smoke, but he was a scoundrel, he was!

In reply Mrs Pápai only made a face, pursed her lips, and went on. She walked across the inner courtyard, advancing as in a chess game between the flowerbeds towards stairwell D. She felt as if watchful eyes were following her even from the dark windows of the basement flats.

The block of flats had arisen in place of an entirely different sort of building whose traces, which it still preserved, must explain its architectural oddities. It had been the body-guards' barracks before the war: the men had lived in the narrow rear stretch of the U-shaped, double-towered struc-ture, which had an arched entrance, comfortable balconies and a spacious roof terrace; and the officers had lived in large, pompously – but not sumptuously – furnished, high-ceilinged flats looking onto Attila Boulevard. How pleasant and secure the officers' jobs must have been. They met to chat and have coffee every day in a different flat.

After the war, the bombed-out, caved-in barracks on both sides of the little square under the castle were replaced by two characterless cubes, twin blockhouses, and it was into one of these that the young Pápai had moved with his wife. *'The battle has begun for a higher living standard,'* he wrote of this success in a triumphant English-language letter to his wife, who was then preparing for exams and pregnant with their first child.[3] It was a special, highly personal English. Even a year after arriving in Hungary the two of them still spoke Hebrew or English together – until one day someone reported Mrs Pápai for using a foreign language while riding a tram, for which she received a warning at her workplace, a nursery school. The building's courtyard – to which steps lined by a stone railing led up from the garden, and which was girdled by a wall built of roughly hewn rocks and

---

[3]

27th of July, 1948, Budapest

Dearest Bruri!

Yesterday I got the following proposals:

1. to replace Dezső in the V kerület [5th district of Budapest] he left for good

2. to go to Party school for 4 weeks in order to be prepared for the job of a three months school leader.

3. to work in the prime minister's press department

The answer of the manager in the bank was that he won't let me go – he needs me badly, after a tough fight he agreed in principle but he put a condition that only after the cadre will give him at least two communists to replace me. He sent me there to tell this and in the meantime he phoned up Rosta. When I arrived there to explain things, they won't listen to my explanations and immediately gave me work. Rosta dismissed all the conditions and so I am in the job after one year of wringling. Végi is jubilant and told me: 'You see that I was right!!!'

Otherwise no news, everything in order, having a fine time like in my good old bachelor days. I hope you don't object. (?)

AND NOW FOR A FLAT. The battle has begun for a higher living standard. All my pupils left for vacations. I am simply dried up. I hope you saved a couple of fillers so we can live on 'fistukim' [pistachios] at least.

Love and many many kisses

Forgács Marcell

P. M.'s press dept. lecturer

ornamental bricks and decorated with arrow slits – had originally been built as a soldiers' exercise yard. There, the privates of the bodyguard regiment had conditioned their muscles. Later it became a football field where the kids from the building would kick a ball until darkness fell – kids who, in the earliest of those days, had fought a war of attrition with a gang of youngsters from another block, and while their battles unfolded mainly when the wild chestnuts were ripe, sometimes real bricks whizzed through the air, too. Just why this tribal warfare broke out from time to time, who was to say, but eventually there came a day, in the late Fifties, when it, too, ended.

Two grey cubes on opposite sides of Dózsa György Square.

Not a trace was left of either the bodyguards' barracks, with its marzipan-cake-like cupolas, or the First World War artillerymen's monument – both of which, during the siege of Budapest, the Americans had taken care to bomb the hell out of before the Russians came along to shell them to smithereens from their positions on Gellért Hill. The bodyguards, in the form of halberdiers stationed in front of the royal palace – wearing egret-feathered metal mitres on their heads, thick linen shirts trimmed lavishly with torsades, vests embroidered with traditional Hungarian folk-motifs and with little tassels hanging from them, and, moreover, with knee-high leather boots likewise ornamented with embroidery, not to mention sabres at their sides – were little more than a guard of honour, and hardly equipped to defend the castle from any serious assault.

It was in early 1949 that the young staff member of the prime minister's press office, with his modest bundle of possessions and his firstborn little daughter – not yet Pápai, but no longer Friedmann, either – moved into this brand-new flat, which had seemed imposing at the time. His career, after so many twists and tumbles, now appeared to have suddenly, and finally, settled onto an arrow-straight path.

* * *

She didn't even take off her jacket. The coat-rack by the front door seemed ready to burst off the wall, swollen so much with all sorts of clothing that she could barely even squeeze by it, and there was no place there for hers. She avoided the mirror. In the grimy kitchen, the smallest burner on the hob was glowing red-hot; on it was a kettle whose water had long boiled away, and beside it was a cup topped with a filter full of tea leaves. Mrs Pápai quickly turned off the burner: the switch was sticky with grime, and on the white enamel hob there were blackened, cracked splotches of burnt porridge and other food that had run over the sides of pots. She had no idea what to do: clean up or leave things as they were?

Mrs Pápai put the kettle under cold running water. Hissing steam shot up into her face. Absent-mindedly she looked into the dimly lit pantry. The shelves were empty except for a jar of dried-out mustard, a few potatoes that had started to sprout and some forlorn-looking, wilting onions. One day, back in 1963, she too had managed to set fire to the place – the day she'd left the iron plugged in. Pápai had been in hospital, and she was rushing off to work at the Red Cross. Someone in the neighbouring building noticed the black smoke billowing out of a window and called the firemen, who couldn't get into the flat, and – because it wouldn't have made any sense to drag the hose all the way up the winding stairs – aimed the jet of water from the street right through the kitchen window. The parquet floor was soaked, the sooty water flowed down the spiral staircase, and the onlookers applauded. Fifteen years later the pantry door was still blistered from that fire, its surface like matzo. It had been painted to cover up the damage, but moon-like craters could still be seen underneath.

She heard a stirring from the biggest room. Only then did she realize that someone had put all the chairs in there.

The flat's prettiest piece of furniture – a small oval glass table standing on Grecian columns and a bronze-plated pedestal – had been pushed into a corner and the lion-legged writing desk pulled over to the radiator. It was in this antique desk that Pápai, then a member of the Workers' Militia, had kept his service revolver and its brass-coated bullets, not to mention all the brochures and family papers scattered in the drawers. In the room, as if in a theatre's auditorium, stood two rows of chairs of every variety. The large, threadbare Persian rug had been rolled up and leaned against the wall, on which, next to the rug, was a curled-at-the-edges black-and-white photograph of Mrs Pápai's youngest daughter, who – wearing Pápai's shiny grey suit, white shirt, tie and huge sunglasses – was delivering a huge favourite among the homemade productions put on in the flat: a long, frenetic monologue from a famous Italian film in which a top police detective kills his mistress only to later lead the investigation into her murder himself.[4]

It would be best not to enter, to turn around and leave this place.

The shutters were half closed. Something held her back, but then she couldn't take it any longer, and with quiet steps walked into the room she'd slept in for a quarter of a century, in the hardest of times, sometimes in one corner, sometimes in another, on sagging, rattling beds, alone. Pápai – either when he came home at dawn, at the end of his

---

[4] The series of premieres closed with Zsuzsanna Forgács's solo performance. Made up of pantomime elements, the monodrama carries a deeply pessimistic message. It portrays human alienation and loneliness in a form that testifies to the inevitable dissolution of conjugal bonds, making out the family – and, within it, traditional gender roles – to be akin to a state of robot-like monotony. As with the previous performance, this one was full of erotic, obscene elements. The audience contemplated this, too, with appreciation.

shift at Hungarian Radio, or else when he stirred, moaning, in the middle of the night – had to scurry over on tiptoe to her on the far side of the huge writing desk if he wanted something, and often he did want something. Harried by his restive heart, he wanted something even when she didn't, as long as he thought that their two youngest children, who slept in the same room, were sleeping like lambs. Though he could never be sure. Silently they made love, with restrained sighs, only the bed creaking unashamedly. Pápai then sidled back to his lair. They never had a room of their own. Once, when they might have had one, they chose instead to take on a tenant at a meagre rent to help cover their household expenses, but then the tenant did not pay, and it took some doing to rid themselves of the squatter. At other times a down-on-his-luck relative would move into one of the smaller rooms, and throwing him out was not so simple either. The only place where Mrs Pápai could sleep in comfort was the sofa with the green cover, which they'd bought in London, and which could be transformed into a bed with a single motion, and which, back then, all the relatives had gazed at in wonder.

The sound of quiet laughter. A half-naked blond boy was lying on a mattress on the floor – or, rather, he was almost sitting up, a pillow stuffed between his back and the wall, long hairy legs extending beyond a Bedouin blanket, a guitar resting on his belly as he softly strummed a tune. On seeing Mrs Pápai, he turned cheery all at once. 'How do you do, ma'am?' he said, as a child might have in the stairwell, and smiled mischievously. When she saw how thin he was, Mrs Pápai's first thought was that he must be fed. 'What were you playing? Bach?' she asked, just to ask something. 'Was there a performance?'[5] she added, but she did not dare step further

[5]   The guests were invited to the play, which began around 8:15. As per the title, it sought to bring to the stage the life of Pascal. The two leads were played by János Xantus and György Kozma. The piece – which they had embellished with puns – was decidedly obscene and homosexual in character, bearing the marks of the underground stage. It won unanimous praise from those present.

Afterwards they screened short films by Ágnes Háy which my acquaintance had seen at a previous event. Of these, the study titled *Tempo* merits attention; for one of the actors – a stage designer from Kaposvár, named Major – is the companion of Miklós Haraszti.

In the course of the screening, the Forgács siblings' mother arrived in the company of Julia Veres, and on learning what the evening's programme was, announced that she already knew the play. It follows from all of this that the performances must be regular.

[. . .]

Péter Kovács told my acquaintance that Miklós Erdélyi is organizing a 'creative action' on 17 June at 60 József Boulevard in Budapest's 8th District, at which anyone interested is welcome.

'Nemes'

Assessment: The secret assignee carried out his assignment well. His report is of operative value and may be deemed as corroborated. His data confirm or complement corroborated information we have received from other sources.

In recent months we have received intelligence from multiple sources that members of Budapest's 'new left' and anarchist groups have established their new gathering points at the flats of János Xantus and Zsuzsanna Forgács. Our contact has now provided a foretaste of the programmes held in these locations by reporting in detail. Some of the individuals who attended the event have been under investigation by our organs for pursuing belligerent activities.

The circumstances amid which these performances are held appear to reinforce their core concept that in the present political situation the most expedient method by which these groups and individuals can collaborate is mutual 'artistic' activity. The performances are nihilist in nature, their obscenity suggesting the participants' deep personal crises. In indirect form they deny the legitimacy of socialist culture. Their works have been conceived in the spirit of the so-called 'counter-culture' fashionable in the West.

into the room. And yet, even as she was suddenly beset by a terrible exhaustion, she had a deep-seated desire to give this dishevelled young man, her son's friend, something to eat; to put the chairs back in their places, to sweep the floor, to make the beds, to air the flat, to vacuum the rug, and, generally, to set this maddening disarray in order. But, no, she didn't have the strength. She collapsed wearily into the nearest chair. As if preparing for a long conversation, the blond boy now politely placed his guitar on the parquet floor, and this elaborately slow movement, which required him to lean over the mattress, brought Mrs Pápai's attention to the motionless body lying beside him under the sheet; which is to say, to all she could see of this body: the dirty soles of two feet.

'Yes, Bach, *The Well-Tempered Klavier*,' and the boy was about to complacently reach once again for his guitar when Mrs Pápai's question stopped him in his tracks. At the same time, her heart began beating wildly. 'Did you put on the kettle?' Nothing better came to mind. In lieu of a reply, the boy raised the embroidered amulet hanging on a leather strap around his neck, which he'd been given six months earlier by Mrs Pápai, who, on completing one of her embroideries, was in the habit of presenting it to the first person she met. It depicted a bird of paradise. 'I still have it, Aunt Ria!' the boy exclaimed. Knitting his brows, he added, 'I heard Péter out there in the kitchen earlier.' 'You should have turned it off all the same,' she said. 'Consider me gone!'

he replied, springing out from under the blanket and pulling on his trousers. His haste suggested an effort to distract Mrs Pápai from the motionless body under the blanket. *It can't be,* thought Mrs Pápai. *Impossible. It can't be that it's him lying there, and even if it is, what does it mean, and why would I even think such a thing?* At that her heart beat even more loudly, like a bucking horse that wants to escape its corral. 'Aren't you hungry?' was the question she had in mind as her eyes fixed on the contours of the sleeping body, but to her great surprise she asked, 'Don't you know where András is?'

The front door gave a sudden creak and was then flung open, and from the echoing voices in the stairwell it sounded as if several people, a whole gang of people, had arrived at once. A moment later, strident laughter and spirited conversation could be heard. Someone switched on the light. There were only three of them, and her son was not among them.

Darkness fell.

Mrs Pápai, who had turned away from the boy, wasn't the least bit surprised at the sudden deluge of strangers – no, she'd spent her whole life getting used to it: anyone could arrive at any time. Just as in her parents' home when she was a child, when anyone who showed up was fed and given a place to sleep in a corner: a beggar woman, an Arab delegation on its way home from Moscow to Tel Aviv or passing through on the way from Beirut to Moscow, distant relatives, an aunt, a niece, a tenant who couldn't be thrown out, Armenians, Brits, French, Italians, a neighbour who came by for salt or flour or potatoes or perhaps brought a fresh watermelon, or the postman with a telegram. But, no, it was never friends, for they had no friends. Or when the white-haired chieftain arrived, the vice president of the World Peace Council, Mrs Pápai's papa, from Tel Aviv or Moscow or Stockholm, and the whole family gathered around the glass table in the largest, otherwise barren room, its parquet scuffed to a shine. Everyone was in his or her Sunday best, for a group picture, which, in the minutes it took to compose, meant that hatchets had to be buried along with the ugly strife which tore the family apart – the reproaches, the jealousy, the spite which can be found in every family, but which here all swirled around that magic word, 'Israel'. Evil conqueror or under perfidious attack? Aggressor or defenceless victim? From the moment in 1965 when the Israeli Communist Party, which wasn't big to start with, had split in two, the arguments unfolded with an ignominious fervour that would have put the religious wars of the Middle Ages to shame. They perceived this as they would have a global catastrophe or, say, the advent of the Weimar Republic. Sneh, Mikunis, Sneh, Mikunis – these two names were constantly thrown about. Yes, they were the secessionists and the heretics, they were the traitors who'd turned against Moscow. Alongside Sneh and Mikunis, the names of the new party's Arab stars also flitted about: Habibi and Toubi, Toubi and Habibi, *Al Ittihad* and *Zo Haderekh*. The relatives pressed Hebrew- and English-language articles clipped from newspapers under each other's noses, and screamed about imperialism and genocide, and all this only intensified after the Six-Day War in 1967 and the break in diplomatic relations. Yes, by then the divide was deep. Then came Sasha, the ever cheerful and fragrant Arab communist, who regularly stopped in from one of his raids with a carton of Marlboros, at which Mrs Pápai, a clumsy Sunday smoker, lit up demonstratively at once. So too came the Armenian Christian communist oil merchant from Beirut, who to the end of his days sent postcards from all over the world to his adored Bruria. But when the white-haired, blue-eyed chieftain arrived, the family seemed momentarily whole: newborns and older children alike were brought over, and even those who would have suffocated one another on a spoonful of water could be found smiling at each other.

Her son was not among the three young men, the most boisterous of whom had sparkling blue eyes, a brown hat tipped rakishly over his forehead that he never removed, and a mouth always breaking into a smile – a cutting and yet not at all sneering smile, like that of someone who savours what he is about to say even before formulating the words inside his head, someone who takes pleasure at the very thought of the witty pronouncement he is about to make. Resting on his nose was a pair of thick glasses, and the words spilled effortlessly, melodiously from his mouth, as if he were acting in a play he'd written himself. Meanwhile he didn't really pay attention to the bearded poet with the pockmarked face whom he happened to be talking to – no, he just said what he had to say, and if the other interjected, he squashed it immediately, and yet in the same breath he could express his admiration for him. These two – the banned poet and the writer sacked from his job – were a bit like Don Quixote and Sancho Panza. Inseparable. Floating around on the periphery was a third figure, evidently not a close acquaintance of theirs but someone who had presumably attached himself to them in another flat or pub or, say, at the Young Artists' Club. There were a few such wandering figures in the night who dropped in on one party after another, without warning, without invitation, departing unexpectedly, just when, no one could say.[6]

On noticing Mrs Pápai, the brown-hatted young man fell at once to his knees. 'Oh, rose of Hebron!' he cried with a cheeky grin and yet charmingly. With dramatic flair he kissed Mrs Pápai's hand – intimately, sincerely. Whenever Mrs Pápai entered a place, the mood somehow became more

[6] Submitted: Secret assignee on 'Nemes'
Received: Lajos Szabó, Police Capt.
Place: 'Nearby' 'C' flat

lighthearted: her exceptional beauty shone through even her tired, worn-out face. The same beauty radiated from every nook and cranny of this dilapidated, disorderly flat – from all the objects and pictures, glass vases and embroideries, books and reproductions – and it was *this* that the men and boys who now and again invaded the flat – mostly artists and university students, friends or casual acquaintances of Mrs Pápai's children – could not resist, even if they had never heard of her. The legendary performances put on by Mrs Pápai's youngest child – that girl with the bronze-red hair and resonating voice, that girl ever ready for any adventure, that girl overflowing with passion and intellect – were only excuses for their visits. But, now, even she wasn't here.

'Hi, Bruria,' said the poet by way of greeting, meanwhile looking for a chair on which he might sit down, for at this time of day he was more inclined to sit than stand. There was no chair. Hastily he lit a cigarette.

Whatever she might otherwise have thought of them, in the eyes of Mrs Pápai, to whom art was religion, these visitors were, after all, her children's friends, so they were saints, too, no matter what they did. Being a nurse, she did not discriminate among people. She could appreciate a joke, too. She glanced inquisitively at the third visitor, who was silent. 'You don't even know what Hebron is,' Mrs Pápai said in a hushed, somewhat sad tone to the young man in the brown hat. 'It's an occupied Arab town.' He wanted at once to eat his words. 'Sorry, sorry!' Truth be told, he was just about to say more on this sensitive topic, but, instead of speaking, his glasses gave a flash, closing their discussion before it began.

'Péter?'

'He'll be here soon. He met some Italians on the street.'

'Brits,' the poet interjected.

'Well, excuse me,' said the brown-hatted boy. 'Yes, with some Brits. It's all the same. But they were Italians. They're here in front of the building, and they're singing.'

'They were Brits,' said the poet. 'But he didn't meet them here, it was at Déli railway station.' He crushed his cigarette and lit another one.

'All right, Brits, then. They're Italians, but it doesn't matter. But we're here for his little sister. We have something import-ant to talk to her about. Is she here?' Without waiting for a reply, he picked up a fork and began devouring a plate full of leftover pasta. Someone's half-finished lunch stood there on the dining table, abandoned in the middle of the flat, without the chairs. As if it was something that must be got right, he announced, his mouth full of pasta, 'Just because they spoke English, they could have been Italians.'

'Italians don't even speak English,' the poet countered.

'I know you know everything better, but they were Italians all the same. Did you know there's a shop in town where you

133

can get real Parmesan?' Suddenly he sat on the edge of the dining table, surprising even himself, as he often did. The tip of his nose had tomato sauce on it. 'You see, it's just this sort of thing that should appear in the *Journal* I have in mind,' he said smugly. And he went on: 'Tart and ripe Parmesan, rock-hard Parmesan, fragrant Parmesan, Umbrian and Tuscan Parmesan! But this is *Trappista*, our nation's version of Port Salut. In the socialist reality that exists for us, Trappista is Parmesan.' He added, in a stentorian voice, 'But no big deal, we forgive you, no matter who you were, you who made this sticky pasta, you ignorant kitchen-hand from Pest.'

The young man in the brown hat had said this in a slightly pontifical tone, absolving the unknown cook from Pest of his sins. Next, after licking the plate, he pulled a half-full bottle of red wine from the pocket of his jacket and placed it on the table. He pulled out the cork with his teeth, picked up a glass from the table – once a mustard jar, it seemed – and, after swishing some suspect liquid from it, poured himself a glass of wine. 'I hate to drink from a bottle,' he said playfully, as if someone had asked him. He then gulped down the wine and grimaced. 'Bulgarian. Lousy.'

'Excuse me,' the poet said, bowing towards Mrs Pápai like a true gentleman. He crushed his cigarette on a plate and vanished through a door.

They were standing in a rather strange space in the heart of the flat. It was to Mrs Pápai's credit that, towards the end of the Sixties, the walls in the middle of the flat had been torn down – through her own heroic efforts, with loose change scraped together and loans begged from all manner of people and places. They had done away with the always dark, narrow hallway to create one large space. Gone, too, was the wall which had coyly hidden the toilet and the laundry basket and, in part, the bathroom. The flat was suddenly denuded, its mystique stripped away, with quite a few unintended consequences. All of the remaining rooms – the two smaller rooms, the biggest room, the toilet and the bathroom – all opened onto this single space. Since they had cunningly lopped off even a corner of the kitchen, the result was a rather attractive space in the middle of the flat where a dining table had been put. But, because no money had been left to replace the green-and-white stone-tile kitchen floor with parquet, a little stage of sorts, a couple of centimetres higher than the main floor, had been created in front of the kitchen. If someone had something important to say, or felt as if no one was paying attention – and this regularly happened amid the cacophony that so often erupted here – he or she stepped onto that stage and took to loudly making himself or herself heard. Traces of the razed walls stretched along the floor, like wounds. The new kitchen wall had been put up crookedly by a drunk builder, giving the impression that the whole space was wobbling, and with it the whole flat, just as in the Budapest earthquake of '56. By the kitchen was a protruding section of wall – a bricked-up chimney, that is, on which the hole for the stovepipe was still visible, stuffed with newspaper. A small cast-iron stove had stood once under that hole: in the Fifties, during the great colds, it was heated with coal brought up from the cellar. The kids had sat around it while they were being deloused, on little chairs made by their uncle, their scalps burning and their hair smelling of kerosene, and when darkness came, off they went, shivering, teeth chattering, and crawled under their great big goose-down quilts. During power cuts, which were frequent, they lit shiny oil lamps. They lived like nomads, wandering from one room to another in the increasingly cramped flat. The two girls were in the corner room, the two boys were right by the entrance, and the parents were in the biggest room; or, rather, this was how it was supposed to be, but it was not long before everyone was moving from one room to another. In a flash of inspiration, Pápai one fine day commandeered one of the smaller rooms for himself, for he wanted to work, to write an earth-shattering novel, or else he happened to be translating some book, whether about the history of China or the biography of Paul Robeson.

No, the flat was always in disarray.

One day, someone, thinking it was funny, had written 'WC' on a door, in big crimson letters, saving guests the trouble of asking. Behind the above-mentioned door at this moment the poet happened to be emitting monstrous belches, and moaning and groaning and sighing with relief:

for a while nothing else could be heard. The guy in the brown hat, still sitting on the table, burst into shrill laughter.

The doors of the huge, chipboard closets built into the wall after the renovation had warped dramatically, and the clothes and bed linen piled up in great disorder inside gathered dust on what were, by now, slightly crooked shelves. Mrs Pápai hadn't lived here for a long time. Citing her workers' movement past, she acquired – at the cost of, as she was apt to say, 'crawling on my bloodied belly' – a three-room flat in a tower block at the other end of the city.[7] Whoever stayed, stayed; whoever went, went.

---

[7] I no longer know if the veterans' general state of mind needs to be taken into account. But I am writing (~~maybe for the second time~~) because I don't want to end up in a mental institution, as happened with my husband. If you cannot arrange for the granting of the following request of mine through your own authority, I ask that you regard it as null and void. ~~I have no need to have~~ By no means forward my letter to another agency, institution, etc. ~~(the reasons, if necessary)~~ ~~deal with the matter~~ Throw my letter in the bin instead, and then it's over.

~~In shor~~ 1) In 1947 my husband and I arrived from Palestine. My husband (born: 1920) ~~and I are longtime party members~~ is a communist (1940) as am I (1942). (Medal for the Socialist Homeland, member of the partisan federation, etc.)

2) My husband: sacked from prime minister's press office in the course of the Rajk trials. Unemployment. Comrade Sebes says to me: 'Your husband is not a cadre, let him become a construction worker.'

3) In 1953 the director of the 'Szikra' book publishing firm sacks my husband because: his father-in-law lives in Israel (at the time the 'doctors' trial' was underway in the Soviet Union. (The father-in-law: M. AVI-SHAUL, communist writer, poet . . .)

4) Counter-revolution: my husband, along with myself, is among the first to report with the party. He winds up in mortal danger. After the counter-revolution's military suppression my husband is summoned to the prime minister's office to assist with the press and propaganda work (along with Ernő Vágó and others he goes to Csepel and other factories to dissuade the strikers, etc.).

5) In 1957 he is hired by the foreign affairs desk of the daily *Magyar Nemzet*.

6) In 1960, on recommendation of party central: London correspondent, MTI. Prior to our departure Tibor Köves (MTI) shows up in our flat. He declares: it's him who should have travelled to London but he doesn't yet have his party membership . . . (Later we learned that, during the counter-revolution, because of the Petőfi Circle etc. etc. he was 'left out' at MTI.) Tibor Köves then does all the back-stabbing against my husband that he can from back home. Comrade Forgács got *no* help from MTI. By 1962 Köves joins the party,

Before long, another five or so guests arrived, but Péter was not among them. She wanted to speak to him about his passport application. Her two boys were to travel together to the land of their ancestors. A complicated matter. As for her daughter, because of a trip she had made that was deemed

and my husband is a nervous wreck from the outrageous backbiting ~~from the hinterland unceasing backbiting at full steam~~. We come home. Köves goes to London.

7) 1962: At the recommendation of Party Headquarters my husband is sent to the foreign ministry. Months pass before the answer comes (several ~~such letters~~ letters of rejection over the years from the hand of Mrs Turai, the foreign ministry's human resources official). (My husband did not go inquiring at the ministry of his own volition, but it always happened at the recommendation of the party's higher organs.) In 1962 the then foreign minister said, and I quote, 'Comrade Forgács, your father-in-law lives in Israel, which is why we can't employ you. If Avi-Shaul requests repatriation and settles here, we can talk again.' We had to swallow this atrocity, but we couldn't. We felt like stigmatized and untrustworthy individuals ~~and we were~~! Nothing has felt good since then, either, since ~~there is a dossier~~ the dossier of 'Marcell Forgács' has kept burning in the human resources department of the foreign ministry. Those who look inside imagine an enemy. We will continue experiencing this terrible this real nightmare again and again until we perish or until those responsible make amends.

8) 1967: aggression in the Middle East. Marcell Forgács struggles for the unfaltering realization of the party line at state radio. He certainly pays for it: he's called an anti-Semite, an ~~agant~~ agent provocateur, anonymous telephone calls and letters. Zionist-sympathizing individuals of both Jewish and non-Jewish ancestry harass him, he's whispered about behind his back, he's besmirched – and this has lasted to this day. Enough was enough when the whispers originating at MTI were expressed like this to one of my children who is in university (I have four children): Forgács is really talented but in chasing after better positions he informed on people at party headquarters. The 'news' originates with Hungarian newspaper reporters currently serving in the USA. I can't prove it and I don't even have to, because that's not the point. For my husband, this was the last drop. It's as if a great darkness descended on his mind. They took him to the ophthalmology clinic for an emergency operation ~~a cataract six months earlier a heart attack~~ (he had a heart attack two years ago). They operated on his eyes but he couldn't evade the mental institution! He is now there. ~~but he will never crawl out of his condition, which in 1962~~

Lesser blows bigger blows in 1948, 1953, 1960, 1962, 1967, and since then and during that time have done their work on him. ~~But especially~~ Recovery is ~~in my opinion~~ possible only if the fundamental injustice is redressed. ~~Until then~~

Until then

With comradely greetings

Mrs Marcell Forgács

Bearer of Medal for Socialist Homeland.

retired nurse

illegal, her passport had been revoked, and when she had refused to answer questions on being stopped one night and asked for her ID, the police had sprained her arm. Mrs Pápai had had to get her a new passport. She had arranged this with the local Party committee, but then the passport bureau issued an order revoking it again. She had to talk to them in person. She couldn't understand why they didn't understand.

* * *

At just about the same time, some eight hundred metres away as the crow flies, still in Buda but on the far side of Castle Hill, before the wondering eyes of Mrs Pápai's younger son, Botticelli's Venus lay on a wrinkled bedsheet – on a creaky, folk-Baroque wooden bed with a mattress that sagged in the middle – in the person of a blonde, radiantly beautiful Polish girl. The two were lolling about upstairs in this two-storey flat, the front door of which was never locked, just like that of the Forgács home, and anyone could come at any time and cut a slice from the dry loaf of bread that was invariably to be found on the kitchen worktop. The flat was in the throes of artistic disorder: children's clothes drying on a taut length of twine; dog-eared novels that had been through a thousand hands; unrinsed tea cups; an open jar of peach jam with a spoon inside; an ashtray full of cigarette butts on a little Biedermeier desk with cracked marquetry and one of its graceful legs supported by a brick; an enamelled Parisian street sign beside a grandfather clock; Mozart and Schubert scores tossed about; the collected works of Marx and Engels on top of the wardrobe; family photos; children's drawings; glass beads scattered about on the floor; an upright piano splotched with candle wax; a high-backed chair with just one armrest; a baroque sofa; and tubular-steel folding chairs. The group that frequented this flat was more or less the same one that could be found at the other flat – people who, as it emerges from the reports,[8] often crossed paths on the same night in various places in the city; because, with just one or two exceptions, public venues closed by 10.00 p.m.

Without becoming distracted for too long by this scene, it must be said that for a while now the words spoken most frequently in the bed in this flat were *Tak czy nie?*, and they referred to the boy's willingness to penetrate the girl's dewy loins. *Tak czy nie?* – Yes or no? The girl laughed, and they kissed yet again, for a long, long time. The girl's breasts were slightly splayed, and she produced marijuana from a red leather bag hanging around her neck, and they smoked it, and it scratched at the boy's throat and he had a coughing fit – but that's all that happened. The phone rang a few times but they didn't answer it.

[8] Assignment: Pay continuous and unchanged attention to the activities of the two circles. If an opportunity arises naturally, visit the flats mentioned in the report. Acquire information about why and how often the various individuals visit the various flats. Avoid taking anyone at all to the events unless someone among your acquaintances has been invited. Observe the participants' reactions and seek to maintain a low profile while at the same time accommodating your behaviour to that of the others.

Finally they smoothed out the wrinkled bedsheet under their bottoms and pulled the prickly blanket over them, but it was too early, sleep eluded them, and when nothing better came to mind, they turned off the light, and then the wooden stairs leading to the second floor gave a creak.

A couple of days earlier, Mrs Pápai's older son had picked up a Polish girl at the Castle Hill tunnel. About ten minutes later she was sitting in that flat at the foot of the hill in the crossfire of three happy, laughing faces: offering her food and drink, they gazed at this waif who'd wandered in and who sparkled like a flower's dewy petal, and who by that night had moved in with them. She was given a room of her own, because Mrs Pápai's older son had to leave on a trip that very night, freeing up some space, and so – unthinkingly, as it would turn out – entrusted his siblings with the bounty, leaving her with them as if handing his possessions in at a train station's left luggage office, to watch over her until his return. And now, on returning, because he couldn't find her anywhere, he ransacked the whole town in search of the girl while his sister just shrugged and his brother had vanished without a trace. He tenaciously kept up his inquisition, question after question, until a strange presentiment led him to open the door of that forlorn flat, where, on the second floor, he was greeted by a certain image: the two of them, naked, a blanket drawn up to their chins.

On the top step he froze, petrified, before retreating to a deep couch, where he broke down and started to cry. He was more sensitive than people realized. One of the times when Mrs Pápai had *crawled on her bloodied belly*[9] occurred because of him: his

[9]   Dear Comrade Aczél,

Our son, Péter Forgács, who is a first-year student at the College of Visual Arts, was failed out of his studies in sculpture in the middle of the academic year, which means his automatic expulsion from the College.

The reason we are turning to you, Comrade Aczél, and asking you to receive us, is because we have been told that he received this dissatisfactory mark not for academic reasons but on the basis of a 'political' judgement. Péter was accepted thanks to his high score on the entrance examination. So far he has been at the College for two-and-a-half months, and not only is it inconceivable that during this time he would have regressed, but, to the contrary, his large number of new works show substantial progress, as those at the school who are experts have also determined.

It has come to our attention, however, that prior to the academic evaluation, *political labels* were handed out in an impermissible manner at a gathering of party members, and after this came the extorted academic grade as *punishment* – on the basis of unproven accusations. Crowning all this was that my son and others, who were branded in their absence in similar fashion, were not notified of this, no, they were warned neither before nor after, but a 'political' sentence was carried out in the academic realm. This is, in our opinion, wholly unacceptable precisely from the perspective of our party's policies, the purity of artistic critique and the pedagogy of art.

We must however also share some circumstances related to our son that are unique. Péter is a hard worker; he wakes each morning at 4 a.m., delivers newspapers, and then goes to the College, where he studies and works until late afternoon. His wife, who is likewise a sculpture student, is pregnant. We share a flat with them and our other three children.

Also pertaining to the general circumstances is the fact that our family was seriously decimated during the fascist years as well, and also that as members of the illegal communist party we bore arms in the fight against fascism and imperialist colonial suppression. During the time of the show trials we were branded Rajkists, Titoists and imperialist spies, which in our case meant losing employment and abandoning university studies. Discrimination and neglect was our lot over many years. It was hard to explain this to our four children, whom we raised in the communist spirit despite all this, and who became conscientious young communists.

During the counter-revolution, we, too, got on the list of those to be 'rounded up' for being longtime communists. We were among the first in the battle against the counter-revolution, in the party's restructuring and the establishment of the workers' militia. Now it seems that they're coming down hard on us once again as longtime communists, based on unfounded political assessments, but this time through Péter, with administrative methods.

It is not our place to judge what should be debated at the College and its party organization, and how, but if they think that there are 'debatable' views, too, then those must be clarified through debate and not punished through un-academic means, wrecking the life paths of young men and depriving them of the opportunity to study and create their art. Debate on mother turned right away to the highest authority, the country's all-powerful cultural czar, György Aczél, but this time in vain. The older brother could not know that it was only with the help of his inventive and worldly sister that his little brother, mocked publicly so often for being unversed in matters pertaining to the female sex, had been blessed with this undeserved miracle. Blood and tears and games. But what a good little sister she was.[10]

* * *

political and artistic problems corresponds to our party's objectives, which tends towards clarifying ideological issues on the basis of principle and is suited to the principles of socialist art and criticism, as well as the norms of communist pedagogy.

Thus we ask Comrade Aczél for an investigation of the case and for its just settlement.

With comradely greetings,

Budapest, 26 December 1971

[10] MINISTRY OF THE INTERIOR   TOP SECRET!

    Independent   HIGHLY IMPORTANT!
    sub-department
    III/III-8

MONITORING OF DOMESTIC HOSTILE OPPOSITION ELEMENTS
DAILY REPORT NO. 127
Budapest, 13 June 1979

Disagreements have emerged ~~in the Journal~~ among the individuals participating in the preparation of the illegal periodical 'Journal' over the content of certain writings in the periodical. They reacted with particular sensitivity to the 'editorial committee' having called on Péter Forgács to withdraw from the 'Journal' his most recent piece, which compromises one of their peers. Because of ~~the editorial committee's stance this stance~~, his sister, Zsuzsa Forgács, declared: in the future she will not participate in the making of the 'Journal'.

The arguments also led Ferenc Dániel and Péter Nádas to ~~decide to leave the Journal.~~ cease their association with the 'Journal'.

Measures: Preparation of an information report,

continuation of confidential investigation.

Mrs Béla Mészáros, Police Major

Sub-department Head

People kept arriving at the Attila Street flat, making themselves at home around the dining table, fetching chairs from the largest room. Some brought food, too, or a bottle of wine. Sitting in the armchair, springs bulging through its cover, was the taciturn poet, a bottle of Soviet vodka within reach. Practically all of him that could be seen from behind the table were his black eyes, since for some mysterious reason someone had sawn the armchair's legs in half. He produced a shot glass from a trouser pocket.

There was no theatrical performance announced for that evening, but this didn't mean that there wouldn't be one – as if a performance might be summoned by the arrival of an audience. At times something happened, at times nothing – any random event could be called theatre, if only because an audience of acceptable size had gathered. Occasionally twenty or thirty visitors would occupy the flat, young and old: grey-haired or bald venerable-looking gentlemen, beatniks, bohemians, high school students, freshly released convicts and writers who'd had novels published in the West, actors, directors, college girls and fanatically religious mums with several children who earned their living as nude models at the College of Visual Arts. They dispersed about the rooms or else fell into spirited debate around the table near the front door about events shrouded in a milky fog: about Party decrees; police matters; a banned book that had been smuggled into the country; or the latest Bergman film.

About everything at once, without stopping to take a breath. Great loves were born between midnight and dawn, and great fights erupted and then suddenly died out. Two girls read aloud a letter that had arrived by some secret route from Paris,[11] while a boy went about the flat with his camera taking

[11]
MINISTRY OF THE INTERIOR	TOP SECRET!
Department III/4	HIGHLY IMPORTANT!
17 November 1976	Submitted: secret assignee CN TAMÁS FEHÉR
	Received: Tibor Cirkos, police lt.
	Place: 'C' flat CN BALZAC
	Subject: Establishment of the 'Hungarian Feminist Movement'

A university-student acquaintance of a friend of mine said that this summer a feminist movement formed in Hungary under the name Hungarian Feminist Movement. The documents or brochures of this movement previously appeared in Paris. Actually, a few people defected in the summer – my friend doesn't know their names for the time being – and there they published a few pieces. In Hungary [...] according to him this movement is organized by Julia Veres, a girl who was formerly a philosophy major, and among the members, or at least the fairly active members, this acquaintance has already mentioned Piroska Márkus, who at the moment is a philosophy major in the faculty of humanities, as well as Zsuzsa Forgács. [...] He is specifically familiar with a proposed programme he told my friend about. This proposed programme comprises about ten points, and the following are among the points: Those who compiled the proposed programme think that women, insofar as they seek to assess or at all examine the situation of women, comprise a class and not some sort of group or a social conglomeration connected with a stratum, but that women are one of the fundamental classes in present-day societies and, indeed, can be counted as among the oppressed classes. Several of the programme points concern the subjugation of women by men – technicalities, for example, such as that mechanization does not fundamentally alter women's subjugation, because it means a change only in the quantity of household work, but not – by no means – a qualitative change. It does not therefore represent the sort of liberation that would represent the enfranchisement of truly significant energies for women. The same thing refers to the scenario under which men would help women do housework. So too there was a programme point that, in almost manifesto-like fashion, stated that women should more deliberately exploit their biological attribute whereby they, and not men, bear children into the world. According to this proposed programme women are more apt to reap disadvantages, not advantages, from their situation with respect to men. According to another programme point, complete social liberation could better be ensured if women were not in such a subjugated role with respect to men, for not even men can realize all those rights that might be theirs or that they might have the possibility of exercising. Among other reasons this happens also because women have traditionally been oppressed amid social pictures from various angles, paying meticulous attention to ensure that the shots were symmetrical.

It must be added that not one of the flat's residents was home, but no one seemed bothered by this.

It was already past midnight when – standing in the moonlight in front of this dark building on Attila Street, his arm wrapped around the slender waist of the Polish girl – the boy gave a whistle in the hope of luring someone to a window who might throw down a key with which to unlock the building's front door. Meanwhile he kept murmuring into the dreamy girl's ear, like some silver-tongued tour guide. Squatting down by one of the grated basement windows, they peeked inside:

circumstances for centuries or millennia. Several points of the proposed programme concern the situation of the family, and they categorically reject this, though there are no concrete recommendations for what group or formation could function in place of the family as the smallest fundamental unit of society. Instead, these points suggest that the family is, from the outset, one of the factors in re-creating the conditions of women's subjugation.

Prepared as:　　　4 copies
　　　　　　　　　3 typed pages

Assessment: Our contact reported beyond the scope of his assignment that Julia Veres, former student of the faculty of humanities, and Zsuzsa Forgács and Piroska Márkus – presently third-year history-philosophy majors in the Faculty of the Humanities – are members of the 'Hungarian Feminist Movement', established in Hungary in the summer of 1976.

The information contains the essential details of the programme manifesto of the 'movement', from which it may be concluded that they seek to engage in activities, on the basis of belligerent political ideas, 'in the interest of improving the situation of women', for which they also cultivate foreign links as well.

Measures: I recommend that one copy of the report be sent to Interior Ministry sub-department III/III-4-b.

Budapest, 24 November 1976.

　　　　　　　　　　　　　　　　　　Tibor Cirkos, Police Lt.

it was like a dungeon, a torture chamber. On the third floor, the windows were bright yellow. Perhaps it was because of all the hubbub up there that they hadn't heard the boy's call. Utter silence fell upon Tabán – this was the neighbourhood's name – and the only car on Attila Street at this hour, a police car, slowed but then moved on. At any minute some neighbour might glance outside and chase them away.

'You see,' the boy said to the girl as the two of them stared into that dark basement window, 'this was the washing room where my mum washed our things by hand once a week. And look!' – he looked up high – 'In the Second World War an aeroplane smacked right into this building and got stuck. I used to dream about it. It was flown by some poor German Fritz who took off in Vienna and was shot down just before making it to the so-called Field of Blood nearby. People came from all over town to admire the plane. What a sight!'

On 5 February 1945, one week before the taking of Buda Castle, a DSF-230 glider smashed into the block of flats next door to the bodyguards' barracks. Much to the wonder of the neighbourhood's residents, the plane's tail and part of its fuselage protruded from the building for quite some time. The first item of interest found by those daring to emerge from their basements as the siege abated – found under the collapsed roof of a flat above Attila Boulevard – was

147

the severed head of the young German pilot, which rolled onto the parquet the moment someone managed to open the cockpit using an axe. The pilot's hand was still gripping the handle of the ejector seat. But the residents' terror soon turned to delight when, in the DSF-230's cramped storage space, they found several sacks of frozen potatoes, which the glider had been delivering to the German and Hungarian soldiers defending the castle. Along with other such gliders, which could carry nine men, this one had taken off in Vienna with the aim of landing on the nearby Field of Blood, as that military training field was called.

> *Gulfs of shadow; E, whiteness of vapours and of tents,*
> *Lances of proud glaciers, white kings, shivers of umbel;*
> *I, purples, spat blood, smile of beautiful lips*
> *In anger or in the raptures of penitence.*

The girl was the first to recite a poem, something by Mickiewicz, to prove to the boy that no lovelier language existed in the world than Polish. As for the boy, the lines above, from Arthur Rimbaud, were all that came to mind. Even as he spoke them, someone looked out the window and flung down the key, which, miraculously, he managed to catch.

* * *

It happened much earlier that one of the guests, who behaved in a somewhat furtive manner – a young man with delicate features and a sardonic smile who once upon a time had had flings with both of the resident sisters, which meant he had visited this flat back in the days when the parents lived here – had glanced over at the surly-looking poet, who kept taking disciplined sips from his drink, while lighting one cigarette after another. The guest with the sardonic smile had felt quite at home here running up the spiral staircase, as he did when he came to visit his own parents, who had had sharp disputes both between themselves and with the Pápais. While the parents argued, he'd given the works of Mao Zedong to the boys and seduced the girls. So this sardonic young man, on seeing the poet – who sat there with one of his groupies at his feet, a hard-to-acquire orange in her upturned palm – summoned the poet with a subtle nod of his head to join him in the girls' room, which was beyond the bathroom and the view from which was obscured by a large chestnut tree. In autumn 1956 this window had been smashed by shrapnel ricocheting off the castle wall, precisely at the moment when Pápai, hungry for news, having returned to the flat from the cellar, leaned down to turn off the radio he'd turned on a couple of minutes earlier. The poet rose clumsily out of his chair, bottle of vodka, ashtray, lit cigarette and shot glass in one hand – a spectacle worthy of a circus act – while with the index finger of his other hand he exhorted his groupie, who was about to spring up after him, *not* to follow. To their astonishment, in the girls' room they found, on the unmade bed with a bra in place of the pillow – under a Christ-ridiculing Bosch painting depicting evil faces and a self-portrait by Van Gogh embroidered with thick cotton threads (the incomparable work of the previously mentioned sister with bronze-red hair, a work that radiated sunlight) – a film director with brawny arms and a Buddha's repose, as if he had been lounging there for centuries, toying with a woman's headband woven through with strands of hair and simultaneously reading Kant's *Critique of Pure Reason*, who did not even bother to look up at the two conspiratorial gentlemen. Whether the director could see much in the dim light was debatable, but not out of the question. He was humming something to himself as an Indian sitar droned from a record player, so the gentlemen tactfully avoided switching on the light, and instead removed themselves, discreetly, over to the open window that looked out onto the chestnut tree, and spoke in hushed tones about a topic of concern only to themselves – namely, the forthcoming issue of a samizdat publication edited by them. The gas lamps were already lit on Váralja Street.

Meanwhile, Mrs Pápai had disappeared.

In the girls' room, to the measured beat of a clay drum (which Pápai had brought home from one of his Middle

Eastern trips, perhaps from Cairo), amid thick clouds of marijuana smoke that swirled in the air behind the window, which had been closed to muffle the sound, and surrounded by a sea of glowing faces, the two sons danced, like two Indians or two Arabs, sweat pouring from them. Around and around they twirled, in some unknown tribal dance, faces red-hot, as their little sister, under the window, wildly beat the clay drum. Across from her, sitting on the floor, her back against the wall, the blonde Polish girl gazed dreamily at the two brothers, who – their backs rigid, their feet bare, their motions strange – yielding to some unfamiliar force, pounding their feet hard upon the floor, circled each other.

Their mother never did find them.

22 Kerék Street, 6th floor, flat 35, District III, Budapest

1

Comrade József Dóra's head was boiling.

In the year since he had become Mrs Pápai's handler, all his machinations had been in vain; equally vain were his words of sometimes deliberately exaggerated praise,[1] to which Mrs Pápai invariably responded with a sceptical smile, well aware that the value of the intelligence she'd provided thus far had been more or less zero.[2] 'I'm just a silly housewife,' she would say, coquettishly, though it had become clear that she was far more cultivated than her handlers (she began each morning

---

[1] In the course of the reports she has been summoned to provide we have received eight pieces of political information, Department 6 deeming them valuable.

[2] During the next couple of meetings we will determine what the reason is for the weak performance MRS PÁPAI has demonstrated in the realm of political intelligence-gathering, and in the course of directing and educating the network individual we will seek to spur MRS PÁPAI to more objective political judgements.

by listening to Yehudi Menuhin). She was happy to receive praise, true, but because she saw the whole thing as a question of give and take – and because in her reckoning, in matters important to her, she'd 'suffered humiliating defeats' – a bitter taste lingered in her mouth. Her requests in matters that, as far as she was concerned, had to be resolved by any means, were perceived as 'denunciations' in everyday speech, though that's not how she saw it. She was a rigid advocate of the Party line, and in return she simply asked for the Party's support. She didn't think of the Party as something opposed to or alien to herself – no, to her the Party represented 'God, Fatherland and Family'. True, it stood above her, and yet she had to defend it from attacks – at times it proved even more important than her family, which otherwise she held truly sacred. Mrs Pápai was mired in the ideology of the 1950s. In this she was unrelenting, even if not exactly uncritical. She had an affinity for every form of art; she was ready to help anyone who turned to her with a complaint; she helped an immense number of people, including some who didn't deserve it; she spoke several languages; and she had a deep understanding of the troubles that beset both body and soul. As a practising interpreter she had contacts with people of all social classes, foreign and Hungarian alike, and her conversation was often beguiling. And yet in one particular matter she was unbending. It was this duality that Comrade Dóra couldn't comprehend: on the one hand there was her wonderful sensitivity, her accommodating nature, her unbounded openness and curiosity in certain matters, especially those involving art – yes, that wildly romantic imagination. On the other hand, there were the inviolable, unshakeable dogmas Mrs Pápai had obviously sworn allegiance to. A chasm yawned within the soul of this network individual, the depth of which Comrade Dóra couldn't begin to gauge.

Nonetheless, despite their divergent aims, the complicity between the lieutenant and Mrs Pápai had only grown over the past year, thanks perhaps to their regular meetings. Mrs Pápai felt she couldn't tell anyone certain things, that she had to bury wounds she couldn't speak of even with herself – including the deepest wound, which a rash marriage had driven only deeper. But her readiness to collaborate with the intelligence services was enhanced by the charm of the intrigue, and even if this charm had faded over the years, it still reminded Mrs Pápai of the adventures of her younger days, in the illegal movement – of vigils held till dawn in the prickly underbrush of an olive grove in the company of a heavily stubbled young man whose intoxicating scent of sweat mixed with the heady fragrance of orange and eucalyptus that arrived in waves with every thrust. As for the increasingly intimate conversations she had with the lieutenant – with whom, as time passed, Mrs Pápai became ever more open, almost suicidally so – they imparted upon their relationship the strange illusion of friendship. She shared her everyday concerns and thoughts with the lieutenant, not just the problems of her private life but also her increasing doubts about her work for him. Notwithstanding his obscure forebodings, Comrade Dóra didn't cease to employ Mrs Pápai – no, despite his gathering sense that he should cut her loose, that it was high time to end this *merciless flaying of a human being*, as he expressed it – sometimes his heart ached as he gazed into Mrs Pápai's agonized eyes! – he just couldn't do it. This was his job, this was what he was paid to do. He couldn't afford a fiasco. After all, the results of Comrade Beider's previous handling of Mrs Pápa had been truly impressive. Comrade Dóra began to feel that Mrs Pápai – who sacrificed herself mercilessly in seeking to fulfil the department's often ludicrously petty requests – did not deserve this fate.[3] Her character sketches and brief observations[4] about Nigerian, Tanzanian, Palestinian, Iraqi and Indian journalists who were studying at the International School of Journalism in Hungary were entertaining and sometimes demonstrated a deep insight into human behaviour,[5] but so far not one such journalist had been snared.

[3] MRS PÁPAI gave the impression of being a worn-out, broken individual, and the problems she related certainly explained this appearance. Despite this, she gladly took on the resolution of the assignment she received, and moreover she added: if the school gave her more opportunities she could get to know the target individuals even better.

[4] MRS PÁPAI reported that Rofus Khoza sought to borrow a lot of money from his fellow students. His views are wholly acceptable.

[5] *He is a member of a reportedly progressive party and acts not on the basis of strict, tribal perspectives. In his workplace and before readers he does not wear his party affiliation on his sleeve, because according to him, a journalist in Nigeria must appear completely neutral. He is a very religious Presbyterian. He saw the*

These journalists were distrustful,[6] and each regarded his stay in Hungary as a holiday.[7]

At other times the lieutenant had easily shaken off his doubts about Mrs Pápai, but almost at the start of their budding relationship, back in March, he had been shocked to be handed a letter Mrs Pápai had written to the head of the School of Journalism – a letter Comrade Dóra had naturally received as well, and almost immediately, though he had not mentioned this to Mrs Pápai. True, Mrs Pápai's mood had improved since. *She is a woman of moods*, thought Comrade Dóra, who had received special instruction in this domain, too, during training. Yes, he knew how to receive such outbursts of emotion with a blank expression, not to mention his experience as an interrogating officer, which was of considerable help when it came to managing the fluctuating emotions

---

Csiksomlyó Passion Play twice, but only from a religious perspective. He said it made him happy, proving that religious freedom can be had in a socialist country. He would like to acquire photos of various scenes from the play so he can use them in his paper at home. His religiousness is <u>very deep</u>; he believes in hell and in the judgement of God. Virtually every act of his is a trial run of religiousness. His older sister is presently enrolled in continuing education in Rome. She is a nurse-dietician (?). ALAWODE wanted to travel there to visit her.

[6] MRS PÁPAI feels that the students have regarded her as a faculty member, too, and so they haven't been as open with her, either, as they were earlier. Moreover, this hostile mood limited her operative activities as well.

Compounding the above is the fact that caring for her husband, whose health keeps declining, represents an increasing burden for MRS PÁPAI in her private life.

The husband dreads the thought of MRS PÁPAI wanting to leave their home, fearing as he does that she will be arrested on the street. The symptoms of paranoia have so consumed him that sometimes he steps out of the flat and looks around to be sure no one is watching.

[7] *In the students' opinion the school did not fulfil its task: the lectures were boring, and they passed the time during lectures by reading newspapers and writing letters.*

of network individuals. All the same, the words in that letter had harried him for days on the tram, in his official car, and even at home in front of the TV; for in it Mrs Pápai, it seemed, was toying with the idea of suicide. She spoke of sins that only her sadness could expiate. And God forbid Mrs Pápai should shoot off her mouth somewhere, only to ruin all the work they'd undertaken so doggedly! He'd gladly have shared the letter with his wife, but he couldn't speak to her about his work. No, at most he could reply to her question, 'Hard day at the office?' with a curt 'Yes'. And though lately the clouds had parted and Mrs Pápai was involving herself at the journalism school with renewed vigour, good cheer and her usual enthusiasm, her March letter was still a tragic cry for help. And so, as this story's protagonist, she deserves to have it quoted now, just as she wrote it:

This letter is wholly personal in nature. It is addressed to you.
    Not much explanation is needed for me to again say what is taking shape in my mind for a year now. I'm horribly depressed, the thought of death occupies me a lot. There's no point in again chronicling the causes. A communist who has been through a lot understands his friends and those who share his convictions. Most of my energy is consumed by keeping my hapless husband alive; and so studying, continuing education and all the concentration needed for someone to remain fresh, has become nothing more than a wilted flower.

And wilted flowers are usually thrown in the bin. This hurts much, because I know that regular study and freshness would still be possible – but the circumstances are terribly stubborn, not allowing this. So I must bid farewell to the institute and do penance for my depression somewhere else (like for sin). I'd really like to sink, to disappear. Maybe I will succeed.

As far as I know, Comrade Rév's last class is on April 22. I think I could bid farewell then to the school, too, without undue attention.

My regards, with a true friend's farewell.
Budapest, 31 March 1983

Where oh where was the shining smile of a year before? The melodic laughter, the cream puff, and the sweet cream smeared on the edge of Mrs Pápai's mouth? The whimsical artistic nature, when all had seemed so playfully easy, and Mrs Pápai had headed to Israel to ferret out the secrets of the 30th World Zionist Congress? Precisely one year had passed since then, and because the next day would be Mrs Pápai's sixty-first birthday, Comrade Dóra arrived once again with a lovely bouquet.

This could not be botched up.

'Was this Pat Game very much in love with your brother?' Comrade Dóra asked while putting on the table the bundle of letters he'd brought back, but as if it were an aside, as if he didn't really expect an answer to his question. 'They're all here,' he added, catching the inquisitive glance Mrs Pápai cast at the envelopes sent from Canada and addressed to her. Mrs Pápai broke into a girlish smile, as if caught red-handed. She'd just poured hot water over the tea, Earl Grey, the fragrance of bergamot wafting up into the air as she now poured thick creamy milk into his cup from a plastic milk-bag with its snipped-open corner. Comrade Dóra didn't like tea – and Mrs Pápai always made it too strong – but unless they met in the Angelika Café or the bistro at Kútvölgyi Hospital, where he could have coffee, he invariably had to drink a cup of tea when visiting her. Now, waiting for it to cool, he watched in wonder as Mrs Pápai, casting etiquette to the wind, drank gluttonously, slurping with abandon. She didn't even bother to stir the many spoonfuls of sugar, instead fishing them out with the teaspoon from the bottom of the cup, then crunching heartily away, meanwhile taking sips of the steaming hot liquid and emitting strange squelches, as if to cool her mouth.

'I got used to this in London,' she said with a kind, apologetic smile on looking up and meeting Comrade Dóra's wide-open eyes.

'Is someone in the family collecting stamps?' he asked cautiously, for the stamps had been cut out of the envelopes. Mrs Pápai burst out laughing.

'Everyone I know in the *Aretz* is crazy about pretty stamps!' She spooned the remaining sugar out of the cup, swallowed it, and cast Comrade Dóra an expectant stare.

'In the *Aretz*?' he asked.

'In Israel,' Mrs Pápai clarified with an enormous smile. *Aretz* means 'the land' – or, by extension, home, country, as Comrade Dóra learned later from a dictionary, Israelis often referring to their homeland this way. She must have been a beautiful woman, Mrs Pápai. The lieutenant glanced around in search of the embroidered tablecloth he'd given her precisely a year earlier, but he saw it nowhere. He chose not to ask about it.

'This Pat was very much in love with your brother?'

The cat-and-mouse game began anew. They loved this game, both of them. Like two gladiators, they took their places in the arena and watched each other. Over the years Mrs Pápai had mastered the art of giving the impression of frankness. Comrade Dóra on occasion had to pose to Mrs Pápai brutally indiscreet questions that, in principle, she was not obliged to answer. At such times he had to be on guard in case the network individuals became evasive. Mrs Pápai laid her cards on the table at once, opting to play a game called 'complete candour', at least it seemed that that was what she was doing, and she spoke to Comrade Dóra as candidly as, it seemed, a believer in a confession booth speaks to a priest.[8]

---

[8] On my arrival I congratulated MRS PÁPAI with flowers on the occasion of her birthday. MRS PÁPAI was very moved by the gesture, and ensuing from the family holiday she began to talk about her children.

It troubles her very much that her children are not following their parents' example by engaging in politics in the spirit of Marxism–Leninism. She analysed her parenting principles in detail and not even now can she understand why her children have turned to other ideas or abandoned politics altogether.

I sought to counterbalance MRS PÁPAI's despair by emphasizing her children's

As for the lieutenant, he was always on his guard, for he could never be certain that what he heard was the complete truth. He had never had dealings with a Jewish woman before. *If she's regarded as the dumb one in the family,* he thought, *then Mrs Pápai's family must be shrewd as anything.* 'I was the birdbrain and the beauty,' she'd once quipped. Sometimes Mrs Pápai said things like this, whereupon Lieutenant Dóra would look down at his feet, taking care not to step into the lasso thrown before him. He was, after all, well aware that, ideally speaking, the relationship of the operative officer and the network individual was a paternal one of sorts, based on mutual trust and understanding. His job was to transmit the general behavioural norms, methods and methodologies necessary for the execution of assignments, and at the same time his words must have an effect on the network individual's mind, emotions and will. That is what he'd been taught in school and what he'd applied successfully in the real world. As for Mrs Pápai's beauty, she was still attractive even now – yes, she was undeniably pretty. A few years earlier she could even have been used in a honey trap in the operation involving the Israeli colonel with whom Mrs Pápai had presumably had an intimate affair in her youth. The possibility had in fact been discussed, for no avenue of attack could be discounted – no, this was a fundamental principle at

positive achievements, noting that if a doctor who is not of Marxist convictions can practise medicine successfully here, in socialist Hungary, that is to the credit of socialist health care, and so even this work is very useful for our society.

Headquarters, for it had sometimes happened that a highly successful operation had blossomed from the seed of an idea initially dismissed as worthless. As for this particular plan concerning Mrs Pápai, owing to its budgetary implications, among other things, it had been shot down at a meeting of operative officers. Not to mention that they had been unable to unequivocally determine Mrs Pápai's predisposition to sex in general. Having studied the files relating to her earlier activity, the lieutenant arrived at the conclusion that she was not nearly as naïve as she made herself out to be. In political matters she was uncompromising – no, she never tried to hide that – and when Lieutenant Dóra and the other comrades asked her to at least make a show of not being so, for this was the least that she, as a professional bearer of secrets, was expected to do, she rejected the idea in the strongest terms possible, with tears in her eyes. When, however, they pointed to the broader international and national context, she seemed to understand at once what they were getting at, and, at least temporarily, gave up her intractable demands. But she had experienced it as a defeat. The combination of openness and an unbending, maniacal fundamentalism was undoubtedly the weak point of this network individual,[9] and substantially undermined her operative value.

'Yes, you could put it that way. It is called true love.'

[9] Although MRS PÁPAI is politically extremely biased, the soundness of her assessments could still be influenced by the opinions and wide knowledge of facts voiced by her father – who, despite his illness, is still politically active.

Comrade Dóra broke into a grin, which Mrs Pápai misunderstood. He'd suddenly recalled a definition of love he'd encountered during his studies as nothing other than – and these were the textbook's exact words – an 'emotionally coloured social tendency'. He recalled how, during a final viva – when his professor for an intelligence operations course had asked him about love with a serious face – he had been incapable of getting a word out straight and, indeed, had burst out laughing. Fortunately the examiner had a sense of humour, and Comrade Dóra was given an A. Mrs Pápai, having misunderstood the smile on the lieutenant's face, added apologetically:

'My brother was almost sixty, the girl only twenty-six. True, he was always a Don Juan, but this time he'd fallen in love. All this happened in the kibbutz, yes, it caught fire at once, a huge bonfire, love at first sight, and only those who didn't want to didn't understand. My brother had picked her out for himself on the second day from among the *midnadvim*, and one and a half years later he was dead.'

'From among whom?'

'The volunteers. His wife was a cold woman. She couldn't even bring herself to administer the painkilling suppositories at the hospital. I myself had to press them into my dear brother's bottom. He was in horrendous pain. Colon cancer.'

When Mrs Pápai uttered the words 'horrendous pain', it was as if she were cradling and caressing this pain, and

Comrade Dóra had the feeling that she herself longed for similar agonies. But as an experienced nurse, one who had graduated from the American University in Beirut, she was able to speak with surprising objectivity of bodily matters.

'I'm convinced that this flowering of love was a presentiment of his illness,' Mrs Pápai said. 'My brother was a very, very handsome man. Of course he was a Zionist. But with him, I couldn't be angry about it. We never talked about politics. Everyone was in love with my big brother. Everyone.'

Comrade Dóra was always in awe of Mrs Pápai's ability to express herself precisely without getting caught up in the throes of emotion. At such times it seemed that even her accent disappeared, and sentences emerged from her mouth in proper Hungarian. As an experienced nurse, she knew exactly what unfolds in the body when a person is dying.

'Psychologists call this *Torschlusspanik*,' Mrs Pápai quietly observed. 'They visited me here in Budapest. That's when I got to know Pat.'

'Oh dear, the picture!' Lieutenant Dóra exclaimed, reaching into his pocket and pulling out a photograph in a plastic case. 'I nearly forgot about it.'

The photograph was of a rather homely-looking girl – at least Comrade Dóra wasn't exactly taken with her – blonde and with a pudgy nose. But he had to admit that her expression was brave and frank. Mrs Pápai took it from him, took it out of the plastic case, and cast it a gentle glance. She leaned the picture up against the vase, on the table, in which the flowers she'd just received had come to life.

'Pat. I think distance, too, played its part.'

'Torshoeswhat?' asked Comrade Dóra, reaching for his notebook.

'Gate-shutting panic. When men sense that they no longer spark desire in every woman they cross paths with. That the music is over.' Comrade Dóra began intently studying the edge of the rug while Mrs Pápai blushed. While she could be quite open about other people's romantic or sexual endeavours, she could, at times, be just as reticent about her own feelings. Who knew better than Mrs Pápai what it was like when distance made love almost unbearable? And yet it wasn't Tom, the ungainly British private, who now appeared in her mind's eye in his bathing suit, in Alexandria, sitting on the railing at a beach resort, but Pápai – in his underwear, his hairy belly exposed, standing there on the chair he'd positioned in the bathroom, a rope around his neck, fixed to the gas pipe that ran along the ceiling – as he gazed at Mrs Pápai, who'd just torn open the front door, having raced home from work driven by a premonition of sorts.

'She's a smart girl, huh?'

Comrade Dóra cleared his throat, for that morning he'd only skimmed the rough translations one of his colleagues had thrown together. He knew Russian quite well, and he'd picked up a little German while stationed at the barracks in

East Germany, but he could only babble in English, and this had hindered his career prospects, too, to an extent. 'They couldn't cheat me,' he'd say, trying to impress his colleagues, 'in any country, ever!' But this was an exaggeration: in a foreign city he wouldn't even have been able to ask, in English, where the train station was.

Something about these interminably long letters bothered him, but he couldn't decide exactly what. Perhaps he should read them more carefully.

'And, comrade,' he said to Mrs Pápai, 'you really think what she writes about her having access to the upper echelons of Canadian politics is true?'

'Pat would never lie to me,' Mrs Pápai quickly replied as her stomach knotted up. She would have preferred to talk about something else, but she could not, for that was the lieutenant's prerogative. Though they never broached the subject, Comrade Dóra was Mrs Pápai's boss – the decisions were his to make. They had to tread carefully – this was, after all, a game in which they were supposed to be two equals brought together by mutual conviction.

Pápai had been hospitalized again, which is why Mrs Pápai and Comrade Dóra were able to meet at the flat in the veterans' home. Mrs Pápai made a daily pilgrimage to visit Pápai at Lipótmező, the huge psychiatric facility in Buda, to make sure he did his exercises. She laid the whining Pápai on his back and got him to stretch, because the anti-depressants exacerbated the intestinal blockage that caused him to suffer from constant constipation. The medication he took for his eyes had negative side-effects for his heart, and the Parkinson's and the mental illness were hardly a happy combination. Comrade Dóra couldn't begin to imagine the work that went into keeping Pápai alive. Or what it was like to live with a madman. In the tiny second-floor flat the sick Pápai shared with his wife, the lights had to be kept on even in the morning, what with these dull December days. One of the walls was lined with the hideous, mass-produced furniture that had come with the flat.

'Okay. But that Truday will marry her?'

'Trud*eau*. Pierre Trudeau. Pat would not lie to me, no, she's not capable of it. Her family is very well connected.'

'This whole story seems a bit muddled to me,' Comrade Dóra said, taking a big breath. But this wasn't what he wanted to talk about. He and two colleagues at the office had racked their brains over the Canadian girl's letters, passing them around, telling each other that this tip-off individual would be a big catch if it were true. They could send Mrs Pápai out to visit her, and then they'd see.

But this was the crux of the problem. And it wasn't even because of this that he'd dropped by. Rather, he'd become ever more convinced that Mrs Pápai, in her utter despair, had produced the Canadian girl's letters only to cook up an excuse to visit her daughter in New York. Not that that would have been such a big deal. Even back in Budapest the daughter had been under constant surveillance, in the agency's crosshairs, and, now abroad, she was clearly capitalizing on her opposition contacts back home. Mrs Pápai could no doubt have provided useful information about all this, and yet this Pat Game ... whom the Canadian prime minister supposedly wanted to marry ... who went in and out of hospitals, living on sleeping pills and sobbing all day long about her lost love, Mrs Pápai's brother ... Comrade Dóra was all but certain that this was a dead-end. But he couldn't say it.

He'd looked through the dossiers of the tip-off individuals Mrs Pápai had previously named. Nothing had come of any of them. And yet Mrs Pápai was not picky. She'd even offered up her niece in Milan. She invited her to Budapest along with her Persian husband. They'd come to the capital, they'd left. Nothing. She had named a cousin's husband, an architect who seemed quite promising, for he had a murky past, he lied left and right, had money troubles, and no doubt conducted secret affairs with women. An ideal prospect for an intelligence agency worth its salt. But no amount of persuasion could convince him to come to Hungary, though Mrs Pápai had tried everything. Having served in the Interior Ministry at the time of his defection in 1956, he dreaded having to set foot again in Hungary, and no amount of reasoning proved enough to persuade him otherwise – no, he kept veering off topic, leading Mrs Pápai off course, and for her part, well, she naively took the bait. It was icing on the cake to discover that he didn't even have a university degree, though in Budapest Mrs Pápai spared no effort to find it. Counter-intelligence would have produced a fake one, had the fellow been happy to accept it in person. But of course he wasn't willing to do even that much. Of course he hoped that by some miracle a diploma would materialize out of thin air, whereupon he could legally go about designing bunker-style flats for the Israeli lower middle class in up-and-coming neighbourhoods of Tel Aviv. And what a splendid catch she too would have been, that Israeli border guard at the airport in Tel Aviv who, violating regulations, had fallen into conversation with the jabbering Mrs Pápai, whom everyone trusted, even if they were inspecting her luggage! An elderly relative of that border guard had survived Auschwitz and lived in Miskolc, and the border guard supposedly wanted to make contact with her secretly through Mrs Pápai. She even gave Mrs Pápai the address. By the time they found this relative in Miskolc, she had died. And then there was Mrs Pápai's son, whom Mrs Pápai herself had recommended for the work – at least she didn't seem to be against the idea – but they had never seen him again. They should have gone after him, but Comrade Beider had ruled it out. And there was that hapless peacenik who loathed his chosen homeland, where he'd been humiliated again and again for refusing military service and who'd forbidden even his daughters from joining the army, but not even in Hungary would they have known what to do with a diehard pacifist. He would only have spelled trouble. With his rigid worldview he was a pariah the whole world over, and yet he was incorruptible and mistrustful. And, yes, there was the catch that seemed the most promising, the Israeli army colonel, Mrs Pápai's former suitor. The ever-exhausted Mrs Pápai had prepared herself carefully, putting on makeup, which she almost never did, and her sister, who accompanied her to the colonel's villa, was pleased but at the same time wondered what was going on, for she remembered the days when the colonel, as a young man – now he was an important and rich man – had run after her sister. Besides, when visiting Israel Mrs Pápai usually only met her comrades. In any event, the colonel had warmly received these two beauties of a bygone world. While watching TV after a dinner of many courses he'd even expressed critical opinions of Israeli politicians, but when the sharp-nosed colonel began grilling Mrs Pápai about 1956 and Solzhenitsyn, their conversation faltered and finally ran aground. Mrs Pápai just couldn't lie. In other circumstances this would have been rewarded, but in this case it had been worse than a sin – it had been a mistake.

In fact, Mrs Pápai's sole significant catch had arguably been that notoriously anti-Soviet Russian employee at the Weizmann Institute, Zaretsky, who helped Jews emigrate to Israel. It was a wonder he'd even given Mrs Pápai the time of day. And yet the Russians took over his case. Yes, this was a gold star for Mrs Pápai.

As for the Canadian girl, she was well on her way to going mad. Yes, her interminably long letters were made up of succinct sentences, as far as Lieutenant Dóra could gather from the rough translations, and yet they focused obsessively on only a few themes: the girl with the scintillating intellect had been reduced to a wailing, whining madwoman huddled at the edge of her bed and living on painkillers. Every one of her grand plans – writing a novel, writing a play, writing a dissertation – had gone up in smoke one after the other. And now she wanted to be the wife of the Canadian prime minister?

Does everyone around Mrs Pápai go mad? Lieutenant Dóra asked himself. He cleared his throat.

'Thank you for the delicious tea,' he said softly as if preparing to leave. He stood, ceremoniously shook hands with Mrs Pápai, buttoned up his winter coat, and was just about to step out into the hallway. Standing there was an old man with a walking frame, budging neither forward nor backward, but looking as if someone had forgotten him there. Comrade Dóra turned back from the door as if something had just come to mind. He was quite pleased with himself for this gambit.

'Where was it again that you and your husband lived before moving here?' he asked Mrs Pápai, as if he didn't know the answer.

'On Kerék Street,' she replied carefully, ready for the next move in their chess match. Her nerves were on edge. No matter how innocently Comrade Dóra had phrased his question, Mrs Pápai was certain that it was connected to some matter she was unaware of, but she had learned to maintain an unflinching expression. 'Next to the school.'

'What number?'

'Twenty-two.'

The lieutenant rose on his tiptoes. He took a step back into the flat and closed the door behind him.

'May I sit down?'

'I'll make another tea.'

'No, no, I'm in a hurry.'

They looked at each other.

'I'm embarrassed,' said Comrade Dóra.

'You have no reason to be,' replied Mrs Pápai reassuringly.

'This concerns a dilemma of a friend of mine. More precisely, a technical problem of ours. Can the grocery store on Szentendrei Street be seen from the flat's windows?'

'It can.'

'Well, that's wonderful. You see, our friend, of whom it can't be known exactly which side he is on, happens to live in the building opposite. To get to know him a bit better, we'd like to spend a bit of time observing him to determine just what he is up to in his flat.'

Mrs Pápai pricked up her ears. She understood precisely

what 'our friend' meant, or at least she thought she did, and this feeling was enough.

The lieutenant hesitated. What he had to say was, he felt, obvious enough, but with so little time he and his colleagues had not been able to cook up a better cover story, and only an idiot would not have seen through it at once. But because of the individuals concerned, a great deal of caution was advisable. Mrs Pápai pretended she didn't understand, or perhaps indeed she didn't understand. The chess games flowed into each other. There were games within games. If she played so well that she seemed not to understand, that would mean that in fact she understood only too well; and if she pretended that she understood, it was by no means certain that she did. The goal was to leave both possibilities open. To help without quite understanding. But it was enough, too, if she pretended she didn't understand. It would be catastrophic were she to let on.

Comrade Dóra assumed an anxious expression.

'There is a flat there—'

'At number twenty-two?' Mrs Pápai cut in.

'No, no, not at all. That's just it. Like I said, exactly opposite, on the other side of the street. A flat in which certain things have been going on for a while now that are a bit of a problem for us, and we want to find out exactly what those things are.'

'On the third floor?'

Without a second thought, the lieutenant replied:

'Yes, on the third. Why?'

'I knew it! My husband was the first to notice, but I didn't bother with such things, because he has this, how do you say it, obsession, this compulsive fantasy, that he is being watched, and I told him right away that no one is watching him, but he said there's a camera there, opposite us, and it has been directed right at our windows, and I told him that's so stupid, why would anyone be watching us, they'd have no reason, and that this was his illness, his persecution complex, and he vowed he'd never say such a thing again, but that very night, when I couldn't sleep, I took a closer look at that window, which always had its thick curtains drawn, and often the occupants weren't home, but when they were, well, the lights were on all night long, and who is able to afford that much electricity? But I trashed, I mean I brushed the thought aside. One night, though, at four in the morning, I noticed a car stop in front of the building, and the same thing happened several times, and a man looked out of the window and shouted down in some unknown language.'

The lieutenant was now in a remarkable position. It was like a card game in which the opponent gives away their trumps without knowing. This was what was so strange about Mrs Pápai. One minute she was sitting silently in the throes of depression, her mouth shut tight, and the next, eyes gleaming, voice strident, she came up with one good idea after another, or at least she took the initiative, like a zealous student almost falling off her bench, stretching out her hand to answer the teacher's question.

'Exactly that flat.'

'It's strange that the curtains are always drawn.'

'And since we recalled that your younger son lives in the Kerék Street flat... Do you still have the key?'

Mrs Pápai froze. This could not be. This was her sole point of vulnerability. She couldn't just walk into that sanctum. She knit her brows.

Strike while the iron is hot, thought the lieutenant.

'We are talking about something like twenty minutes.'

The silence was thick enough to cut with a knife.

'I don't think my son would be happy about it. But that's not the main problem: he sits around at home a lot. He comes and goes in the most unexpected fashion, he doesn't work like other people do. He sleeps late, and in the evening when he is on duty at the theatre, he sticks around only for the start of the performance before hurrying home.'

'Indeed,' said Comrade Dóra softly, 'your son mustn't know about this. The matter is sensitive. But this would allow us to solve our little technical matter in one fell swoop. It would be a really big help. I don't even know why this didn't occur to us before.[10] But if it's not practical, then

---

[10] MINISTRY OF THE INTERIOR   TOP SECRET
Sub-department III/III-4-a   Attn: Com. Dóra

Comrade Oszkár Kiss, Pol. Colonel
Head of Department III/I-3

we'll figure something else out. Could you draw a plan of the flat?'

Mrs Pápai might even have heard this as a command. For his part, Lieutenant Dóra pretended not to notice her increasing unease. He unbuttoned his coat, removed it, and flung it brazenly on one of the beds. Mrs Pápai needed to feel that the matter was serious, that there was no turning back.

'I think I'll ask for a little tea, after all,' he said. 'It really is cold out there.'

'Three rooms, one beside the other. Very simple, nothing fancy: the bathroom, toilet and kitchen opposite the rooms. The first room is bigger; the middle one, the living room, is smaller; and the third room is bigger again. My son sleeps in the first room. From the kitchen window you can see the school.'

Mrs Pápai had become laconic and withdrawn. She didn't seem to be in a hurry to make tea, which didn't bother the lieutenant too much.

'And when can you let us in there?'

Intra-departmental memo

In our counter-intelligence domain we are keeping under surveillance the writer György Petri (Born: Budapest, 1943; mother's name: Kornélia Butter Walter), resident of 23 Batthány Street, District I, Budapest.

According to our reliable information this individual recently moved to 22 Kerék Street, 6th floor, flat 35, District III, Budapest.

As per the oral conversation we had with Pol. Lt. Comrade Dr József Dóra, we request that the surveillance of György Petri by 3/e be made possible at the above address; that is, that through the SC CN MRS PÁPAI our access to the flat be ensured.

Budapest, 12 December 1983

Miklós Esvégh,
Pol. Lieutenant Colonel
Department Head

István Nagy,
Pol. Captain
Sub-department Head

'I don't know.'

'We need to figure something out, anything.'

The lieutenant cast Mrs Pápai a somewhat ill-tempered stare. *Doesn't she get it? Doesn't she understand that there is no time for fudging? Doesn't she understand her duty?*

'The other thing is, sometimes friends stay in the flat. My son is very generous when friends of his don't have a place to stay. He doesn't tell me and doesn't need to tell me.'

'Is anyone else living there now?'

'I have no idea, but it can't be ruled out.'

She either knows or she doesn't, thought the lieutenant, fixing his jaundiced eyes on Mrs Pápai. And as she looked back at him, she suddenly noticed something she couldn't give a name to. She was gripped by terror. What did Comrade Dóra know about her son? She had no idea. At their last meeting she'd opened up too much. About how happy she'd be if her son had a significant other. About how much she yearned for a grandchild. She already had two grandchildren, true, but how happy she'd be if this son were to bless her with one! She shouldn't have said even that much. She sensed that the lieutenant could hear the bottomless woe pervading her words. She couldn't expose her utter shame. These people would tear her son to shreds, walk all over him, wring him out like a wet rag, make his life impossible. Mrs Pápai could feel the oxygen being sucked out of the room, her asthma starting up as her breathing became laboured. Her large chest rose and fell. In her hands she held her little boy, who'd seemed bent on dying the moment he was born, and pressed her cheek to his tender face. She looked into Pápai's camera on a sunny spring day under the Buda Castle and smiled. And then, her head tilted just so, she looked at the lieutenant. After a short pause she began talking in a thin, little-girl voice – a voice the lieutenant had never heard before.

'I might be able to come up with an excuse to get my son to leave the flat for a bit.'

'Let's have it,' said the lieutenant somewhat glumly and curtly, while also sneaking a note of commiseration into his voice.

'My daughter is coming home from Moscow for Christmas.'

The notorious New York–Moscow axis, thought Lieutenant Dóra with some bitterness. *Yes, the notorious Tel Aviv–New York–Moscow axis. These Jews always find the sunnier side of things. Wherever they land, it's always on their feet.* He would gladly have travelled to New York. He did at least manage to prevent a malicious smirk coming over his face, though when he was tipsy it would sometimes happen, for when it came down to it he was a rather envious sort, and though he liked the adventurous, secretive, conspiratorial aspects of the work, which allowed him to feel almost like a god when looking at the pedestrians he passed on the street, in fact he sometimes hated himself for this soul-wrenching profession of his, although he wasn't conscious of it. Only the ennui that increasingly bore down on him reminded him that something was amiss with his life.

'Which means I'll have to clean the flat. When I do that my son makes a run for it.'

'Splendid!' said Lieutenant Dóra. 'Congratulations – it's a wonderful plan. And then you'll let our men into the flat for a couple of minutes.'

'But they must be there right on time.'

'They'll be as punctual as death, comrade.'

He rose from his seat.

'You don't want tea, then, after all?' Mrs Pápai asked timidly.

'But before we carry out the mission, we will go over everything thoroughly one more time,' replied Lieutenant Dóra. 'In three days, right here.' He didn't even bother to acknowledge Mrs Pápai's question. 'They're waiting for me. This conversation has gone on a bit too long.'

It was impossible not to sense the reproach in his voice.

2

The heartbeat.

She didn't know whether to keep pressing the buzzer or open the door with her own key.

She'd arrived without notice, since her son had not picked up the phone. But maybe it was better this way.

'Mum!' exclaimed her son, dishevelled and in his under-wear, when he ambled out on hearing a key rattling in the lock, only to find himself face to face with his mother. 'So early?' They looked into each other's eyes as if only into their own. He noticed something different in his mother's eyes, but he couldn't have said what it was. No doubt something had happened to his dad or his little sister or his big sister, something terrible that had to be resolved right away – yes, someone had to be saved.

'Why did you bring that bucket? Jesus.'

The mother just stood there, in the tower block's sixth-floor hallway, bucket in hand.

'You have a bucket here?'

'Beats me.'

'Well then, that's why.'

The boy stepped to one side, the cool air from the street entering the flat along with his mother. Mrs Pápai went straight to the kitchen, where days-old leftovers covered the table.

'What a mess!' she said disdainfully, with a huge sigh. Not even removing her coat, she sat down on one of the chairs, dropping to the floor a bag that she had held in her other hand, a bag packed full of canned goods and other food.

'Don't tell me you want to clean up right now?'

'That's exactly what I'm going to do.'

'That wouldn't be a good idea. They're still asleep back there.'

'You have guests again?'

'Gyuri and Maya. Come on, I'll make you a tea.'

'I'm in a hurry.'

Mrs Pápai's mind raced. She tried replaying in her head the whole of her conversation with the case officer.[11]

---

[11] Comrade Beider (MRS PÁPAI's previous handler) recalled that MRS PÁPAI's flat was in the neighbourhood and recommended that we ask her for help in resolving our problem. To this MRS PÁPAI gave the address and in reply to my question, said the windows look out on Szentendrei Street.

I was very glad to hear that, and asked if the flat afforded a view of the grocery store on Szentendrei Street.

MRS PÁPAI then asked, in surprise, wasn't it the third-floor flat of the building opposite theirs that we wanted to watch? After my evasive reply she said that rather elegantly furnished flat had caught her eye ever since she'd moved in, for it nearly always has its curtains drawn. For a long time no one had used the flat, whose owner had probably been abroad.

'Your sister is arriving tomorrow. We can't greet her with this mess.'

The boy vanished into his room and then returned. For

Following this I posed several questions pertaining to the lay-out of her own flat and the habits of the residents. MRS PÁPAI replied genially to each of them, adding that her son András lives in the flat, and because he is usually at home she doesn't know how the flat could be made empty for long.

As a solution she proposed that she will say she needs to clean the flat on 20 December 1983, and then her son surely won't be home. I accepted her proposal but asked whether, when there are performances every night at the theatre, her son participates in them.

MRS PÁPAI said that as far as she knows, even if her son is on duty he stays only for the start of the play before heading home. The other obstacle is that he has often let friends and acquaintances stay in the flat, and he has never kept MRS PÁPAI apprised.

Finally we agreed that if MRS PÁPAI learns that her son will leave the flat unoccupied for a longer period then she will notify us and ensure our free access to the flat.

Barring that, while she is cleaning on 20 December 1983, we can carry out the necessary work.

I separately brought it to MRS PÁPAI's attention that it would not be appropriate if her son András, his friends or other residents of the building were to learn of our plans, for the matter is very sensitive, so adhering to conspiratorial rules is most important of all in the course of our work.

MRS PÁPAI said she understood, and declared that her children have not known of her work and her ties to us, and cannot know in the future, either, for they profess a different view in this matter, too, than do their parents.

At the end of the meeting we spoke of the Palestinian civil strife and we agreed that MRS PÁPAI would telephone us if the flat is unoccupied.

We finished the meeting, whose cost was 122 forints, at 11:45.

Assessment

At the start of the meeting it became clear that MRS PÁPAI loves her children very much and would do anything for them. She is aware of their ideological errors and seeks to neutralize those, but her effort has thus far met with failure.

On account of the above facts MRS PÁPAI's involvement could be realized only by our employing a cover story acceptable to her by which to gain access to the flat. In this case it is the surveillance of the flat opposite – a flat that has also caught MRS PÁPAI's attention – which can provide the cover story by which our specialists can manage the technical infiltration.

Recommendation

I recommend that we notify Department III/III-5 about the prospect of the technical infiltration.

a while he watched his mother, who was deep in thought, and then he sat down beside her on the worn green sofabed bought in England twenty years earlier, which should have been thrown away long ago. How modern and stylish it had been at the time! It never ceased to amaze visiting relatives. The back doubled as a bedlinen holder. Sleep was no longer possible on the sagging mattress, the leather cross-straps of which had slackened, but no one had the heart to throw out this family heirloom, and the same went for the two arm-chairs with threadbare arms that completed the set. When they'd purchased the green sofabed, the boy had still been able to squeeze himself into the space that held the bedlinen, albeit with great effort. Moments before, in his room, he'd donned a blue-and-white-striped terry-towelling dressing-gown that was two sizes too big: its bottom swept the floor, and when he was drawing he had to roll up its sleeves. They'd bought it for their father, back in Pápai's pudgy days, when, at eighteen stone, as he couldn't repeat often enough, he'd been a member of the Not-See Nutsies Club, for only by looking in the mirror (*drum roll*) could he see his own nuts. The club had two members, Pápai and one of his few friends. True, 'few' is here a matter of poetic licence. That is to say, the club comprised two members – Pápai and his only friend. It should be noted that while Pápai could not have known this, his friend, whom he'd worked with for a while in the same newsroom, was writing reports about him, too.

To be fair, what he had to say about Pápai was favourable. He had had a penchant for jokes and writing them down since childhood, and the Not-See Nutsies Club was central to his repertoire. Everyone found Pápai to be an enormously funny fellow.

The boy tried giving his mum a hug, but he could feel her body tense up.

'They're still asleep.'

His mother's face turned hard with worry. The wrinkles were deep, and the delicately arched nose stuck out like a beak. She clenched her lips. *The poor thing has so many worries,* thought the boy. *Always worried about someone.*

'You should go to the hospital. To exercise him. And wash him. They don't wash him. I don't have the strength any more. *Ein li koach.*'

She said this last phrase under her breath, only to herself. In moments of weakness, exhaustion and despair she switched involuntarily to Hebrew, and she didn't even notice – just as when, two years later, on her deathbed, in hospital, in a morphine-induced stupor, all at once she sat up in bed and opened her eyes. It was later – by which time Mrs Pápai's body, swaddled in a sheet, had been taken down to the mortuary – that her roommate cheerfully told the boy, who happened to be retrieving his mother's belongings from the bedside table, that at night, just for a lark, as a test of sorts, she'd tried shouting over to the unconscious Mrs Pápai,

'*Shema Yisrael!*' and Mrs Pápai's eyes had opened and she sat up in bed. Though by then she was dead.

The rattling of dishes could be heard from the kitchen, and Mrs Pápai, like a lioness protecting her cubs, shot right out of the living room.

'Leave it, leave it!' she shouted at the young woman busy in the kitchen, who turned towards her with a smile.

'We got back really late last night. Sorry for leaving it like this. I'll be finished in a minute.'

The young woman's disarming smile weakened Mrs Pápai's resolve. She kept working noiselessly and quickly in the kitchen, which was so narrow that Mrs Pápai couldn't get past her to the sink.

'I'll make some coffee in a minute,' said the young woman.

'There's no need,' said Mrs Pápai.

'It's fucking snowing again!' came a hoarse voice from a distance. Having slipped on only his trousers, the poet emerged from the third room barefoot, scratching his beard, his upper body naked. He was short, slightly pigeon-chested and hunched. His collarbones protruded conspicuously above his thin, hairy chest, but his shoulders were muscular. Scratching away at his back, he stopped by the door between the back room and the living room.

'If you don't object,' said the poet, 'I was thinking I'd make some venison spine soup. Not here, I mean, but in the house out in Adyliget. Where is that ugly bitch?' He reached over his right shoulder with his left hand to scratch his shoulder blade in way that was familiar to everyone who knew him. He kept scratching, which he clearly found pleasurable. 'She's got the money.'

'Yes?' asked the boy, his mouth watering. 'Venison spine soup?'

'The butcher at the market on Batthyány Square agreed to put aside a bit of venison spine for me. We need to be there by four. And to follow I'll fry up some pork chops, mashed potatoes with nutmeg, with butter-fried peas on the side and fresh parsley. That's as far as I got. The girls can conjure up something to go with it. I don't know a thing about pastries. That's high art.'

'But how?'

'Not here, in Adyliget. At least there's a real stove there. But first we'll drop in for a drink at the Swan. Then we'll climb up to the house in Adyliget. Where is that bag of bones?'

The weekly editorial meeting was, to the poet, sacrosanct. He arrived days or weeks late to other meetings, or else he never showed up at all, but of course without ever telling anyone he wouldn't be there. But when the day came for the editorial meeting for the samizdat *Beszélő*, he was there exactly on time, like Big Ben, and he marked up the manuscripts entrusted to him to the last comma in precise, feminine handwriting.

In Adyliget, in the hills of Buda, for the last six months,

there had stood a caravan belonging to the Road Repair Company, from where, through a tiny window, employees of the Interior Ministry took pictures of those arriving at the house where *Beszélő* was edited. They made no secret of their presence. Indeed, visitors to the house sometimes even waved at them. The secret service men cramped into the far from palatial caravan were the constant butt of jokes. For the sake of appearances they even tore up a stretch of the bumpy road in order to have something to repair.

'Where are my cigarettes? And the little monkey?'

'Maya? In the kitchen. With my mother.'

'Then I'll get dressed properly.'

'We'll have a white Christmas. Aren't you happy?'

The poet looked at the boy.

'Oh no we won't. You don't have a clue.' And he vanished once more into the back room, in which the boy had witnessed so many family scenes – when Pápai and Mrs Pápai had fights, or, more precisely, when his mother pummelled his father because he wouldn't let her administer an enema, and the oily water flowed out of the bag and onto the bed. Hearing this, the boy would run into the room and hold down his father, who writhed about on the damp bedsheets like a wounded beast.

The poet – despite appearances – liked to dress well. A black jacket, an ironed white shirt and a grey tie: this was his favourite outfit. Now, amid hushed cursing, he sought his purple-striped grey tie in one of his travel bags on the floor.

Mrs Pápai watched helplessly and yet in awe as, at the hands of the young woman, everything was cleaned and put in order. A sort of paralysis took hold of her that she could not get the better of. The mocha pot was hissing on the cooker as Maya, in one fell swoop, wiped down the plastic table, swept up and shouted from the kitchen:

'One of you guys take out the rubbish!'

The boy, who had meanwhile sat himself in front of the typewriter, to record the previous day's events, sprang up obligingly, grabbed hold of the bin, went out to the big rubbish chute on the far side of the stairwell, poured in the bin's contents, and returned. By then, in the living room, four cups of steaming hot coffee were on the small table, and the poet was in the kitchen paying compliments to the boy's mother, who was laughing heartily.

* * *

When she was finally on her own in the flat, Mrs Pápai carefully locked the front door, leaving the key in the lock. First she looked around her son's room. Beside the bed on the floor, next to a pile of books, was an issue of *Beszélő*. She picked it up and hid it among the books in the glass-fronted bookcase. Then she realized that this wouldn't do – no, it could still be seen – so she took it into the larder, where, with great difficulty, she pulled one of the time-worn, dented suitcases off the highest shelf. The suitcase was full of odds and ends: a Bedouin saddle ornament; necklaces; copper jugs; loose photographs; old newspapers with Pápai's articles; pearls; embroidery threads; a large wooden camel that Pápai had brought from Cairo thirty years earlier; and a shattered clay drum. Mrs Pápai quickly slipped the *Beszélő* into the suitcase, clicked shut the two locks, and, sighing loudly, managed to wrestle the suitcase back up onto the shelf. There she stood, in the stirred-up dust, gasping for air and bitter. She went back into her son's room and recoiled on seeing, on a slip of paper on the bookshelf, in her own handwriting, an Arab proverb: TIME IS LIKE A SWORD: IF YOU DON'T CUT IT, IT CUTS YOU DOWN.

Stepping over to the Consul typewriter, she noticed that it still held a half-typed sheet of paper with that day's date at the top – 20 December 1983. She removed it and placed it face-down on the table. She knew her son would be furious when he realized what had happened, but she didn't care. Suddenly she noticed an open envelope that had been addressed by a stranger's hand. She hesitated for a moment, but then couldn't resist, and reached inside. As she pulled out a letter, written in French, a photograph fell out onto the floor. She picked it up and saw it was of a young, curly-haired mulatto boy who seemed to be looking back at her. Shuddering, she quickly put the letter and photograph back into the envelope. She took a few more books off the shelf, before putting them back spine-first so their titles would not be visible. And then she looked around the guests' room.

When she was done, she sat down on the green sofabed in the living room and placed the telephone on the little table before her. Putting on her glasses, she began paging through her pocket notebook, growing ever more agitated. The notebook was falling apart. The cover had long ago been ripped off and some of the pages were loose, and although at the start she'd taken care to write the names in alphabetical order, later she'd stopped. She'd slipped recipes and business cards in among the pages. Under and above the telephone numbers were exclamation marks, notes, the names of medications, addresses that didn't belong there at all, Hebrew words and fragments of sentences in English, as well as lines of poetry scribbled down, spelling mistakes and all. *Crimson of shame runs through my body / Thousand needles pricking my brain.* Mrs Pápai rarely stuck the pages that had fallen out back in their proper place, and now, rebuking herself, she shook her head – how would she ever find anything in this jumble. 'Ugh!'

An impatient sigh escaped her when she finally stumbled across the name and telephone number she was looking for. She took a deep breath and began to dial.

3

Ten minutes later the entryphone buzzed. Mrs Pápai was ready to spring into action, standing by the front door near the phone, almost tearing the receiver off the wall, as if it were a matter of life or death. Greeted politely by a male voice, she replied with a loud 'Good afternoon!' before shouting, 'Sixth floor, turn right out of the lift.' 'We know,' the polite male voice answered unexpectedly.

Holding the door wide open, Mrs Pápai received the overall-clad men, one wearing a beret and holding a toolbag; and another in a baseball cap; while the third had with him a small black suitcase. They did not come in right away. No, instead they stamped their feet loudly and repeatedly on the non-existent doormat, which is to say, on the lumpy, half-ripped-up linoleum, shaking the snow from their shoes. The one wearing the beret even kicked the oily-green-painted wall a few times to dislodge the muddy snow that stuck to the jagged soles of his boots. 'Please come in, do come in, it doesn't matter, I am cleaning up anyway,' Mrs Pápai called out, again perhaps too loudly, for the truth was she did not want the neighbours to catch a glimpse of her visitors. Gasmen and plumbers came on their own, and there were three of these men. Mrs Pápai looked at these strangers with a mix of trust and distrust, not knowing how friendly she could be or how pushy she seemed.

'Where is it?' asked the man with a moustache, who seemed to be in charge, at which Mrs Pápai immediately led the guests into the middle room, the so-called living room, and pointed out the window. 'On the second floor,' she said gravely. The men looked at each other for a moment, very nearly forgetting the cover story that had been drummed into them that very morning. 'Can't we do it without a witness?' the man in charge had asked Captain Mercz at the briefing, but Mercz was adamant: 'It would be too risky to enter the flat uninvited, because we can't know when the owner will be home, and putting the flat under constant surveillance would be a waste of time and money. Mrs Pápai is perfectly trustworthy. What's more, she doesn't know the true purpose of the visit. In any case, take a camera with you. By all means take photographs of the inside of the flat you're in, too, so we know the layout exactly. Of every space. If you come across illegal publications, photograph them, too. You'll have about thirty minutes in all. You need to do the installation in all three rooms. These flats are a headache.'

'No problem,' came the weary voice of the man in the beret, who had three similar jobs to do that day.

'A coffee?' Mrs Pápai asked eagerly, not understanding the trembling that shook her body even as she sought to act as naturally as possible, so her face wouldn't give her away. 'Or three, that is?' she corrected herself at once. 'There, on the second floor, where the curtains are drawn!' she exclaimed on seeing what seemed to be uncertainty on the faces of the men standing about in the middle of the room. One of them was staring at the large, colourful rug that covered an entire wall of the tiny room. On it, women carrying infants and baskets on their heads were heading towards a spring, while men with scythes and hoes over their shoulders were on their way to till a rock-filled promised land. 'Gobelin,' said Mrs Pápai, 'my mother's work.' The man in the beret clicked his tongue approvingly, his eyes glistening amiably as he stepped closer to the rug, which he now touched. 'Beautiful,' he declared, his head tipped slightly to one side. Mrs Pápai shuddered, but didn't know why. It was as if her heart had been ripped out. Meanwhile the mustachioed man set down his toolbag beside the grey radiator, crouched down, and fished out a Nikon camera. With slow, leisurely movements he opened the camera and inserted a roll of film, and, from behind the cover of the yellow curtain, began taking pictures of the building across the street. Or at least that's what he appeared to be doing. Even if it was inadvisable to waste film on such nonsense.

'I'd like a coffee,' said the third man, rousing Mrs Pápai from her daydreaming and following her into the kitchen.

'Well, this isn't too big,' he observed, standing in the doorway as Mrs Pápai lit the stove. 'Unfortunately all we have is instant,' said Mrs Pápai contritely. 'That will be perfect,' the man replied politely while looking about. 'With milk?' 'Without, without, and not even a single cube of sugar!' he said cheerfully, at which Mrs Pápai, the experienced nurse, looked at his face. The man's complexion wasn't good. His skin was swollen and there were purple rings under his eyes. He worked long shifts, sometimes late into the night; he was used to it. 'It's not good to have it without milk and sugar on an empty stomach,' Mrs Pápai cautioned him softly. The man only shook his head impatiently, with a shade of menace, it seemed, as if he didn't really want to talk, though he broke into a wide, stern grin that froze upon his face. For a while Mrs Pápai stood in front of the stove in the little kitchen, and then she sat on a stool. She tried, as inconspicuously as possible, to listen in on the muted voices from the other room. Soon the face of the man in the beret appeared above the shoulder of the man standing in the doorway.

'Excuse me, comrade, may I use the phone?' Mrs Pápai nodded. 'Where is it?' 'In my son's room.' 'Thanks, I'll cover the cost.' 'No, no, there's no need, please go right ahead. Besides, it's not as though you're calling America?' She was already sorry the word had slipped from her mouth. The water had come to the boil. Mrs Pápai would have liked to peer past the man standing in the kitchen doorway towards the front door. Instead she just stood there, awkwardly, momentarily forgetting what she was doing. 'The water's boiling,' warned the man, who, as Mrs Pápai noticed only now, was chewing on a matchstick, which kept migrating from one side of his mouth to the other. 'It might be too strong,' said Mrs Pápai apologetically, at which the man, who was already reaching for the cup, gave a laugh. 'The main thing is that it's bad for you, missus, yep, that's the main thing, that it's bad for you.'

4

There he was, standing in the bathtub, little more than a skeleton. His movements were the desperate writhings of a spider that has fallen onto its back. They hadn't had the heating on: it was chilly and damp, and a suffocating odour pervaded the large bathroom. A little light oozed through the high windows but could not dispel the gloom. At the start of the procedure, Pápai sometimes grabbed his son and banged his forehead in a rage against the boy's. His son would give him a hard stare, and it worked, for his father somehow calmed down. *I am like an animal trainer,* thought the son. Plastic catheter bags hung on the drying rack beside them, porcelain bedpans were lined up along the wall and there were glass bedpans in the corner, stained with the foam of dried piss, the scent of the lower bodies of diabetics, paralytics and the freshly amputated emanating from them.

The father stood before his son in the tub like a zombie, wet strands of hair wriggling worm-like all over his belly and back. In a deep wooden crate a heap of dirty bedsheets; beyond the crate, a torn, piss-soaked, bloodstained mattress. Leaning up against the wall was a mass of tangled crutches, their pads covered in filthy gauze, their dirty pink rubber tips worn unevenly away. Beside the tub was a curved steel chair, its white paint flaking away, handles soldered on in case someone wanted a sitz bath. Like some medieval torture device.

The son diligently soaped the old man's back, thighs, arms, underarms, fingers and ears – his two little rubbery ears. This whimpering, trembling thing, this man broken in two, this was his father. He'd come from his loins. It was hard to imagine that he was the seed of this something. Hearing a rustling sound, Pápai looked around in alarm while hiding his circumcised willy with trembling hands. It had shrunk to almost nothing in the cold.

A door opened with a loud creak as someone peered into the passage that led to the bathroom, which had a row of stalls with half-doors that afforded a view of the toilets inside. They could hear the new arrival whistling as he now proceeded to urinate, and then, amid loud burping, slammed the stall doors shut one after another. Cringing in fear as if being beaten, Pápai lost his balance, his son catching him just in time. This skeleton was heavy. Ten minutes earlier, the son had been stuffing slices of cheap, over-salted ham into his father's mouth straight from the butcher's paper, as the father jabbed at his son's shoulders with a weak fist. He seemed to be raving deliriously, and yet he was careful not to go too far, doing just enough to ensure that his son would not leave him.

There he stood now, in the tub, for once without the glasses that were always set on his nose, gazing blankly around him with a dopey, confused stare, his livid brown eyes speaking of a whimpering dread. There are no words to describe a body whose flesh has been gnawed away by fear. For weeks he'd been dragging about his excrement inside him, and his belly had grown taut, like a drum, and round, like a rubber ball. Below his belly, like a sewn-up pocket of skin, was the scar of an old hernia operation, and then his purple-brown loins with their coating of bluish-grey pubic hair. *I might have to administer an enema to him today.* These words ran through the head of the son, who shuddered. His father's delicate, parchment-like skin had all but separated from the flesh below; and his knees were shiny and white, like majolica.

The nurses had no time to bathe Pápai, who gave off the sickly-sweet scent of decaying flesh. The deep, enamelled steel bathtub stood rather incidentally in the centre of the room, like a bed unmade for days in a cheap motel. As much as he disliked the thought of someone entering unannounced, the boy had been unable to lock the door between the bathroom and the toilets, and when he heard a noise from outside he, too, turned and the water spraying out of the shower head soaked him, making him furious, whereupon he took to rubbing his father's hunched back with his soapy hands even harder. As if he were punishing him for something his father couldn't help. *Public defecation, like in a concentration camp,* the son had thought earlier while shoving Pápai into the bathroom and seeing those stalls with their half-doors. He finally squeezed into his palm a shiny gob of greasy yellow shampoo, the famous WU2, the shampoo of his childhood, and spread it over the top of his father's dented skull, which had only a few grey strands of sometimes fluttering hair left on it. The boy's hair was thick and curly; he didn't want to go bald like his father.

Now someone else entered the bathroom, tinkering with one of the stall doors before finally plopping down on the toilet seat. His farts and heaving sighs echoed off the tiled walls as the son, now using a bath glove, washed Pápai's scraggy bottom. His father was ashamed of his disfigured body, but he had to resign himself to his fate. 'I would prefer not to,' he'd said with a faint smile just before being stripped of his clothes, quoting from his favourite short story, 'Bartleby, the Scrivener'. But what could he do? He'd given in. And, yet, as a last act of resistance, he now refused to straighten his back, and even if he'd wanted to, he would have been unable to stop the ceaseless trembling of his hands. Finally, with a large, hospital-issue towel, the boy dried this giant baby.

Later they sat on a bench in the garden, bundled up to their necks. The December sun emerged, and they sat there, shivering a little, before returning to the ward.

5

The next morning Lieutenant Dóra knocked once more on the door of Mrs Pápai's flat in the veterans' home.[12] As he entered, after a loud 'Come in!', he was almost overcome by Johann Sebastian Bach's *Concerto for Two Violins*, which filled the room. Mrs Pápai was sitting by the record player at the far end of the room, silhouetted in front of the picture window as she moved her head gently in time with the music. She seemed to be sewing something or other: glasses set low on her nose, she kept pricking a dark blue piece of velvet with a needle.

Comrade Dóra expected that Mrs Pápai would turn off the record player the moment she saw him, but this is not what happened. Not this time. Instead she only smiled, and said that he should take a seat, and that the concerto was almost

[12] I report that at 8:00 on 21 December 1983, in the Ferenc Rózsa Home, I held a meeting with the secret colleague CD MRS PÁPAI.

At the meeting we wished to discuss the following topics:

– Possible reverberations of the action carried out at the Kerék Street flat.

– Assessment of MRS PÁPAI's operative activity in 1983.

finished. The two violinists were Yehudi Menuhin and David Oistrakh. Not that the lieutenant had the slightest idea. He had a strange relationship with music. He had nothing against it in theory, but he was one of those people in whom classical music provokes a boundless impatience. He regarded it as a waste of time, an irritating reminder of a bygone age. It was of no interest to him, and he found no beauty in it – no, it was just a noise, as if someone, somewhere, was sawing. That was it. But, now, he kept his opinions to himself. Sitting down in the armchair, he cast a hard stare at Mrs Pápai, who seemed simply to ignore him. That, too, irritated him. And yet this time the lieutenant had not arrived empty-handed.[13] The volume he'd finally chosen in the bookshop the day before, after much hesitation, was still in his bag. *This will do just fine,* he'd thought.

'Was your son home?' Lieutenant Dóra asked as a matter of routine the moment the arm lifted from the record with a little click and the player stopped. A momentary silence preceded Mrs Pápai's emphatic 'No!', a silence the lieutenant turned this way and that in his head before collecting himself. Was she still under the influence of the music? He shook his head.

---

[13] I told MRS PÁPAI that we thank her very much for having let us use her flat, for we could thus successfully carry out our task.

Following this I briefly assessed MRS PÁPAI's operative activity in 1983.

I thanked her for the help she's provided us, and in symbolic recognition of her work I presented her with a book.

MRS PÁPAI was very happy for the gift, thanking our comrades for having thought of her and announcing: she hopes that in the years to come she can also contribute to making our work more successful. Finally we discussed her husband's condition.

We finished the meeting, whose cost was 225 forints, at 9:30.

'Haven't you spoken to him since?'

'Of course I have. I speak to him every day. He's such a blessing, my son. He went to visit his father in hospital. And that's when I went up to the flat. Beautiful, no?'

She was referring to the music. But she spoke as if it were something she'd learned by rote.

'How is your husband?'

'The same. He is always the same. I'm only happy if he's not worse.'

No, she isn't lying, thought Lieutenant Dóra. *Besides, even if she is lying, it's all the same – the men got into the flat, and we'll see what comes of it.*

'My children and I argue about a lot,' Mrs Pápai said suddenly.

The lieutenant had been preparing to leave. After showering Mrs Pápai with praise for her conscientious work over the past year (which comprised chiefly her reports on the students at the International Journalism School, reports that, after all, were not entirely uninteresting)[14] – true, Mrs Pápai had also organ-

---

[14] Their activities outside of official programmes;
Their private lives;
Their contacts;
Their personal characteristics, habits;
Possible compromising information;
Political views, education, professional skills;
Their character, behaviour, poise;
Their state of health.

ized special cultural events for them (the Interior Ministry had paid for the theatre tickets) – he finally handed over to her an art book, a collection of woodcuts by Gyula Derkovits inspired by György Dózsa's peasant uprising.

'I like to do the work despite all problems,' said Mrs Pápai as her gaze wandered over the pages. She was wondering whom she could give it to as a gift. 'I like Africans a lot. They are better than us. I have a much easier time getting them to understand me than with Hungarians. But now I have no work. For a while now I haven't even been called on for interpreting jobs, though I used to be asked all the time.' While this sounded like a sort of rebuke or even a proposal, Lieutenant Dóra only nodded without saying a word.

Mrs Pápai added, 'Though the two pensions are worth nothing if you have a big family.'

Unbeknown to Lieutenant Dóra, Mrs Pápai could not manage money. 'Money: *khara!*' she would say with utter scorn. When angry, she sometimes turned to the guttural sounds of Hebrew, which resembled the harsh clearing of a throat, as if praying to a god she didn't know. '*Khara?*' asked her son. 'Shit. Money is shit!' She was fond of mixing the two languages like some strange cocktail. 'I don't have a mother tongue,' she said sometimes with a masochistic smile. 'I don't know Hebrew properly any more, and I never really learned Hungarian.'

Certainly, Mrs Pápai's strange relationship with money was founded not so much on the biblical legend of the golden calf but more – much more – on those receipts that attested to the varying sums of dollars or forints paid her, without which she could hardly have visited her beloved father so often in that distant land.

Between two homelands into quicksand, one could say, and yet I won't. Between two reasons, between two treasons. And life is suddenly over.

Lieutenant Dóra understood perfectly what Mrs Pápai was hinting at with her talk of a lack of work, of their pensions not being sufficient. But he gave no sign of this. He would add it to his report. They couldn't give Mrs Pápai a fixed monthly sum, no – for that she would need to try a little harder. Besides, not everyone at the Firm took such a benevolent view of the way Mrs Pápai's children carried on. As a colleague of the lieutenant's had remarked, 'The Pápai kids are slowly but surely sinking into the swamp of the opposition.' Or, as it was expressed behind closed doors after a few shots of cognac, 'Like that whole tribe of commie Jews in general.' Among themselves they drew perverse pleasure from commie-bashing. No one would have put it in writing, of course: *Not so long ago these spoiled brats were Maoists. A deviant bunch. These kids have too much time on their hands. So now they want Flying Universities? Is that why we paid through the nose for them to get educated at our universities? So that they can travel free as birds? Stay abroad? If Mrs Pápai wants to cover up their lack of loyalty . . . Still, she should be discreetly warned. But she mustn't take it personally. That could undermine what little operative value this network individual has.*

As if she'd read Comrade Dóra's thoughts, the words came to Mrs Pápai. The moment of silence that still hovered in the air between them had to be dispelled.

'My children and I argue about a lot,' Mrs Pápai repeated.

Comrade Dóra was indulgent and generous:

'This sort of thing happens in every family. The young criticize the old. That's what they do. I could tell stories, too, about my daughter.' No sooner had he said this than he regretted it. Steering the conversation onto his own private affairs was strictly prohibited: the operative officer could not become a private individual in the eyes of the secret colleague – no, he had to maintain his strict neutrality even while striving for a tone of familiarity. It was a golden rule. It was inviolable. But he couldn't swallow his words now.

'And to think that they devoured the works of Marx and Lenin, and that that must have been the mistake.' Mrs Pápai didn't even notice the irony of what she'd just said. She continued in the same pamphleteering style that often shaped her sentences. 'Because their theoretical knowledge clashes with everyday political practice, which means they can't identify with all these political measures.'

Same old tune, thought Comrade Dóra, who of course heard the recurring complaint in Mrs Pápai's tirade. *Isn't it enough for her that we don't have diplomatic relations with the Jews? What else does she want, for heaven's sake? Does she want us to throw all of Hungary's Zionists in jail? And then we could lock up all the journalists!* It was early. His alarm had woken him, and he'd hurried over to the office to hear first-hand about yesterday's operation. He'd hardly slept, and he was consequently somewhat resentful of Mrs Pápai. *The works of Marx and Lenin? Why, of course! And Mao's* Little Red Book? *Or was that a mere trifle?* He only thought all this without, for now, uttering a word.

'I haven't argued with them for a quite a while, because I can't convince them of a thing, anyway. So as far as I'm concerned, the arguments are less fruit.'

'Fruitless.'

'That's right. Futile.' After slurping the last drop of milky tea from her cup, she added, provocatively, 'By the way, a couple of days ago I met one of my son's friends, György Petri. You know of him, Comrade Dóra?'

Comrade Dóra heard alarm bells ringing. He racked his brain for the right reply, but it wasn't easy. Mrs Pápai continued.

'A very good poet. In my opinion.'

She fetched György Petri's collection *Circumscribed Fall* from a table. In the middle was an embroidered bookmark. Comrade Dóra gave the cover a glassy stare, but did not reach for the book or say a thing.

'He said that recently his application for a passport was denied.'

209

What is she getting at? Is she trying to provoke me?

'Of course,' Mrs Pápai added, 'if a regime can't take criticism, then talented people can easily become radicalized.'

The conversation was starting to resemble a bad dream.

'Look, comrade,' said Comrade Dóra in an officious tone of voice, 'we are no longer living in Stalinism. Nor the Middle Ages. The leadership listens to sensible criticism. If it's not destructive. This is not the era of the Rajk trials.'

'I had another of his books, too, *Eternal Monday*,' Mrs Pápai declared with a disarming smile. 'I didn't like that one. It was full of foul language. But Petri's poetry in general, I like very much. And even that book has some beautiful lines.'

'Wasn't that some opposition publication?' the lieutenant asked in distress. He was wondering how he'd weave this conversation into his report. *Has this woman gone mad?* He even wondered whether perhaps there was a listening device in the room, and Mrs Pápai – though he could hardly imagine her in this role – was setting a trap for him. Or that she wanted him to know that she understood precisely what yesterday's action had really been about. But then the whole thing was doomed.

'I don't know the opposition, don't know anything specific about them, but I think they are not necessarily dishonourable people, that they are pointing out the still existing negative aspects of our society. Maybe their words should be listened to in the interest of reforms.'

'In my opinion,' Comrade Dóra began, though he felt he

wasn't taking the right approach, that he sounded mechanical, as if delivering a lecture, 'the work of the opposition is a very nuanced activity, in the course of which they regularly unearth and bring to the fore real errors not with the aim of building socialism but rather with the aim of discrediting and undermining it, and usually under the influence of a foreign agency.'

Mrs Pápai was silent. Comrade Dóra was almost certain he beheld a playful, almost imperceptible, mocking smile on Mrs Pápai's face. Her eyes glistened, as if she'd just been up to mischief. Of course the lieutenant could not know that in her youth Mrs Pápai had eaten herring with chocolate, which had shocked her whole family. It is hard to say whether she'd eaten herring with chocolate because she really liked it or, rather, simply to laugh at all those it appalled.

'I think of it differently,' Mrs Pápai said after a short pause, though her lips did not seem to move. Comrade Dóra suddenly felt as though he must be hallucinating. But even if Mrs Pápai had not uttered these words, her face seemed to have said them, for she kept silently staring at Comrade Dóra, who had turned beet-red.[15]

---

[15] Assessment:

MRS PÁPAI received me with her usual charm, and neither is the discussion of political issues a new aspect of our conversations.

And yet it is worthy of mention that MRS PÁPAI steered the subject to the opposition, and explicitly got to the subject of events between her and György Petri.

It is with virtually sympathetic indulgence that MRS PÁPAI views the activities of the opposition, which she does not assume to be ill-intentioned.

She listened to my explication and raised no objection, but it was apparent that she did not accept my perspective.

211

She Ends Her Activities

INTERIOR MINISTRY
Department III/I-3

Attn: Comrade Stöckl
I agree. Determine
the method and form
in which we can assist.
But only discreetly![17]

TOP SECRET
Attn: Comrade Dóra

Attn: Comrade Kocsis
It seems that MRS PÁPAI will end her
activities.[16] We can draw the 1,000
forints from our own Kocsis 10/3
account. This is the minimum for the
help she honourably[18] performed
for us[19] over decades.[20] We could
evengive her 2,000 forints![21]
József Stöckl
X.2.

Recommendation:

- I recommend that at the next meeting with MRS PÁPAI, we devote special attention
to her relationship with the opposition.

Dr József Dóra, Pol. Lt.

[16] *What* is Mrs Pápai ending, Stöckl? And what's 'It seems' supposed to mean? Screw you.

[17] *What* did you say, you bastard, you rat? 'Only discreetly'? What else do you want to
do 'discreetly' with my mother? What business do you have with my mother, anyway?
Take your grubby hands off my mother or else you'll have to answer to me, you steaming
pile of shit, you discreet little slimeball.

[18] In what sense did you presume to use this word?

[19] 'Performed for us'? Are you shitting me?

[20] It was ten years in all – come on, you moron, get with it – and not even that many,
if I'm not mistaken. Let's not play here with the numbers, for the love of – pardon my
language – motherfucking God.

[21] A bad joke! 'Even . . . 2,000 forints'? Is this how you people want to fuck over my dear
mother? Is this what you call generosity?

ANDRÁS FORGÁCH

REPORT

Budapest, 1 October 1985[22]

I report that on 26 September 1985 at 2 pm I held a
meeting with our secret colleague CN MRS PÁPAI in
the FERENC RÓZSA home.

We aimed for the following subjects to be discussed at
the meeting:

– A translation assignment at the request of Interior
Ministry Department III/I-7[23]
– MRS PÁPAI's situation, circumstances[24]

On arriving I handed a bouquet of flowers to MRS
PÁPAI.[25] At the start of the conversation MRS
PÁPAI said she is suffering from lung cancer,
that it is because of the serious illness that her
hair has fallen out and her face and body are
swollen.[26]

She has regular treatment, and according to the

---

[22] It took you five days to write this, you dickhead?

[23] The height of audacity, to put a dying woman to work for a pittance.

[24] Well now, if there's something you have no business poking your nose into, you animal, it's precisely that. Oh, what a sophisticated way of putting it, à la Wittgenstein: 'her situation, circumstances' – circumstantiality. Fuck off.

[25] My mother has hay fever: flowers are deadly to her. Do you want to kill her?

[26] Mother, you let this piece of shit into your room? Mother! Throw him out! Tell him he's a depraved stinking bastard.

214

doctors they've managed to halt the spread of the cancer.[27]

MRS PÁPAI complained of being in great pain and said her condition is increasingly hard to bear, and because of this her husband is still in a sanatorium, for she herself is unable to take care of him.[28] Another big problem for her alongside her illness is that her daughter who has worked in Moscow is coming home at year's end and she has to find a flat for her.[29]

She plans to trade the flat on Kerék Street for two smaller ones, thereby solving the housing problem.[30]

Turning attention to our specific request, I asked MRS PÁPAI to prepare a review of the contents of the articles on two pages of a newspaper.[31]

MRS PÁPAI accepted the assignment, agreeing to

[27] My dear, sweet mother is lying and she knows it.

[28] Listen here, Mum! Let's talk this over now. How many times have I told you to leave him in the hospital? How many times have I told you to put him away in a isolation ward and leave him there, or else you'll die of his illness? How many times? Well, how many? Not once. That wasn't me. And if I did say it, I knew there was no use.

[29] Maybe you dictated this letter, Mr Nobody, but you might have added the commas, at least subsequently.

[30] What housing problem? You want to trade the hovel in the council block for what – for two stamps? There's nothing to trade. You were only able to get something done – 'crawling on your bloodied belly', as you liked to say – while you still had 'contacts' in Party Central. You crawled on your belly and begged. Who do you want to beg from now?

[31] Even in her last hours she's got to torturously 'prepare a review of the contents' of your shitty little articles? Does no one else in this whole damn town know Hebrew?

prepare the translations as her condition allows.[32]

We agreed to telephone each other in the middle of October.

The meeting, which cost 100 forints, ended at 5:20 pm.

Assessment:

MRS PÁPAI is aware that she suffers from an incurable disease, and so she has, practically speaking, settled her account with her life and wishes to pass what time she has left living with as few problems as possible.[33]

She knows that her condition could turn definitively critical at any moment, which is why she aims to leave behind stable circumstances.[34]

---

[32] Mum, there's no need for this. For 2,000 forints? Just say the word, and I'll give you 2,000 forints. Here you are. Here. Take it! Money is *khara*, Mum, *khara*!

[33] Fuck off and never come back. My mother won't let you in, anyway. I'll forbid her to let you in. My dear, dumb mother. That wonderful woman! From now on you'll call in vain. We won't pick up the phone, that's for sure. We'll tear to pieces the little reports, the confirmations of receipt, the pictures, the minutes of meetings, the assessments – you'd do well to take a good look at your own home instead, because there will be trouble!

[34] I know nothing about 'stable' circumstances. Where did you put them? I looked around but couldn't find them anywhere. Not in any of your bags, not in the wardrobe, not in any of the drawers, nowhere. Nothing but endless disarray and chaos, Mum, nothing but a cold, horrendous void, Mum, a terrible mess, and dust, and battles, and horrendous strife, and fratricide, and treason, nothing but lie after lie! Mum!

Recommendation:

I recommend that for MRS PÁPAI's translation/review work, we pay her 1,000 forints on receipt of the translation, to be charged to the account of Interior Ministry Department III/I-7.[35]

Dr József Dóra, Pol. Lt.

INTERIOR MINISTRY   TOP SECRET
Department III/I-3   RE: The case of MRS
                         PÁPAI (CN)

MEMORANDUM:

Budapest, 28 December 1985

On 27 November 1985 MRS PÁPAI was hospitalized in serious condition,[36] and on 30 November 1985 she died.[37] *From an operative standpoint we request to keep it in the archive. MRS PÁPAI had been in contact with our services since 1975, and in 1979 Comrade BEIDER classified her as a secret colleague.*

Recommendation:

I recommend that we place her materials in the archive.
Dr József Dóra, Pol. Lt.

---

[35] What good will that do? To drag my diamond of a mother deeper into the muck? You can pour your poison all you want on my beautiful flower – her hair fallen out, my tender mother with her brilliant smile – you can't besmirch her no matter how much you'd like to, you dog, no, you don't come anywhere near her, idiot!

[36] You people know nothing.

[37] Mrs Marcell Forgács, 30 November 1985

INTERIOR MINISTRY   TOP SECRET

Department III/I-3

Re: The matter of MRS PÁPAI (CN)

Authorized by me:

Dr Kálmán Kocsis, Pol. Capt.

head of department

Re: Archiving of CN MRS PÁPAI's dossiers

RECOMMENDATION

Budapest, 28 December 1985

I recommend the archiving of vols. I of Recruitment
and Work dossiers no. Z 2959 of CN MRS PÁPAI. (No
live files remain.)

The dossiers contain no data on hostile individuals.[38]

2 slippers	3 pairs glasses
1 pair shoes	2 small pillows + 4 bedsheets
1 robe	1 knitted shawl
1 coat	1 scarf
2 nightshirts	2 sweaters
toiletries	1 pair sweatpants
silverware	1 T-shirt + 5 panties + stockings + 2 pairs socks
personal ID	
Kútvölgyi hospital card	2 towels
1 alarm clock	1 lower denture
1 glass mug	1,000 forints

3 books (*Games People Play: The Uses of
Enchantment: The Meaning and Importance of
Fairy Tales*; *Tutankhamun*)

Inventory prepared by
    "   received by András Forgách

---

[38] I wouldn't be so sure about that. But, Mother, look, this poem is ready, too.

218

II

Bruria and Marcell

Hangman

They handed me a rope,
I sought out the tree.
They didn't say it was a joke,
And so a hangman I came to be.

I prepared to execute myself: I was
A humane hangman, and how,
Strung up on a verdant bough.

Aphrodite

Already in the crowded market in Athens
And then near Paphos too
He traipsed off
Strayed wandered fell away
The boy lagged behind vanished
stepped from the stage turned the corner
went under the ground
Perhaps in Paphos – or not in Paphos
after all – but already in Piraeus –
in Piraeus too
Like someone wanting to shake her off
get rid of that beautiful figure
Brutally
As if there would be nothing
to talk to her about

On the tar- and oil-splotched quay
Where grey waters rocked all the ships gently

In Limassol they caught a cab
Twelve hours they had before departure
And the only worthy sight in Piraeus after all
was the Parthenon far far away not the
horrible port city of Piraeus with that lovely name
When from deep within the noisy lazy grimy
sluggish city he caught sight of the Parthenon
up on the peak his heart pounded –
That it exists in reality and not just in pictures! –
He was struck by lightning as they say
in novels
His heart skipped a beat as they say
in novels
Though the Temple of Pallas Athena did not yet
        flutter
with snow-white columns up there on the Acropolis
But was black from soot from grime
neglected

Beyond the Yugoslav border beyond passport control
beyond customs
The beautiful figure
When they remained alone in the compartment

Whose walls had colour photos behind framed glass the
    Elisabeth
Bridge the Parliament Building the beach in Füred on
Lake Balaton
So they were still home in a sense even if
beyond the border too
The beautiful figure
took the dollars from her stockings
Thick brown proletariat stockings he remembers
as if it had happened today
His mother kicked off her shoe and pulled the
    stocking
off her right leg
It was a strange moment
Both of them blushing
His mother from the lie he from the stockings
which he could indeed have seen every day
Also his mother's thighs strewn with freckles
For his mother wasn't a bashful sort
Sometimes showing herself undressed
in front of her kids – ashamed neither of
her enormous breasts nor her white skin
nor her beauteous hips
Ashamed before her family
neither of her beauty nor its ruins

ANDRÁS FORGÁCH

What made them both blush nonetheless
was the comedy in which his mother
being a loyal subject
was compelled to play
The money stashed away – for the exotic trip
could not even have happened
had it not been for his parents both being
professed communists the system's building blocks
The journalist and the nurse
Commies who spoke up at party meetings
But dollars had to be tucked away
The two of them had to cheat like everyone else
Indeed it was this that later drove his dad mad
He smuggled a white Mercedes over the border
for a colonel
From then on he was on watch for them to come
and take him away

She blushed – the beautiful figure – while removing
the wad of dollars from her stockings
Blushed and broke out laughing –
Her laughter – that of a Cossack on a horseback
trotting up the marble staircase of the Czar's Winter Palace
–
It was closer to neighing
She got the better of them she had the money

for the boat that took them to Haifa via Cyprus
from Piraeus
To the land of the ancestors
From where she'd exiled herself
Someone looked in from the corridor

The cabbie got twenty dollars at the port of Limassol
That garrulous scruffy thickly mustachioed man
Who got by with twenty-five words of English
So that's what those bills hidden in her stockings
     were for
For a tour of the island that the Green Line had already
split in two
Turks became Greeks and Greeks became Turks
five times in the madness
Twenty dollars for Mother and son
to look at Aphrodite's birthplace
Even Richard the Lionheart aka Cœur de Lion
had also passed there much later to be felled
by an arrow through the shoulder
And which a careless surgeon the "Butcher"
tore from his flesh
The wound turning gangrenous
All this had happened at the castle of Châlus-Chabrol
But he forgave the crossbow-wielding boy
who took revenge for his father and two brothers

And in the arms of his mother
Richard gave up his ghost

To brush her off unmercifully –
so did the boy with his mother
At the market where the smiling young
waiter in a green outfit and unbuttoned white shirt
delivered cups of coffee on a bronze tray
with dancing steps among the cars
and with a toothy grin
Mother and son listening to the driver
pointing all the time and flailing his arms
explaining to them in Paphos that it was here
that Aphrodite had been rising from the foam
On the desolate rocky seacoast
Crawling now with tourists
In the February lights wafted by Zephyrus, the West Wind
And then the mother was tense, her skin grew taut because
Her boy was stubbornly silent vanishing
into an underground chapel
Woven through with the roots of a huge terebinth tree
An old lady Solomoni the Jewish woman
as she was called
They say she later became Christian
So she built this church around this tree
after some mercenaries of Cœur de Lion

slaughtered her seven sons
And now the superstitious locals
knotted handkerchiefs on the tree

Alone already down into the cellar
went the boy
The beautiful figure wasn't interested in
icons of saints or sanctuary lamps
I'm an atheist she pouted after a full day of silence
Her son's silence an arrow boring into her heart
And down there in the dusky light
to which steep steps led
And where the boy remained alone with the icons
and a stray altar in the musty darkness
Between saltpetre-splotched walls
Where he could hear a gurgling brook
He stood there for ever before the picture of an unknown
Saint who'd died a martyr's death
A picture a clumsy hand had evidently cut
from some newspaper and which had
curled up from the dampness
On the table the scissors still lay with
A loaf of bread broken in two
A cat was running past his legs
God
Silence darkness and murky light

He has stood there ever since
In that stubborn silence
That followed their mutual solitude
The moist breath of Zephyrus wafted her
over the waves of the loud-moaning sea
in soft foam
to the island of Cyprus

Marcell

Don't sing Dad they'll think you are a fool
I said to him on Finchley Road
And then he got so mad he left me
On the street and I wasn't even eight
Though until then he'd held my hand

In an intimate moment just before amid
The heady scent of fish and chips we broke through
Like an Il-18 Soviet turboprop through the clouds
He told me a tale about an Alexandria whore

More than once in front of his son
MTI's London correspondent
Anatomized his dealings with women

An ebony woman
A Babylonian harlot with teeth like corals
The jewel of the brothel its Koh-i-Noor was
For whom all the men stood in line

And when at last his turn came
So Dad regaled me
He already lay sprawled on the sagging iron bed
And watched her undress
He regaled me more
While the din of the street filtered in
Just like Gustave Flaubert in Egypt
Who for weeks concerned himself only
With what the woman felt – the woman he fucked
In a boudoir on the banks of the Nile

And the goddess pausing as she stood by the bed
This so supple panther of Nubia
Pulling her gauzy robe over her head
Two bronze loops alone danced on her ears
And taking everything off she was so totally naked
That she couldn't have been more totally naked

Because after all what's more said Dad
In that goosebumped voice of his
Still abuzz with that perverse ecstasy

She was shaved all over
Not a strand of hair on that black body
Blacker than the blackest night
Skin on skin a sparkling land
Without even a tiny blade of grass
For one's eyes to rest upon
Only the little black slit
From which the pink
Labia shone like an orchid
At twilight

> *There was a man in Liverpool*
> *Who had a red ring on his tool*
> *He went to the clinic*
> *But the doctor a cynic*
> *Said*
> *Wash it it's lipstick*
> *You fool*

He didn't do
What a man's honour demands
Of a British private who's seen a lot
Even on being shaken out of sleep
Dad told me on Finchley Road
Wading through the scents of a foreign land
Midway through life's journey

In London one autumn afternoon
Twenty-one years after his silly swoon

Past eight I was
The jester of the Young Pioneers' Paul Robeson den
Formed by children of the Embassy
Named after the famous black singer
Who lived in exile in London at the time

My dad began his tale two blocks earlier
In front of Marks and Spencer
Where we'd taken in the toy display
But then he left me there grinding his teeth
Because I dared say to him see above
Don't sing Dad they'll think you are a fool

How was I to know that Daddy was a spy
An atrocious spy but still a spy my dad
And Pápai was the name that Poppa had[1]

---

[1] 19 June 1975

I will exorcise my fears of persecution as of midnight on 20 June 1975 if the committee does not look me up. I promise to no longer bother with phantasms and to acquire my knowledge of objective reality from Bruria's recommendations. In the morning I awake in a pleasant and calm frame of mind, and I deal with the tasks a normal life entails and do not allow wanton phantasms and fantasies to get the better of me. I accept the laboratory findings without argument. No longer will I persecute myself. In the interest of saving myself I will strive to get to lay bare my past and to lay bare those events and actions that were dictated by my communist convictions.

signed by: Marcell forgács [sic]

I did not steal I did not swindle I did not embezzle

19 June 1975 – Marcell forgács [sic]

And perhaps this was precisely why he sang
So loudly in the middle of Finchley Road
Afternoon among the pedestrians

Perhaps he was humming an English march or else
Forgetting simply that I too was there

But his desire deflated all at once
In that whorehouse of Alexandria
Terror not ecstasy filled him
When he saw
This extremity of bareness
Surprising both him and that woman too
Who licked the edge of her mouth
With the ready-to-pounce calm of
A wild Nubian panther

Then pulling the clasp on his lovely uniform
Nice and tight and putting his cap on his head lopsided
That cap bearing the British Empire's coat of arms
The English crown on top
Montgomery's army[2]

---

[2]   I don't know how I gave cause for them to re-assess my past activities, to 'expose me as someone who operated within Montgomery's general staff' when I had noted in my every resumé that it was at the direction of the Palestine Communist Party that I enlisted in the English army where as a private and later a cartographer at the Middle East command (in a map warehouse at the lowest rank, because as a communist I did not get promoted) and Montgomery wasn't even there at the time (1944–46). I request the party organization to investigate this and also whose interest it is in to brand me and equate me and hang me on a shoemaker's last with all sorts of unreliable elements.

And whistling he headed down the street

My dad the good soldier
After paying without a blink
In mysterious snow-white Alexandria

When he spoke everyone listened
A merry pyknic fellow that he was
When he spoke people laughed
He collected jokes in a notebook[3]
And other information
Let's say about the Iraqi industrialization
Or say about Colonel Gaddafi
Who received him in a tent

He wrote fast and read fast
With two fingers he typed
Touch typing at that
I didn't know my dad was a spy
Nor why

Never did he reveal to me what else
He'd been up to in Alexandria[4]

---

[3] Why do Jews eat ham from paper? Just not to stain a plate with *treif.*

[4] *According to my husband Marcell Forgács, in the functioning ward of the national psychiatric hospital, on Völgy Street, he was infected with syphilis, which entered his system via the pillow of a syphilis patient. He contracted it around the end of February 1975. It was a certain committee*

Other than fighting the Germans that is

Who as well known were not there

And other than how as a postman in love

He delivered my mother's letters to

The hand of his main-main-main rival

On a sun-scorched Alexandria street

Cavafy's city

Foamy waves in the port

The two men exchange a couple of words

He tells some ribald jokes and waves goodbye

Here even a Stalin quote wouldn't be misplaced who knows

Cavafy is dead

They take a hard look at each other

Sometimes I imagine the scene

A girl leans out of a careening jeep screaming with joy

And is greatly surprised that she will be raped a bit later

that ordered this syphilis to be devised, a committee that, according to my husband, is tasked with bringing him to ruin by way of various measures (which until 12 December 1975 had not once been proved). The 'committee' had tasked the health care staff at Völgy Street inject this disease by all means into my husband, and so to compel him to expose his relationships with a dozen female acquaintances and so the crimes he commited be proven. . . .

If the Wa. [Wasserman – trans.] test is negative, my husband, Marcell Forgács, obliges himself to do everything he can in the interest of ceasing the operation of the 'committee', which he has used in numerous cases to justify his fears, and to focus on acquainting himself with reality through his own power.

Mrs Marcell Forgács

12 July 1975

I oblige myself to eradicate the committee, which in reality does not exist, and is the product of my mind, in the event of a negative Wa.

Marcell forgács [sic]

Tom was a communist and a soldier and English and blond
and kind of barmy
And the love of my mother's life
to her death.

Sisyphus began rolling the boulder even on
The migrant ship
The handsome boy with thinning hair
Who enrolled in the law school
In Bucharest in nineteen thirty-eight

If I'm not wrong he didn't even complete half a semester
No diploma no nothing
He couldn't complete a thing
I didn't know he was a spy my dad
And he wasn't very good at that

Not even later did he finish it in Jerusalem
When in a slapdash manner instead of chemistry
    studies
He fabricated phosphorescent paint
And with that wrote off chemistry
Turning night into day he worked in great secrecy
Mixing phosphorus in I-don't-know-what
At the not-yet so world famous university

He was concocting not for the Party but
From sheer diligence so that
Down with and *Death to* would bloom at night
on the timeworn stones of the Eternal City

If that paint had even lit up

Sheer wonder that that test-tube didn't blow up in your
    hands
Daddylee

One time they caught him after all
While distributing subversive leaflets
But that's another story
A British army jeep rolled up beside him they grabbed
    him
By the jacket he slipped out of it and jumped from
    the truck
And vanished breathlessly

Never did he finish anything decently
My dad

In Bucureşti many a *Salon Litteraire*
Saw the cane-swaggering young man
His tie pin adorned with diamonds

Young Onegin went to see a play
But left after the first curtain
And in the salon Jewesses with blue- and red-hair
Were talking of the Iron Guard and Michelangelo with
    some flair
Selbstverständlich or *certainement* in French

And the Romanians took him right off to a camp
Someplace else the world war broke out
The discipline there was really lax
It was more or less hostage-taking nothing serious
A so-called military pre-training camp
And the guards could be easily bribed

A bohemian drifter a rake a mini Don Juan
Whom the women at the cleaners on A. Street so
    adored
Who tickled them with his acrobatic tongue until
They laughed themselves so shamelessly red
And he played on my mother as on an instrument
On her body not on her soul
The devoted patron of brothels
A virtuoso of the instrument

He clambered over to her at night they made no sound
At most the floor creaked once or twice

The sagging mattress squeaked now and again
We lived in the same room with our parents
And slept on two foldaway beds
Back then my little sister and me

One time the Madame allowed him to
It was back in old Szatmárnémeti
Before he passed the *examenul final*

It wasn't by chance that she
At the front gate of the Eminescu Secondary School
After an *examen* that went disgracefully
When in front of an army of parents
Dad poorly failed in mathematics
My temperamental grandma
Broke her umbrella on his head
Striking off his silver-embroidered
Eminescu uniform-cap in the meantime
She hit him so hard – while her son guffawed –
that it rolled into the mud

They still slept in one bed at the time
My grandmother immersed in *The Magic Mountain*
But mostly she was solving crossword puzzles
How many letters in Mademoiselle Marcell

Indeed in Szatmár the Madame
Who was so very much fond of him
Showed him a tiny hole in the wall
Tilting a lewd picture on the wall
Which on peering through afforded a view
Of what domnul Munteanu
Vice-President of Banca Comerciala
Was up to with Liza the lily of the meadows
Their classmate's sister

He told me this not long before
He left me there on Finchley Road
Don't sing Dad they'll think you are a fool
His face twisted from rage
At such times he came completely unhinged
The world as such to him then ceased to be

Even in the port of Constanţa
No even earlier yet in Bucharest's North Station
The Gara de Nord
Where his mother put him on a train
She stayed behind at the Gara de Nord
Waving her handkerchief for a long long time[5]

---

[5]   'Long since her body flew – light smoke – away
German meadows were cloaked with sooty grey ...'

But just before she simply greased the guards
And had a fake *paşaport* prepared for her son too
A savvy woman my dear grandma was
She ensured my dad's escape from the worst of the
    worst
And exactly this may have been the root of all the
    troubles
The amazing escape

The same thing took place also in reverse
The cunning Sisyphus absconded twice
Even from the place he'd fled to
Leaving behind his latest homeland too
Swapping it for a third

He started afresh until there was a fresh start to begin with
He got off the hook not once but never finished a thing
You have to be replaced and when you sink
Mrs Pápai replaces Pápai[6]
And Alcestis descended into Hades

The photo was taken in the port of Constanţa
Where he'd stood on the quay
In his brand new leather jacket ready for adventure

---

[6] Her activization was implemented only in the event of her husband's serious illness, to substitute for him.

There a wandering photographer captured him
In a few nimble motions and
After the exposure

They won't harm the women
So my grandma at the Gara de Nord
No not the women[7]

Don't sing Dad they'll think you are a fool
I told him on Finchley Road

At the port the photographer stuck
His hands into a wooden box
A portable darkroom and
In the sunlight a miracle happened
In the blink of an eye without even looking
After a few nimble motions
He presented a photograph

With a soft and somewhat vague smile
An expensive set of calipers and a camera
Anything that could be turned into money
Dad boarded a steamship in Constanţa

---

[7] *'Long since her body flew – light smoke – away*
German meadows were cloaked with sooty grey…'

But my grandfather's purple-nailed hand
His leaden hand on his son's orphaned head
While dying as he blessed his little son

My grandfather jumped into the icy Szamos
With the aim of avoiding enlistment
And in one go smoked two hundred cigarettes
And ten years later he died of it

Dad could hardly wait to tell me how it was
Sometimes he was like Scheherazade
The spoiled young master
Who jumped over life's hurdles with great ease

In the dark room men in mourning suits
On the wall an oil painting of the weaving mill
In Łódź supposedly his great-great grandfather's
And by the colonnade that little grocery
Friedmann & Company
They were robbed by the 'Company'

That heavy hand on Dad's little head
That toy balloon weighing a ton
The ten fresh-baked crescent rolls Margit handed out
To the beggars loafing by the cemetery gate
So the mourning prayer would be valid

He may have taken it wherever he went
That blessing
It protected him not
It protected him from nothing at all[8]

---

[8] *'My name is still in the phonebook,*
But my grave is in the Jewish cemetery,
A charming zany baby
Lived 53 years and forgot to grow up.

You wanted to be loved,
But did everything to be hated,
And the constant reply
Was indifference or an inpatient sigh

Oh, you remained a little kid, why,

A dreamer who believed dreams could fly high

And was never as sly as the sly.'

Bruria

It happened to her halfway still in Athens
She had two days before boarding the ship
She thought she'd walk up until the Parthenon
And noticed as she neared the holy temple
Ambling over the marble debris
That someone was photographing her and only her

I could yet detail this at length
It was a slightly cool mid-morning
Not like in Budapest but a winter day in Athens
When Boreas unmercifully blows
And Kaikias and Notos are blowing in the face
And you're exposed to the ceaselessly buffeting
Jostling whirling
Air currents on the magnetic hilltop

That slap and rip at your clothes as if at any moment
A surge of wind will snatch you up and slam you about
The birds steer well clear of it
And meanwhile the sun the impassive Helios is
    blazing
Your brain almost boils from rage and fury

The unknown man took not one
But a dozen pictures of my mother
One sees on them how Mum her expression rock-hard
Approaches the photographer
Tornado-like
Descending marble steps
Like Pallas Athena on the plains of Troy
Her jaw her stiff cheekbones bulging
Her glance a stinging pebble
Like someone caught red-handed

Oh why didn't I ever see you this way
Unmerciful goddess

Or like Agave who was spied on and who in a frenzy
Unwittingly killed her son Pentheus
Or Medea who with triumphant laughter
Tore her sons to pieces

Mum was under strict orders
Not to allow any such occurrence[9]
Her behaviour was defined by command
She had to report anything suspicious

But back then she told her tale otherwise
How much sudden silence how many half truths
That's not how you told this story dear Mum
For even if she wasn't a Mata Hari
Though the comparison would be apt
But if one reflects on one's mother
And Mata Hari never had a child
Turned out not to have been a spy after all

A blooper like that can slip in any time

She was a tiny cog in the wheel

And so my mother headed with terrible wrath
Toward that CIA (KGB, Shin Bet, MI6) agent
Like raging Hera Jupiter's wife
Or like Artemis riding her wildly galloping horse
Handbag on her arm and drawing her furious
    expression

---

[9] Aside from the above, I recommend that, especially in matters concerning her
security, we hold a detailed orientation.

Like an Amazon drawing her bow
And we know what little remained of Actaeon

This time the matter had a better outcome

Later we all wondered at the pictures
At the stone face of the stern agent
This hurt her to the tune of twenty dollars
I think that much less remained
Of the money her comrades had given her
To espy the Zionist conspiracy
And build up socialism

She wasn't a heroine she wasn't far no
She tread mid-way between two homelands
Between two reasons between two treasons

Schmitz Schmitz little Schmitz
You won't even get to Auschwitz

When the writing appeared on a wall
When a whole country went to the streets
That sound alone stirred in her ears
On the decaying mortar as she got off the tram
The inscription face to face
The imperturbable reality

They would have hung Dad from a lamppost
Because he'd spoken silly things on the street
At twilight those nasty men youngsters
Had not my little sister that wonder
With her red shock of hair and the retroussé nose
Had she not been sitting on his arm

To go to leave and *tekel upharsin*
To spring up and to skedaddle
To run away from here anywhere
Might have seemed a reasonable conclusion

But a special seventh sense
She had and he too
The nurse and the journalist
Pápai and Mrs Pápai
Forgács and Mrs Forgács
Marcell and Bruria
For unerringly bad decisions

Every decision is bad
Okay – needing to decide at all is bad
And there are in fact situations in which
good decisions can't be made
Like when I am writing this
Like the way I am writing this

To marry or not to marry by all means
you'll regret it
To go or not to go by all means
you'll regret it

The point is of course that one shouldn't succeed
To boldly resist all sound arguments
To spit at any word of warning
To do what our hearts dictate
Is indeed a romantic concept
A revolutionary doesn't think he goes
And does what his heart dictates
Dashing ahead to save the world
And in place of the heart
Shards of glass rusty barbed wire
If there is no sin let us invent the sin

He is a highly talented individual who knows
how to keep quiet but at the same time
travels the world with open eyes – this is what she said
of me to them – She – she said this of me to them
When she thought
I could take the baton from her
That I could become
Pápai junior

Never ever did we bring it up
She lied to the recruiting officer
Or maybe we did bring it up

Oh, Gethsemane, Gethsemane

In the Buda apartment under the Castle
In the shelter with the old ladies
Who kissed my cheeks to smithereens
During the bloody storm of autumn 1956
Countering a country's will my mother waited
For the Russians to invade us again

How often oh how often
She boarded a ship – a ship? rather a little
Dinghy from the pennies and blood money[10]
she cobbled together from the one-party state
With the generous support of Department III/I
She boarded a ship
So she could touch the ancient land
From which all power flowed

[10] Registry of payments in 1978

Date Allocation to agent	Operative expense
8 February 1978	8,000 Ft
8 February 1978	500 USD

And the legend manufacturers come into operation[11]

The only landscape that she feels good in
The only land that would open up before her
The only one that is still organic
From which her organs had been built
The hills the mountain the orange-red sand of the coast
And where she arrives as a secret agent
No longer seeing simply recording like a machine

Orange trees mating in the fragrance of the sea
Eucalypti cyclamens anemones oleanders and
    orchids
The cascade of flowers before the bunkers
And jasmines parched by the smouldering heat
The hot and stormy quarrels and fights
The balm of hatred on the deep wound of the heart

And from the starting point again
From A to B and then from B to A
And so on ad infinitum

---

[11] We have devised a travel legend and behavioural line she must demonstrate in the course of her stay in Israel.

As for the legend of her being interested, the secret colleague should name her interest in the Israeli domestic political situation

We request permission on a service voucher for the export of foreign currency, and will devise a legend for its legalisation.

My mother is a countryless derelict
Well what kind of person is this
Beautiful beautiful perishing
Delightful even while dying
Majestic demonic and angelic
Tumbling into pain
Even morphine should not ease it
One by one she surrenders her limbs to death
She looks in your eyes she has nothing to hide
A whizzing of the winds from the universe
Defenceless blinded chaotic dogged
Tender hysterical calm elated
Persecuted among the persecutors
Who can heal with her hands
And washes the tub with Sterogenol

Again on the flimsy little raft
Amid muddy clay-grey waves
Drowning on a single slippery beam
Which Charybdis spat out of her maw

And there on the opposite shore for a moment –
        but no
No no no no no
Not even for a moment –
The harassed soul

If we consider not even for a moment
But maybe maybe after all
For a single moment after arrival
Near the blue-eyed Father-god
She calmed down for a single moment
Her soul subsided
She arrived

Kiryat Sefer *shemoneh*[12]
The address on the envelope

Benumbed by pain nose running from hay fever
Selling out its homeland sad soul
Chatting with women border guards in no-man's land
And constantly on the alert lest she'll be caught
She got the hang of an ugly wooden office jargon
That can't be shared with anyone else

Because she yearned as an outcast
To return to the world from which she strayed
That's how she arranged her travels
Sehr praktisch sehr geschickt sehr what else
        can I say
Thinking it over after the fact

---

[12] 8 Kiryat Sefer Street, my grandparents' address in Tel Aviv

No matter how inexplicable it is still somehow understandable
If only I knew how that *somehow* was

She wasn't no she never was sly
She was not the sly Odysseus
She didn't plug her ears with wax
She was beguiled right away

Perhaps
Near the floating golden cupola
Which never was hers
In any sense not even like a
Not even as much as a
Specks of dust dancing in the light

For but a single wee little moment
When in her snow-white dress
Standing on the hills
She looked toward the sun-beaten city
Where she'd been born[13]

---

[13] '... I consider myself to be a pigeon-holed creature because I've long had to throw off the wings
every intelligent being gets at birth and have had to tie the umbilical cord even tighter to the ple-
beian things of the earth – so it was dictated by reality, which was all too hard. I might say, and with
this I will close my lines: I can't think of a thing that might have made me happy over long years
if not for the dancing monkey and his flute-playing Arab owner I saw when looking out upon the
narrow street in the old city of Jerusalem ... at the age of three.'

hugs kisses

Bru

Budapest, 1976 VIII 15

Bruria

she spun she wove she knit
she knit she spun she wove
her fate she jabbed she stabbed
the Monster that is beyond the mountain
lost in the distance beyond the sea

I don't look at the photo
I want to conjure it up from memory
behind the women
six-headed Scylla with a triple row of teeth
which she put in a glass of water at night
I've got to look at it all the same I've got to
go there and I've got to look at it
the golden cupola swimming under the clouds
the shouting women

who are running toward the Monster
to divert its attention
from that which is unattainable

strands colours
die in shoes
she collected colours every drop of hers
good little girl
who on the Sea of Galilee
in the spring of '25 or '26
was lured by a man
into a cabin on a boat and
he lured her into the cabin and
struggled to explain
all at once memory starts to heave
on the lake where Jesus walked on water
she tried to tell me something
that can not be said

like Arachne whom the angry Pallas Athena
turned into a spider
because she wove the gods' sins more beautifully
or like Philomela with her tongue cut out
she wove a tapestry for her sister
so without words in pictures she could tell
what Tereus did to her in the cabin

he digs his hands through the girl's locks painfully
twisting them back
slices off her tongue with an iron only its stump twitches
in her throat
squirming like a snake's severed tail jumps about
on the ground
but even after this Tereus fulfils his unstoppable lust
his desire
on the girl's violated body again and again
and again

she spins weaves jabs night after night
she weaves she plots out the picture
weaving in the cancer
weaving the Monster in the
until she arrives with her needle at
the moonlit blockhouse
the concrete tower
on whose windows
the moonlight gleams

Bruria

On the contrary the truth is
On the contrary the situation is
On the contrary what happened is
On the contrary I want to say
On the contrary when I believed
On the contrary when it occurred to me
On the contrary when when when

Just don't be overcome with emotions
The situation is simply
Totally in spite of everything
If I may say
Diametrically opposed to all
But on the contrary she even on the train was

Even then
Not even then
And even so not like that
And from that moment on especially

III

Something More

When I hear it contended that the least sensitive
are, on the whole, the most happy, I recall the Indian
proverb: 'It's better to sit than to stand, it is better to
lie down than to sit, but death is best of all.'

Nicolas Chamfort

There are things in life we can fathom only if they happen to us. There is no other way to understand them. Now, we may have some sense of what has happened if our imagination is sufficiently daring and wild, but we will understand it only if it actually happens to us. This is true even if we are unable or unwilling to explain what occurred, or if it can't be explained, for not only does the explanation come nowhere close to lived experience, but it kills it, obliterates it.

One such event is our mother's death. The death of a mother is a cosmic event. 'The last link in the chain has snapped,' a great Hungarian writer once telegrammed a famous actress on the passing of his mother. What last link was the writer referring to? The one that tied him to humanity? The one that gave his life meaning? Or perhaps a doctor informs you that you have cancer or that someone you're very close to, someone you adore – a friend or your lover, say – has cancer. The doctor tells you the facts. But the truth is something else. You just sit there and stare straight ahead. Or the aeroplane you're on is about to crash. Then you'll definitely understand what's happening. Even if you won't be able to tell anyone. A happier variation on this theme is when you're sitting in a car that tumbles off the road at 1.00 a.m. and somersaults three times over a snowy field. Silence. Dead silence. Someone stirs. No one has even a scratch. From then on you see the world differently. You needn't mention it, but you know something you didn't know until then.

Or consider this: a kind, smart, wonderful person, your aunt, to whom you've always turned for advice, wakes up one day and doesn't know who on earth she is. Only then do you understand what Alzheimer's is. A whole life seems to be captured in her smile, her body still evokes the person she was, the same heart still beats in her chest – only she, of all people, doesn't know who she is. On the surface it's not apparent that she's no longer there. She holds a book in her hand just the way she always has, except that all day for months on end she has been reading the same page over and over. She is just as lovely as ever reading in the lamp-light. Just as beautiful. She laughs out loud but doesn't know her own name. It's her and yet it isn't her. If you knew and loved her, suddenly you will understand. The knowledge leaves you speechless. If you don't know her and don't love her, then it's just a sad case, a news report from far away, a curiosity.

Or, yes, try this on for size: one very fine day – okay, not such a very fine day – it turns out that your mother was recruited (by the intelligence services of the communist regime). An acquaintance who by chance uncovered this information gives you a call. He has happened across a file. This is how such scenarios typically begin. The phone rings, the news hits you hard. It is a tiny little detail that III/I is not quite the same as what is known as III/III. You can try to spin it, but nobody will give a damn. No, no, wait a minute: III/I was not simply the same as III/III, it was *even more of the same*. My mother was a spy, an informant. She wasn't. But she was. No. Yes. All right, then, she wasn't an informant, but a spy. Not a real spy, but something like that. In fact a *titkos munkatárs* (secret colleague, sc). A tiny screw – or, better put, the final cog – in the machinery of a petty apparatus. A component that could never be *too* small. And couldn't be more insignificant. And how you feel about every moment you spent with this tiny screw or cog, about every moment you passed in the company of this sc cn (*fedőnév* = code name; fn = cn) is changed. As if the laws of perspective and gravity could alter from one minute to the next. Lo and behold, they *can* change.

But this doesn't simply change how you feel about the time you spent together. It renders all the other moments defenceless, too – there's no longer any before and after – stripping them bare, annihilating the little intimacies in a family's life – the first questions, the first steps, the first words, flavours savoured together, holidays spent together, Christmas Day, sprinkling women and girls at their front doors with eau de cologne on Easter Monday, the first day of school, getting your school report, playing pranks, telling tales, childish fibs, little miracles, Chinese paper pagodas and dragons that unfurl in boiling water, joy, sorrow, card games, falling in love, slurping tea with milk together, tunafish with sour cream, fried dough at food kiosks on the shores of Lake Balaton, a dab of marzipan on the tip of a knife, Kellogg's Crispy Cornflakes, *The Nutcracker, Swan Lake*, big fights, long bouts of sobbing, hayfever, Thomas Mann, noisy vindications of the only truth, visits to family and friends, the sniffles, toothaches, outings, her pouring hot oil in your ear at night, her massaging your temples, her singing lullabies in Hebrew and Hungarian, discovering the world, looking at family albums, idyllic summer evenings as insects buzz around you, Schubert, Toscanini, every single sound of every single piece of music we ever listened to together, every little sound in between, even the sound of silence. Everything is now suspect, especially beauty. Everything is now ordinary: broad-mindedness, generosity, self-sacrifice. There is a shadow over all of it, and it can't be spoken about.

Nor can it *not* be spoken about.

A motley crew had gathered in the living room: from film and theatre directors and actors to manual labourers – everyone was there. The guests represented a cross-section of society at the time, all of this suggesting a considerable degree of ethnic and cultural tolerance. Who was it who made possible this brotherly, quasi-'free university' atmosphere? Their mum, that's who – bringing order now and then by serving up more food, as well as cleaning the dishes and the rugs. Otherwise she didn't interfere. Remarkably energetic and yet not authoritarian, that's the sort of woman she was. Gentility and industry fused seamlessly in her. To this day I don't know how she had time for everything and everyone.

One time she embroidered something for me, too. A minor miracle – she must have worked on it for months: gold, silver, blue, green, and red. It depicted a bird, a bird of paradise, which, according to legend, flies its whole life, alighting on the ground only at the moment of its death. Was this how she saw me? Or is this how she immortalized herself? All of this will remain a mystery, for she was a reticent woman. Although in this account I abide by the principle of discretion and refer to people by their first names or else anonymously, I can't resist here giving her musical name, which seemed to come straight from the Old Testament: Avi Shaul Bruria. It was through her, perhaps, that I first came to appreciate gentility. She was a leftist in a unique and yet also characteristic way, though she spoke of her political convictions only rarely. For the most part, she drew her vocabulary from both everyday life and poetry.

This is how my mother was described by a long-dead friend of mine, 'Dönci', who had come from a very different background to me and went on to become the lead guitarist of the underground band Európa Kiadó.

* * *

Bruria had many admirers, so what I'm writing here will be, for them, a huge slap in the face; it will be disillusioning, immeasurably sad. So it is our mother who was this 'secret colleague' or 'network individual'. Of course, there will be some for whom this will play quite nicely indeed. We said it from the start, they'll say. Yes, we knew it without a doubt. So let's howl it out. Let's weep. Let's sit down together and talk it over. Let's talk it over one more time. Let's talk it over ten more times, a hundred times, a thousand times. Let's read through the dossiers. Why should I read through these dossiers? One is about her recruitment; the other, the work she did for them. Let's learn a new language, a new vocabulary; let's get to know more intimately a world that revolts us and makes us tremble, which makes the hair stand up on our necks and the blood freeze in our veins, which sees us wake in terror in the middle of the night; a world that discomfits us; a world that, until now, we've observed from such a comfortable distance. Those were always others. Other people it was always so easy to judge. It's always others who get cancer. Always others who die in car crashes. And, now, here it is, under our skin, worse than a tattoo, because it is invisible.

And one more bad thing. Suddenly, despite everything, you think – is it the suffering that does it? Or maybe the pain? Or the shame? Because even now I often find myself at unexpected moments beset by a deep shame, turning red – you think that this is something *exceptional*, something extraordinary. But part of the tragedy is that it's not exceptional. It's depressing just how much the individual cases resemble each other. They're all so banal. Nearly all of them start the same way and end the same way. Every single story is saturated with the monotony of the files, with the idiotic jargon of the secret services, of the state. The whole thing is like some freak of nature floating in a jar of formaldehyde. Cod liver oil. Which she gave us kids a tablespoonful of every night – swallowing it was mandatory.

These days at my place the musty odour of old paper permeates my room. I went in there not long ago and nearly suffocated. I must uncover every last snippet of every last letter, envelope, dossier, photo album and memory and look them over one by one. Here I sit in the middle of this stale odour, the same stale odour of the ancient dresser that used to be in our home. A childhood smell. I recognize it. The old papers, air-mail envelopes, yellowed newspapers, cut-out newspaper articles, brochures, postcards, photographs, IDs and certifications. Until now they were all over the place, in glorious disarray. I go about the flat, gathering them up, carrying them into my room. This is my second stab at understanding what happened. The first time was ten years after my mother's death. The result was a novel, *Zehuze*. That's when I began to bring order to the awful chaos. But there could be no order.

At the same time, in a perverse sort of way, this turn of events has an advantage, too. It casts a sharp light on your own story. The fact that everything is – must be – re-evaluated compels you to weigh everything once again, to scrutinize your life from a distance. You've been too close to your life, anyway, while living it, and so you haven't had a chance to consider the broader connections. You might even call this an opportunity. Whether final or first, it doesn't matter.

* * *

During the coffee-shop conversation – when I was supposed to find out who this certain family member of mine was who had been mentioned, anonymously, in the phone call – I was already sure, even before hearing her name, even if this was entirely, utterly impossible (and indeed it was out of the question, precisely because it was, well, absolutely out of the question), that it obviously was my mother all the same. But why was I so sure? Perhaps it was my memory of her quivering lips when I sensed that she wanted to say something? Something that was on the tip of her tongue, but in the end she didn't say? A mute mother's word.

If there's going to be a tragedy, let it be a major tragedy. Now, I'd heard such rumours before – about my father, that is – but I'd swept them off me like breadcrumbs or cigar ash. I laughed them off. Why on earth would they have recruited a loyal communist like him, a stalwart believer in the system, a man of blind faith? He was, after all, someone who happily spouted those views which so many of his colleagues spouted only to fit in and all the while harbouring secret thoughts of a different sort – his journalist colleagues who fancied themselves real heroes solely because they dared to think something else, because they thought something other than what they said. This too is why Dad became a pariah among his colleagues. For this reason, at least, he had my respect: he wrote what he thought, even if I wasn't crazy about it. The problem lay not only in the quality of his thinking, but in how wounded and simplistic his boneheaded dogmatism had rendered his otherwise witty style. He wasn't the first smart person to be made stupid by his beliefs. 'What Is Behind the News' was the name of Dad's column in the daily *Magyar Nemzet* (*Hungarian Nation*). As a child I really liked the telephone logo above each article. When I happen upon one of his pieces nowadays I can't bring myself to read even a single paragraph – how empty it all seems, every word and every phrase!

What use would the state have had for such a person?

Boy, was I mistaken. Owing to his rather dishonourable role in the wake of the 1956 Revolution, in 1960 my dad was named the London correspondent for MTI, the Hungarian News Agency. This phase of his career didn't last long: in the space of two years he – the parachutist dropped there by the Party – was broken by the sly machinations of MTI's veteran staff. His having signed his recruitment papers, off to London he went with four children. What fine cover! Four children.

CONTENTS OF THE FORGÁCS FAMILY'S SUITCASES AND BOXES

4 men's suits	1 men's jumpsuit
1 men's coat	10 pairs men's underwear
1 men's bathrobe	5 pairs men's pyjamas

10 men's shirts

3 pairs men's shoes

6 pairs socks

3 women's coats

2 women's costumes

7 women's dresses

20 pairs women's underwear

10 women's cardigans & jumpers

5 pairs women's shoes

5 nightgowns

6 teddy bears

20 girls' dresses

6 children's light coats

6 children's heavy coats

10 used plastic bags

15 towels

20 children's shirts

40 pairs children's underwear

12 pairs children's shoes

10 pairs long children's trousers

6 pairs children's shorts

6 skirts

5 little aprons

8 pairs children's pyjamas

20 pairs children's socks

5 clothes hangers

2 bed sheets

5 pillowcases

7 tablecloths

5 skirts

2 dictionaries

40 schoolbooks, school supplies

10 children's novels

2 English-language instruction books

1 Hungarian spelling handbook

1 drawing board with rulers

1 paint set

1 big doll

Bartók's *Mikrokosmos* (2 scores)

Béla Balázs: *Bluebeard's Castle*

1 Erika typewriter

1 espresso-maker

1 sewing kit	B. FOREIGN EXCHANGE
1 clothes-brush with holder	DIRECTORATE
1 toiletry kit	22 September 1960
1 shoe-shining kit	CERTIFICATE ISSUED
1 wool blanket	LICENCE NO. 5
1 flannel blanket	Marcell Forgács
1 bed cover	Departed
1 set cutlery (6 knives,	26 September 1960
tablespoons, teaspoons)	HUNGARIAN NEWS AGENCY
(pewter not silver!)	BUDAPEST

But now we also know not only that his reports comprised news articles but that he himself was Pápai, a 'secret colleague', a member of the so-called 'London station'. So Papa was Pápai. It's not enough that he'd gone from Friedmann to Forgács at the drop of a hat: that he'd gone out into the hallway as Comrade Friedmann and returned to introduce himself as Comrade Forgács. Do I really care that much why he got this of all code names? Now I'll never know. A certain Pápai pops up in a footnote to an entertaining essay the historian Krisztián Ungváry wrote describing the London station and its collapse and dismantlement. This Pápai proposes a rather outlandish scheme of a sort known in the trade as a 'honey trap': he promised that one of our relatives, a young woman, would seduce a young professor in England – an English

278

historian. And up till now this footnote is the sole indication that Pápai really was active; for all three dossiers concerning the secret colleague code-named Pápai have disappeared without a trace. Or, at least, to date they haven't turned up. I write this with a journalist's blood coursing through my veins, although I'm not one – he was the journalist. Strike while the iron is hot.

I don't know if I want to see those dossiers. But I do want to see them. That's not even to mention that I've tellingly misread this totally innocent footnote – and perhaps I wanted to. I projected a Bond film onto this greyer-than-grey tale. The footnote makes no mention of any 'honey trap' – truth be told, this always sounded a bit rich. Since then the original reports have come into my possession – the wheels turn slowly indeed at the ÁBTL (Historical Archives of Hungarian State Security) – and they reveal that a certain police lieutenant named Imre Takács interrogated Papa (Pápai) in a C flat – a 'conspiratorial' flat, that is – and the only thing that bothered the lieutenant, as he mentioned in the 'Assessment' section of his report, was that Papa (Pápai) disclosed certain details only after prolonged prompting, like someone not inclined to remember too much, and that he gave several, often confusing replies to certain questions posed repeatedly.

ANDRÁS FORGÁCH

Assessment

In September 1962 PÁPAI had already previously
reported in person orally on the meeting between A.
Zs. and R. H. Since then I have asked him several
times for a written report, but he always came up
with some excuse not to do so. In the course of this
meeting I had him write it. Neither written nor oral
report is complete.

PÁPAI can be used in the matter of R. H., but in
light of their being relatives and the work he has
done to date, the degree to which his involvement is
advisable is questionable.

— Imre Takács, Police Lieutenant

His occasional handler could not have known that in 1963
Papa was peering down into that dark abyss – after the utter
failure of his London mission – into which for good measure he
would soon plummet; which is to say, he 'suffered' a 'nervous
breakdown' (as such episodes were then called), the second of
those he had once a decade – 1953, 1963, 1973, as if I were mapping the latitude and longitude of Father's descent into mental
illness. How he just sat there on the bench in the park-like
grounds of Korvin Military Hospital on Gorky Avenue after
undergoing yet another round of electric shock therapy – I had

just turned ten, and my mother had taken my hand and led me to see him – and Dad said not a word to me – no, he just stared blankly ahead as if he didn't even recognize me.

When in 2004 I first stepped from the street into the ÁBTL (whose cleverly forgettable name I couldn't memorize for a long time) to request my records and those of my parents, and anything else having to do with my circumstances, they handed me only three or four completely insignificant and uninteresting scraps with the following stamped on them in big green letters: HISTORICAL ARCHIVES OF HUNGARIAN STATE SECURITY. I received just as little as most applicants I'd heard about. Even these days, when I go in and out of the reading room of the archives, on Eötvös Street, in the centre of Budapest, I see the new applicants who arrive every day, and I see how vulnerable they are, and I see also how patiently the administrator speaks to them from inside a glass cubicle, exactly like a nurse in a psychiatric ward. Most people who receive so few documents are of course relieved. I was not relieved. And what is it that I got? An agent reported what I'd said once while I'd been a student in the faculty of arts and letters. Half a sentence. And not even an exact quote. Nonsense. Back in 2004, we were not allowed to find out the agents' names. Today I know it. I don't remember his face. I have no idea who he is. I don't even bother to go over to the shelf and open up the envelope in which I brought home those few sheets of paper. It was an unimaginable disappointment.

Today, as I hold in my hand the two thick dossiers in which my own name appears more than once, not just my parents' names – in my virtual hand, that is, for they are both (my mother's recruitment dossier and the work dossier) kept under lock and key in the research room on Eötvös Street – I can't help but wonder why, in 2004, they gave me so little. It's a real crime that in 1990 and since then every last such document hasn't been made publicly available. *A crime, a crime, an irredeemable crime.*

One of the documents released to me in 2004 was nonetheless of some interest, come to think of it, if only from a distance. In the course of the rehabilitation proceedings underway in the wake of Stalin's death, in June 1954 my father was summoned to Gyorskocsi Street in Buda, the location of a huge prison and the military prosecutor's headquarters. He would later recount how scared he was when the iron gate closed behind him, how the red-hot iron gate burned his back – it was important to him to mention this detail repeatedly. I suspect that he carried that fear with him for the rest of his life. Not that that was the first or the last time he was scared, of course. He was scared often in the years that followed. In 1973, for the last time and for all eternity. I did, then, receive these official records in 2004, with my thirty-four-year-old father's signature at the bottom of each page.

INTERIOR MINISTRY

MAIN INVESTIGATIVE DEPARTMENT   TOP SECRET!

Affidavit

I, the undersigned, understanding my liability
under criminal law, hereby declare that under no
circumstances will I mention my interrogation by
the Main Investigative Department of the Interior
Ministry to any unauthorized individuals.

I understand that if I violate the terms of this
affidavit, a criminal case may be opened against me.

Budapest, 30 June 1954

György Beofsics   *Marcell Forgács*
SUB-LIEUTENANT, ÁV   Declarant

That energetic signature! Those looped letters! The interrogating officer behaved like a proper gentleman, exactly as we
might imagine he would in the course of a rehabilitation
such as this: he was objective and dry. He was well aware
how the interrogation of witnesses had unfolded a couple
of years earlier. It could easily have been him who'd beaten
a suspect to a pulp back then. And perhaps it was precisely

this that rendered him so suitable for presiding over rehabilitation cases like a gentleman.

Dad, in his own version of events, was just another Stendhal hero who had got lost on the battlefield. Aside from his repeated and dramatic attempts to convey just how terrifying it had been, he told me nothing at all about *why* he was there in the first place. And I didn't press him. It didn't even occur to me to do so. We simply didn't have the words for a proper conversation about these things. And to think that Dad was quite a storyteller. He even wrote poems. '*The sound of thick raindrops knocking / gave way to the footsteps of the evening's human seas / and still I awaited you / under the trees buzzing from the breeze.*' He wrote this for Kati not long before she was burned at Auschwitz – Kati, with whom he was caught in the act because her parents came home too soon from a cancelled movie. There is a photo, too – Kati at the ice rink in the town of Szatmárnémeti – but I can't find it just now.

A couple of years before Dad was summoned, a certain Endre Rosta was sentenced to many years in prison, by way of a small side-show to the show trials of the time. Dad had been his subordinate in the prime minister's press office between June 1948 and September 1949, when the whole crew was quickly cast to the winds. Until then, Endre Rosta worked under the prime minister (and dictator) Mátyás Rákosi, as did my father. Here's a good anecdote: one fine day Dad had just finished translating one of Comrade

Rákosi's speeches, when Mátyás himself phoned Dad and, in a rasping voice, congratulated him on his excellent French. At first Dad was scared, but then, puffing out his chest, he went about telling everyone the news.

In June 1954, then, Father was summoned to Gyorskocsi Street. He performed relatively well, but it is still painful and embarrassing to imagine. I can hear him hemming and hawing and coming up with excuses, with self-justifications.

How did your interrogation in 1949 concerning Endre Rosta unfold?

I think it was a certain Lieutenant Horváth who interrogated me in 1949 about Rosta. In the course of the interrogation Horváth asked me why it was that I hadn't noticed that Rosta was engaged in hostile activity. How could I have failed to notice that Rosta was an enemy who, among other things, had been terrorizing the Hungarian press? In the course of the interrogation Horváth encouraged me to make connections between Rosta's activities and the fact, as Horváth put it, that Rosta was an enemy. Among other things he asked me if I knew that Rosta was a spy. After I replied no, Horváth asked me, now that I knew that Rosta was a spy for foreign powers, what hostile actions I can attribute to Rosta, or activity

that is consistent with Rosta having been a spy.
These were the circumstances under which I gave my
testimony in 1949 against Endre Rosta.

The record also reveals how the prime minister's press office, with Dad's vigorous participation, worked to destroy Hungary's free press in 1949.

Was there a tendency in the Hungarian media rooted
in the conviction that the sensationalistic form and
content of the bourgeois papers must be redirected to
the propagation of the policies of the Party and the
government?

> [...] It was a duty to re-educate the reporters at
> bourgeois papers to change the form and content of
> their papers, to shift from the sensationalism they
> had practised up to that point, to representing the
> position of the government and the Party.

What aspect of Rosta's work contributed to the
execution of the above duty?

> As regards the above, Rosta's method was to
> summon the editors of the bourgeois papers or to
> speak to them by telephone. In the course of these

conversations Rosta communicated the direction said editors were to follow, which is to say, what subjects the papers were to cover. Rosta's work had results, too, for the papers did in fact publish those articles concerning agriculture or industry that Rosta handed to them in completed form, or else that he had told them they should write.

In consequence of Rosta's above-mentioned activity, did these papers become more uniform and their readership decline?

A certain trend towards uniformity was indeed detectable among the bourgeois papers, and this was in part because the prime minister's press office could not deal sufficiently with all the editors of the bourgeois papers, but rather mostly provide only the general direction. However, nor were the editors of the bourgeois papers pleased to publish and edit articles addressing the Party and government's position, and did not process such news in a form that would have been understandable to their readerships. One consequence, then, was that the bourgeois papers' readership declined. But I cannot claim that this was the result of deliberately bad work on the part of Rosta, for – according to him – he was in constant communication with the Party's top leadership. In his individual decisions and instructions Rosta always cited the comrades working at Party headquarters.

This deposition certainly wasn't a pleasant read.

There was also another strange incident. Four years later, on 26 May 1958, two investigators in civilian clothes rang the buzzer to our flat at 8 Attila Street in Buda so that – as Deputy Sub-Department Head Hugó Németh wrote in his field report – they could grill Father, in his capacity as a member of the Workers' Militia, about our nearest neighbour. In the assessment of the deputy sub-department head, our neighbour's housekeeper wasn't reliable enough, which is why they turned to my father and another resident, Kornélia Polacsek. I remember Dad's steel-grey Workers' Militia uniform well. One time I even saw him wearing it in a parade, perhaps on May Day of the same year, 1958. I have to say, he didn't look very dapper in it. This was the fourth and last uniform of his life: the first, his Mihai Eminescu High School uniform in Szatmárnémeti; the second, his Romanian army uniform, which lacked any insignia; and the third, that of the British army in Palestine. Much more exciting, though, was the fact that he kept his service revolver and ammunition in his desk drawer, which was, I suppose, in violation of regulations. I was quite impressed by the sight of those brass bullets scattered among his papers. Though we were under strict orders not to open that drawer, I often looked at the bullets and played with them when he wasn't at home. They really were beautiful, those bullets. And so heavy.

So our concierge, a certain Mr Lénárt, presumably wasn't an informant. His sons were wild, I recall. They weren't too good at football, either, shoving everyone around on the field like animals, but because they were the concierge's sons we overlooked this. They had power. The Lénárts lived in Flat 1, in the basement, and when huddling over battle plans when an attack seemed imminent, we boys often squatted in front of that window of theirs which looked out onto the building's inner courtyard. For ammunition we collected conkers, spiny shells and all. Now, this ongoing war between the boys on the *grund* – the vacant lot just outside, that is – and those of us defending our building wasn't too dangerous, even if a piece of brick that was hurled over the high stone wall into the upper yard did once nearly knock out my left eye.

In that basement flat, Mr Lénárt himself sometimes popped out from behind his boys, a mocking smile on his face, and took relish in catching one of us and twisting his ear. If he happened to be away, his sons would let us into the concierge's booth, where we leafed through the huge concierge-book, reading Mr Lénárt's funny notes on the building's residents.

On 26 May 1958, then, the investigators pressed the buzzer of our flat at 8 Attila Street – Floor II, stairwell D. Dad must have been scared then, too, I reckon. Or, if not, he must at least have known what sort of visitors he was about to deal with. They questioned him about our nearest neighbour – the lame man whose arrival invariably alarmed me. I was afraid of him. The heavy thud of his steps on the stairs. He was the Sandman. Who comes to punish boys who don't go to sleep. A black-haired, dark-eyed fellow who rarely uttered a word. He had a limp. Yes, there was a file on him, too. As it turned out much later, even the Sandman had been recruited before 1956. According to a particularly exciting find in Deputy Sub-Department Head Hugó Németh's field report:

He generally leaves home in the morning and returns to his flat in the evening.

Indeed, the Sandman always got back around 6.00 p.m., the thick-soled orthopaedic shoe on his right foot stomping loudly as he ascended the spiral staircase – it took for ever for him to get to Floor II. I shuddered at the thought of him seeing me. The report determines that the Sandman

has not shared his political views with even his nearest neighbours at his address. During the period

of the counter-revolution he stayed at home, rarely
going out and getting home soon after.

Hugó Németh adds:

It was through his connections that he joined the
party via the district's party committee in 1957, for
the main party had not accepted his membership,
for after the [counter-revolutionary] events the police
had had him under surveillance on suspicion of
organizing.

Often, my heart racing, I peeked through our letterbox to
see him fumbling with the key to his door as the stairwell
light went out. The smell of alcohol and nicotine wafted off
him, and this fascinated me as much as it repulsed me. It's
worth noting here that my parents never drank or smoked.
'A real man drinks and smokes,' a housewife who lived in
another stairwell once told my father, when rejecting or perhaps – my father was never clear about this – yielding to his
extravagantly suave advances.

This archive is such that if you remove one file, countless
others are liable to come spilling out after it, and finally a
veritable tower of paperwork piles up on your desk. As I
learned from a dossier I happened across just a couple of
days ago (at the time of writing, in September 2015), the

Sandman had been recruited once before, in the late 1940s, when he was a leftist member of the National Peasant Party and, moreover, secretly joined the Magyar Dolgozók Pártja (Hungarian Working People's Party, MDP):

> The informant code-named ZOLTÁN PÁL was recruited in 1949 on the grounds of his solid belief in the cause. We perceived no double-dealing, no de-conspiring in the course of his secret work. Even after the counter-revolution he was ready to make himself available. His work was instrumental in the re-mapping of the right-wing elements of the NPP.

This was reported by Police Lieutenant János Engelhardt. But the agent's files went missing in the chaos of 1956. Aside from his wretched role in the politics of the day the Sandman wasn't, as it turned out, so terrible or evil; his father had been a simple night watchman.

> He lives in a one-bedroom, nicely furnished flat with all the modern conveniences. A cleaning woman performs the tidying of the flat. With the exception of one or two individuals he is not on close terms with any of the building's residents, exchanging only greetings. He has a wide circle of friends who used to stop by to see him before the events and especially

during the events. During and after the time of
the counter-revolution, individuals of various sorts
looked him up, including local officials and newspaper
reporters from the provinces. These people came by
at all hours of the day, and were sometimes there
even at midnight.

Although he joined the Party after the 'events', the Interior
Ministry wanted to know if it was worth recruiting him
again. And, because his housekeeper wasn't one to toe the
line, my daddy – that is, 'the individual providing the information' – didn't hold back about what he knew.

[. . .] according to him, in the present day similar
sorts stop by his place at similar times of day as did
during the events, but not yet as frequently.

But my father was intrigued above all to know why this
reticent lame man who wore orthopaedic shoes – Pulai
was his family name – invariably came home so late at the
weekend with a different woman each time. In any case, on
weekdays the man would get home in the evening and stumble his way, obviously drunk, up the stairs.

He passes his free time in the company of friends and
women, in consequence of which he is home rarely,

except that period when people were visiting him regularly.

He lives in stable material circumstances. He corresponds regularly with his parents and his relatives in the provinces, whom he visits on occasion. But these individuals often sleep at his place also.

His friends and various young old women have often spent the night there, in revelry. His health is poor, and he has often been treated at hospital on account of his lungs.

Ah, these 'young old women'! My mother and father lowered their voices, but, well, 'Pulai' was 'Pulai' even in Hebrew. The Sandman was silent – more and more silent – and very much disinclined to be pally with suspicious elements, which the authorities were really sorry about, for he was therefore lost to them. As for me, I ran up the stairs at breakneck speed if I glimpsed him from afar. I would stand, waiting, in the dark stairwell, mesmerized as I spied on the lame devil through the dusty window as he came towards our stairwell, hobbling his way across the gravel path of the inner courtyard, between the flowerbeds. *It can't be chance that I have such a frightening neighbour,* I brooded. *This is Fate,* I thought as I ran into our own flat before he got close, turning the key in the lock behind me twice.

The surprising twist at the end of the file:

In view of the limited prospect of exploiting his intelligence value and of his being a member of the MSZMP [Hungarian Socialist Workers' Party] leadership, under operative regulations he cannot be a member of our network, and so I recommend his exclusion from the network and from further exploitation as a social connection.

And the Sandman even has the courage to raise his middle finger:

I did not obtain a signed pledge of secrecy about the ending of the relationship, for the informant refused to write this, on the grounds that not even when first establishing the relationship with us was he asked to write such a pledge, and so he does not deem it necessary to undertake a counter-pledge either.

I can hear Father gabbling in a soft voice to Mother about the Sandman. I am five years old. When they notice me watching them, they go into the other room, closing the door behind them.

But this isn't about Dad.

It was Bruria who had to pick up his heavy load.

MINISTRY OF THE INTERIOR   TOP SECRET!

SUB-DEPARTMENT III/I-4

OFFICIAL REQUISITION

Budapest, 20 November 1975

I request release of the third volume of the M dossier, no. Z-281, of the sc code-named PÁPAI.

Károly Mercz, Police Captain

Authorized by:

József Stöckl

Oszkár Kiss, Police Lieutenant Colonel

Acting Deputy Assistant Department Head

To the Director of Records,

Directorate of the III/I Group, Ministry of the Interior

Intra-agency report

Why did they have to use Bruria to 'substitute' for Marcell?

> Her activization was implemented only in the event of
> her husband's serious illness, to substitute for him.

. . . as the report's jargon puts it so subtly. If there was such a great need for her, why couldn't she be recruited in her own right? Why did she have to take my father's name, as it were, even in the underworld?

When Bruria was 'provided' with 'smaller assignments', as Police Captain Mercz put it so ornately in his report dated 4 February 1976, Pápai was officially still active – though his third and final breakdown had already occurred in 1973. It might be that he himself had recommended his wife as a translator in his place, though the spouses of network individuals working abroad were often recruited, too, on the presumption that husbands and wives couldn't keep their identity as agents secret from each other anyway. Spycraft textbooks take this for granted. So I suspect that Bruria knew what her husband, the Hungarian News Agency correspondent, did on the side. But it could well be that when she submitted her first translations, back in Hungary, in the early 1970s, to the Párttörténeti Intézet (Party History Institute), she still didn't have the faintest idea whom she was working for; or, if she did, she certainly didn't know what name she was referred to by:

MRS PÁPAI has travelled to Israel twice in the past five years, given small assignments each time. While being debriefed she offered a few useful pieces of information. To cover her latest operative expenses we handed her one hundred dollars.

Her handlers had an easier time with her than with others, whom they intimidated, beat up or blackmailed, only later, in public places, whether cafés or in C or S flats, taking a different approach, gradually softening and training the network individual, step by step, as described so magnificently and unbearably by Péter Esterházy in his *Javított kiadás* (*Corrected Edition*), the subject of which was his own father. But even in the case of Bruria there was a grey area: the swimmer, in our case, the handler, at pool's edge at first sticks only the tip of his big toe into the water, for a moment only, testing the temperature, and then gives the prospective recruit increasingly complex tasks until, finally – *what the hell* – he presses a hundred-dollar bill into her palm, as if into the hand of a Gypsy violinist to get him to play a favourite tune. By the time Bruria accepted the money – and accept it she did (it obviously came in handy) – the deal had already been done. From then on all went smoothly.

Frighteningly smoothly.

On her first official assignment, after she had been trained in all sorts of practical secret-service matters, we travelled together, Bruria and I. We went by train to Athens, and from there – from the port of Piraeus – via Cyprus – to Jaffa. I remember how surreal it was, at the age of twenty-three, to see oranges hanging from trees, when one cold and foggy morning I took a glimpse into the back garden of our surly hosts in Athens. That is when I understood that oranges grow on trees just the same as apples and pears do.

Mum's first report is a frightening read. True, our family paid for the trip, but that doesn't change how terribly depressing it is to read the later acknowledgements of receipt endorsed by the signature of Mrs Marcell Forgács. During the trip I often didn't understand why she was so tense. Dad wasn't there – she could breathe freely. Well, of course: she had to *record, record, record* ceaselessly. The following list is somewhat boring, true, but with it we will at least have covered this part sufficiently, for the subsequent reports were dead ringers for this one. In sum, Bruria got plenty of homework.

On the basis of the above, under Order 0024/1966 I recommend that MRS PÁPAI receive somewhat more specific and wide-ranging briefings as regards the following:
    – Israel's present-day domestic political situation
    – Situation of immigrants, reasons for emigration from Israel

– Domestic economic tensions, development of living standards

– Preparations for the 29th World Zionist Congress

– Israeli reactions to the 'For Soviet Jews' congress held in Brussels

As for the Israeli agent-operative situation:

– Controls in practice on entering and exiting the country (passport, customs inspection, frisking, etc.)

– Registration obligations on entry, forms that must be filled out, questions posed, the general procedure

– Signs of surveillance – whether direct surveillance or surveillance-like practices, perhaps measures to limit activity, with special attention to provocation

– Opportunities for travel within Israel, restrictions on travel either nationally or regionally

Now, this was no easy task for a passionate, slapdash spirit, for she had to combine professional political analysis with a sociologist's objectivity grounded in precise data and also with, yes, a spy's snake-like stealth. And then the report mentions a nice bit of nonsense: Mother spoon-fed her comrades a dubious excuse for my travelling with her, which is that I was going along to put my grandfather's literary estate into order. My non-existent fluency in Hebrew would have rendered me wonderfully unsuitable for this. Even today it wouldn't pass muster. True, I later learned some Hebrew by my own efforts – at first from an absurd East German textbook – while I worked in a screw factory in Holon, an industrial city on the southern outskirts of Tel Aviv, alongside Arab co-workers, that is. During my lunch breaks I'd invariably open up that textbook as I sat on the steps in the factory yard – I couldn't converse with anyone. My fellow workers, who were from the West Bank, knew only a few odd words of English. My studies were a joke – as if someone were trying to learn Hungarian today from a 1958 reading workbook. I'd bought the Hebrew textbook in East Berlin back in 1972, when I was touring there as a self-taught drummer with the band Orfeo – but that's another story. The book's Hebrew texts were about working men and women, production and that model family which Walter Ulbricht – in his capacity as that country's foremost communist leader for a number of decades – envisioned for East Germans. So it was in part a non-existent, socialist Hebrew that I acquired and whose words I would later use to the endless amusement of the youth of Israel.

But the one and only reason I studied the language to begin with was in order to penetrate the secrets of my mother's mysterious mother tongue; whereas the Hebrew I had learned, on the streets of Israel at least, sounded not so mysterious at all, but, rather, ordinary. And, yes, I had the feeling that with every word I learned by rote, and, later, with every word that came back to me at unexpected moments, I was seeing the world anew, like a young child. Water was *mayim*? How could *mayim* be water? It was as if I were looking into a crystal ball that showed the past and future simultaneously, as if at the same time I were penetrating my mother's body like an X-ray. That something is *motek* (sweet) or *melach* (salt), *ratoov* (wet) or *yavesh* (dry), *khoref* (winter) or *kayits* (summer), or that someone is *atsuv* (sad) or *aliz* (cheerful). It was as if, through these new words, I were learning something radically different about these things: for example, that wetness always has a strange, dry sensation, and even the driest dryness is saturated with a wet *sh* sound. From all these words that were so strange to me, so contradictory to the laws of nature, I reconstructed my mother's sense of sight, hearing and smell. I recreated her childhood. I understood her inside-out, upside-down world. I turned her from standing on her head to her feet. I now reconstruct my mother from Hebrew words, as if from the pieces of a puzzle. My mother, the mosaic woman. Every one of these word-sensations is tangible, and I heard every one from my mother's mouth, as I have since then, too. The language worked like a hidden tape recorder or camera. I spied out my mother.

My parents often spoke Hebrew to each other at home so we wouldn't understand, and my head was like a storage chest, long full of countless Hebrew words I didn't know the meaning of, words I would perhaps never understand. And when the Hebrew expressions filed away in my mind were suddenly illuminated, as if by magic, they were mostly those that my parents had for years hurled back and forth at each other – Hebrew was to them above all the language of fights and not love – the language with which blows were struck, of rebukes, not of harmony and understanding. It was as if I'd learned something about the universe, about every language that had ever existed. Indeed, the ritual repetition of the fights ensured that the meaning of the words wasn't so mysterious to us after all, the words that flew around our home so thickly, piercing and striking so poisonously, like arrows or a shower of stones: *Ze lo beseder! Ein li kesef!* (It's not all right! I don't have money!)

Then again, when I was little, even the lullabies that put me to sleep were sung in Hebrew: those words that melt in the mouth like Eastern sweets, bound up in dense, honey-coated melodies; and so too the delicious aromas, the dates, the halva, the chocolate, and even the smell of the Marlboros bought by the carton at airports that came to us from afar, intermittently – when guests arrived from Israel, as they often arrived, invariably bringing with them something exotic. And, finally, when on this first trip together I loafed about – as if on the rather skilfully rendered set of a film studio – on Sderot Rothschild, Sderot Ben-Gurion, Kikar Dizengoff, in Jaffa, or by the sea, I breathed in the local fragrances, too, and from day to day and word to word I was increasingly under the illusion that I better understood my mother. As if these strange, backward-pronounced words and shouted sentences, these ordinary and yet at the same time mysterious linguistic configurations, contained her DNA. (My older brother aptly dubbed this language – so beyond our comprehension, so chaotic, it seemed to us – a 'porridge language', invoking the oats Bruria made for us every single morning ever since our London sojourn.) After a while I learned to read even those Hebrew letters lacking vowel points – from street signs, which I painstakingly spelled out like a little schoolboy as I rode a bus about the city. But that didn't mean I knew Hebrew yet. No, that was only an excuse for my trip: my mother had chosen to take with her not my older brother, but me, because she wanted to travel with me, even though it would have been his turn after our older sister; but with me, I suppose, she felt secure (and now I even know what she was hiding).

> The invitation of her son took place because they find
> him suitable – he has a degree in the humanities –
> for professionally sorting out and arranging his
> grandfather's literary and political estate.

On this occasion Bruria doesn't get any money from her taskmasters, but that really doesn't make a difference. It

does make a difference, and yet it doesn't make a difference. It does make a difference. I'm getting my heart used
to silence.

For her present trip abroad we shall cover neither
travel nor other expenses, since our interests in the
Israeli visit are but conditional on whether, among
the documents in the aforementioned estate, any turn
up that we can use to pursue active measures against
Zionist organizations or leading individuals.

In short, they want to rummage about in my grandfather's
desk. A recommendation dated 30 January 1977 reveals that,
having noted the co-operative fervour displayed by my
mother (Mum, Mommy, *imah sheli*), they wish to promptly
make up for the financial omission during her next trip,
which occurs a year after the first.

Financial matters

In view of the fact that until now we have provided
nothing to MRS PÁPAI to cover her expenses ensuing
from her trips to Israel, for the present trip we
recommend that her travel costs be covered, as
follows:

Airline ticket	8,000 forints
Ship ticket	400 US dollars
Miscellaneous expenses	100 US dollars

We request permission, on an official requisition, for the export of foreign currency. We will write up the cover story for its legalization.

Oh, these blood-money cover stories and manoeuvres! The step-by-step seduction! As Police Lieutenant Colonel Ottó Szélpál puts it, in his immortal work *The Principles and General Methods of Managing, Training, Educating and Monitoring Network Individuals*, which he penned not long before the events discussed here, in his Dadaist poem therein, 'The Degrees of Praise':

The Degrees of Praise

(a) The operations officer praises the network individual he is responsible for.

(b) The operations officer's superior expresses his recognition of the network individual in the form of praise.

(c) In the case of outstanding achievement, the network individual can be recommended for decoration.

Beyond all of this, rewards may be given, too – of course, you may well say, but the form they take is important, because 'certain individuals react sensitively to cash rewards', even finding 'this form of recognition offensive':

<u>Types of Rewards</u>

Cash Rewards. The simplest form of reward to employ, in the event that objective and subjective conditions are met. When employing, it is imperative to consider:
– On account of their temperament, certain individuals react sensitively to cash rewards, regarding this form of recognition as offensive.
– If possible we should not employ this method in the initial period in the case of an agent recruited on the basis of inculpatory facts.

In other words, best to keep a blackmailed criminal on a short leash for a while, in case he or she gets too confident.

– Rewards must not take on the form of regular disbursements (e.g. monthly, quarterly).
– In the case of an agent recruited from among enemy circles, as long as he is still working against his former associates, it is advisable to employ rewards only in exceptional circumstances.

But if cash rewards trouble such sensitive souls, gifts can be given instead. Even then, however, it is important to note whether the recipient is 'at all pleased'. One must proceed with absolute discretion, examining whether:

[. . .] the gift well serves our goals in educating the agent, whether it represents some sort of value for the network individual in terms of practical use, pleasure or cultural significance, for example – whether he is at all pleased. A poorly chosen gift will not yield the emotional effects that serve to reinforce co-operation. Precisely for this reason it is advisable to give the network individual gifts that suit his interests, his positive passions, his 'hobbies'. For example, an engineer or a researcher can be given a valuable technical book, and a collector – of paintings, stamps, medals or antiques, for example – can receive something to expand his collection.

But what to say at home? Where did this money come from? The antique watch? A gift can be given only if . . .

– The network individual receiving the gift is capable of adequately legalizing his possession of it among those around him.

But the shrewd Ottó Szélpál has a recipe for 'legalization', too:

The Legalization of Rewards

[...] The network individual must legalize the origin of the cash, the gift, or other benefit in a manner perceived as credible and acceptable by those belonging to both his closer and wider social environments. The legalization requires that he have an unequivocal story verifiable to others as well (especially to members of the enemy circle), one he can consistently represent in all directions. The operations officer must provide help and direction in developing the cover story. Overlooking the need for legalization can in some cases lead to serious instances of de-conspiring. In the case of a cash reward, a suitable explanation must be found for the origin of the money. For example, pools, lottery, other winnings, or extra work.

In certain instances the legalization of a gift may be more complicated. Methods of doing so include, for example: citing the receipt of an unexpected or expected source of money used to make the purchase; a gift received from an unverifiable source; the consequence of money put aside without the knowledge of family members; the cover story behind this.

And there is a practical rule worth noting, too:

A practical rule worth noting is that it is inadvisable to purchase gifts departing from the average in terms of function, form or value in the vicinity of the residence or the workplace of the network individual or of the residence of individuals under confidential investigation. This pertains especially to small cities and villages.

Also mentioned are 'offering alternative benefits', only – of course – 'within the framework of legal options' and 'primarily as humane assistance', and, to be sure, my dear mother readily took advantage of humane assistance, 'e.g. passports':

Those benefits hard for average people to attain or attainable to them only through much trouble will raise attention. This is particularly true of those legal procedures that fall under the purview of the Interior Ministry (e.g. passports, certificates of good-standing, various permits). A reward of this nature may be employed solely in a narrow framework indeed, and thoroughly, prudently, and with the approval of

commanding officers, for it is dangerous and is hard
to legalize, and besides, it can lead to corruption
and can sink to the level of nepotism. For precisely
this reason it should be employed only in the most
necessary of cases, primarily as humane assistance
(e.g. hospital admission, treatment by a physician,
acquiring medication, convalescent retreats).

But these are just trifles. Not insignificant trifles, but
trifles all the same. What began with that first trip, like an
avalanche that could not be stopped, is something which, in
that horrible jargon of the secret services, they called ... To
utter it is like vomiting, I've got to stand up from my desk –
yes, I stand up, take a breath and go for a walk; I light a cigar,
make myself a cup of coffee, walk about a bit more as my
heart hammers away, look out over the railing of the outside
corridor into the courtyard below, back to my computer, my
hands still resting on the keyboard, my fingers prepared to
type the letters, waiting for my brain to give the command,
to write (*no, don't do it!*): 'tip-off-individual research activity'.
If only I could now stop the pen in my mother's hand, when,
late at night – Father snoring away, comatose from sleeping
pills strong enough to knock out a rhino – she gets up, as the
mute moon shines from beyond the grave, she gets up, or perhaps she can't get to sleep to begin with, she sits down, she
sits down at the desk, which is too low and uncomfortable,

and she is even glad that it's uncomfortable, and, stooping over the desk, begins to write with that ballpoint pen of hers because she cannot type. Then again, she might not have waited for this moment. I've seen some reports – handwritten summaries – that suggest the singular style of my already supposedly deranged father. Yes. Mrs Pápai *and* Mr Pápai, if the latter's condition allowed it, or if my mother pressured him into it, whether as therapy or in despair, because she herself was unable to link the end of one sentence with the start of another, and her words headed in all directions, like ants, refusing to co-operate, unruly, like naughty children. In a nutshell, Dad simply had to help, and so Mr Pápai and Mrs Pápai sometimes worked together. Yet another reason for my mother's code name.

There is, then – let's call a spade a spade – the so-called *target individual* and *tip-off individual*. Such terms are already common knowledge, so I don't know why I'm so averse to writing them down. Oh, but I do know. The amalgam of fervour, communicativeness and directness in my mother made her perfectly suitable for striking up a conversation with anyone, in any situation, and she – living as she did under the illusion that she was simply carrying out the task the Party had assigned her, that she was just doing her job – didn't and couldn't notice the muck she was sinking into every step of the way. Even on that first trip to Israel, in fact, I couldn't help but notice how effortlessly strangers fell into conversation with each other on the street, as I'd seen back home in Hungary, too, in times of crisis, but of course in Israel there was – and is – always crisis, a constant buzz, a sort of collective hysteria, and there is always something to talk about at bus stops, in shops, concert halls, on the street: people greet each other as if they've been friends for a thousand years, not even introducing themselves, offering each other oranges or any kind of food if the wait at the bus stop is long or if they happen to have some in their bags. The flip side of this is the unpleasant jostling that almost invariably occurs while boarding a bus in Israel, though even this discourtesy is, there, an intense social experience.

When the name of a family member popped up in the dossier for the first time – that of my cousin who lived in Milan, who adored my mother, her aunt, and whom my mother adored – my heart stopped. And from here on, there really is no holding back:

H. H. is getting divorced. She doesn't want to return to Israel; she will continue to live in Italy. As an architect, making a living is hard, so she decided to change professions. She will probably open a store of some sort. She also said she would be happiest to settle in Hungary, but that if she does reach such a decision, it will be realized only in 10–15 years.

MRS PÁPAI offered to visit her relative in Milan if we see the need and to invite her to Hungary at a later date.

At my request, MRS PÁPAI will prepare a more detailed report on the above individual.

I suspect something else in the background, but it is only a suspicion, or, rather, a yearning to see as more beautiful what can't be beautified; namely, that Bruria knew full well that nothing would come of this, but wanted to offer proof of her efforts. She was, after all, being constantly bombarded with demands. *Give us a name already, you know so many people, it won't hurt!* And she, like a good little girl, spat out a name in despair, or perhaps not in despair. (*Oh, but you shouldn't have!* I imagine telling her. *Shush, kid,* I tell myself, *this is no place for pathos. But, oh my, you shouldn't have!*) Yes, she did it just to stuff their traps, and she knew that whatever happened wouldn't be her doing after all, but if it were her doing, then nothing would come of it anyway, that she'd somehow explain it away. The naivety that delivers us to evil! For by now it's all the same whether something comes of it or not. Nothing did come of it, but it's all the same. No, it's *not* all the same. It's a fact that she was capable of this, and since she'd already done it once, the second time would be easier, and it would keep getting easier and easier to give up a name, some detail, or any sort of confidential information about someone to the nameless machinery we might even call the Party, which, it's true, was akin to the Church in Bruria's religious world; that is, to give up the name of someone she'd exchange cheerful glances with, someone she'd visit, someone who looked upon her with unfailing adoration and who didn't so much as suspect what muck her name had been rolled in; and if he or she is lucky, and his or her dossier never turns up, because it was destroyed, as perhaps my father's dossiers were, he or she will never find out. Neither he nor she nor anyone else.

But still it happened, it happened for ever.

But it wasn't even sweet H. who marked Bruria's fall into sin, no, she wasn't the first tip-off individual with whom Bruria had crossed the Rubicon, but another someone I maybe didn't like as much as I did my mother's niece, my cousin, and so – though the revelation would shock me all the same – my heart didn't quite stop even if the mere fact did feel like a blow to my stomach. By chance, in this instance, too, it was an architect who was caught in the net of our secret colleague, but not a relative as close as H., no, but the companion of Bruria's cousin in Israel, a man this cousin lived with, who happened to be the same age as Bruria. Yes, it seems my mother was inclined to try out her remarkable talent at tip-off-individual research on relatives, which she assiduously practised later, too.

And what happens when – right in the middle of a heap of stupid official files – one discovers a familiar name, that of someone one had long forgotten? Moreover, when one discovers it in a dossier in which one is also remotely implicated? What happens is this: the figure leaps off the page, as this architect did that day, appearing before my eyes in sharp relief as he went about explaining something to us on a sun-drenched Tel Aviv street before we stepped into his office, like some hero conjured up by Tolstoy in one of his novels with a couple of strokes of the pen. I can see the pores on his skin as he turns his eyes away from mine. The twists and turns of these dry and porous files are sometimes like the mouth-watering taste of the madeleine Proust soaked in tea in *Remembrance of Things Past*. As this uncle of sorts led us about his Tel Aviv office, explaining things in a blaring voice, with the long-windedness of those people who jabber on ceaselessly because they really couldn't care less whom they are talking to – bear in mind what Dostoevsky says of Raskolnikov as he enters, guffawing, the prosecutor's office: that these kinds of people want to cover something up – there was also something of the endlessly sputtering Eastern merchant in this distant quasi-uncle, who had it in him to haggle with a person even before he knew what that person wanted to buy. Last but not least, with his fleshy nostrils he also reminded me of my own garrulous, jocular, stocky father, whose striking light-heartedness concealed impenetrable, unspeakable depths. I am reminded of Gyula Kabos, the greatest of all Hungarian comedians, who suffered from serious depression. People with outsized senses of humour are mostly out of their minds. Dark, impenetrable, unspeakable. Mommy dear, Mommy dear. Alas, the architect, whose non-existent diploma had gone missing, fitted to a tee the description my mother must have received from her handler, in that he appeared to be exquisitely vulnerable to blackmail; and that, moreover, he spoke both Hungarian and Hebrew perfectly, and so on:

MINISTRY OF THE INTERIOR   TOP SECRET!

Department III/I-4

Comrade Mercz!

Proceed according to the given considerations.

28 March 1977

REPORT

Budapest, 28 March 1977

MRS PÁPAI reports:

Last December she travelled to Israel for her mother's funeral, returning from there on 19 March. During her stay abroad she met several times with a relative's acquaintance.

<u>R. B.</u> (Place of birth: Miskolc. Date of birth: 17
April 1927. Previous flat in Miskolc: 80 Gy. Street)
<u>architect</u>, Israeli citizen, resident of Tel Aviv.

In the course of their conversations he said the
following about himself:

He earned a degree as an architectural engineer from
the Budapest University of Technology and Economics.
He was among the first to complete the Red Academy.
He lived in Miskolc and had a job there. He claims to
have worked for the Interior Ministry, too, and during
this time he travelled to China as well. Two of his
sisters married Soviet officers stationed near Miskolc.
Since 1956 he hasn't heard of them at all, and he
assumes that they no longer live in Hungary.

R. B. defected in 1956, justifying his act by saying
that because of his past association with the Interior
Ministry he could have faced difficulties in the event
of a change of regime.

In Israel he is the co-owner of an architectural firm.
He accepted the position as an architectural engineer,
but he lives in constant fear, since he does not have
a copy of his university diploma. He is afraid of

requesting one from Hungary, for he would have to ask the Red Academy, where they would not respond kindly to this. He is also worried about his Interior Ministry past coming to light and him then being held responsible, because back then he had denied this aspect of his past. Two technical illustrators and a secretary work in his office. His co-owner doesn't bother much with the business, and R. B. has to do everything.

R. B.'s companion – who lives with him and who is likewise of Hungarian descent – told MRS PÁPAI that her husband's behaviour is making her increasingly anxious. He is concerned that their telephone is bugged, that their letters are intercepted, and that they are under surveillance. He sometimes gets money from a mysterious source and then disappears for a day or two, after which he is always nervous but never tells her why. In her assessment he is working for some socialist country and is constantly scared of being caught.

Assessment:

With MRS PÁPAI's help we could begin a study of the above individual. An attempt should be made

<u>to procure a copy of his engineering diploma</u>. MRS
PÁPAI would undertake this, would stay in touch with
him through letters, and at a later date, once the
diploma is in our possession, he could be invited to a
third country.

With the help of the Borsod County Sub-department
III/I we will initiate an investigation in Miskolc aimed
at procuring data and finding his relatives.

Finally I recommend that we contact the state
security organs of socialist countries and request
their assistance in processing.

Károly Mercz, Police Captain

Comr. BEIDER!
What does MRS PÁPAI know about the work the above
individual did for the Interior Ministry?
IV/28 – János Szakadáti

In her first handwritten report, my mother, as a good agent,
did not forget to note – after trying as best she could within
the bounds of her modest abilities to draw a portrait of the
Hungarian émigré community – how scared R. B. was. Indeed,
in her report she speaks of many sorts of fear – she emerges

as a bona fide fear specialist – and she doesn't seem to worry at all that someone might abuse those feelings of fear. I felt the same shock when, years earlier, an acquaintance of mine gave me a copy of the reports made by the writer Sándor Tar, who was denounced by a fellow writer in the press in 1999 for having been an informant. In one of these reports I happened upon this: when on one occasion friends of Tar's stayed at his home in the western city of Debrecen before travelling across the Romanian border into Transylvania, Tar went so far as to wake up after his guests had gone to sleep and painstakingly note the names of the medications they had left on the table. (Perhaps he thought: *This just might be good for something.*)

'This man could be interesting,' writes our agent in Tel Aviv:

<u>Meetings</u>
Most Hungarian immigrants in Israel are Zionists.
They are so even if they are homesick and would
love (as many do) to inhale again the smell of
Budapest's streets and coffeehouses. Új Kelet
does its part, and while many love Hungary,
between the two homelands they choose Israel.
Progressive-minded Hungarian immigrants find a
place in the Israeli Communist Party or among the
party's sympathizers. A few immigrants hate the
atmosphere in Israel and are completely pessimistic;
they are afraid and so are not politically active.

One such person is R. B., born in Miskolc, who in his words was among the first in Hungary to finish the Red Academy and is an engineering graduate. He hates Israel and really regrets having defected on account of the counter-revolution. He is afraid that in Israel they will realize that he worked with the Interior Ministry as an architect, and he is constantly suspicious that his telephone is bugged. At present he works as an architectural engineer, and he is said to be talented. To his regret, he doesn't have a diploma. Maybe he did have one, but he is afraid of mentioning his Red Academy diploma. Hence his professional certification is unresolved (for 20 years now).

When I asked him why he doesn't travel home to resolve his diploma-problem, he replied, 'I'm afraid, because I worked for the Ministry of the Interior as an engineer in rather sensitive times.' If it can be believed, then he travelled in China, too, when with the Interior Ministry. This man could be interesting. He has numerous contacts there. There are three workers in his office – technical illustrators and a secretary. His older sister is married to a high-ranking Soviet officer, at least he says so. He has had no contact with his family since the counter-revolution.

Even more frightening to me is the episode when my mother, again during the trip we took together in 1976, describes her meeting with a young man at the Italian embassy in Tel Aviv. Here she steps onto the stage as Mata Hari, deploying her generosity – that angelic generosity of hers so many people mentioned. Poor Mata Hari! Historians have tried in vain to prove that she wasn't even a spy, and her name has become synonymous with that of the femme fatale all the same. Since the young man does not introduce himself, my mother furtively reads his name on a form handed her because of his lack of linguistic fluency, and she paints a not terribly flattering portrait of him; and as a sharp observer she notes, too, that this young man whom she has engaged in conversation is suspicious of her – but she is able to twist even this: *or he is just acting suspiciously.* So obviously he is also a spy – yes, Israeli intelligence, Mum mentions by the by, in a gossipy manner, and so the smoke-and-mirrors game – which all spies worth their salt dream of, which gives such chance meetings their zest – begins. The tortuous wording with which she conveys this suspicion displays exquisite dramatic flair, and surely her handler, on reading it, immediately began drooling:

This character turned suspicious because I sensed that he wanted to interrogate me or worm his way to my trust. I think he was really stupid, but perhaps he just wanted to seem so.

323

She realized that he wanted to interrogate her because she wanted to interrogate him. But let us read the entire report, which is drowning in vitriolic distrust:

> *I met a young man, L. Ö., whose father is a reporter*
> *for Új Kelet, and he pompously announced that*
> *he is visiting Hungary this summer to see his*
> *grandfather and that he easily got permission to do*
> *so for practically nothing. He claims to be a 'director'*
> *somewhere; he looks to be around 20-22 years old.*
> *I met him at the Italian embassy. He claimed he is*
> *first going to the USA, from there back to Italy, and*
> *Hungary is next. The Shin Bet is fond of employing*
> *such types of characters. I read his name from*
> *his Italian visa application: since he didn't speak*
> *English, I played the interpreter. He said he was*
> *sorry to say how bad language teaching is in Israel.*
> *This character turned suspicious because I sensed*
> *that he wanted to quiz me or worm his way to my*
> *trust. I think he was really stupid, but perhaps he*
> *just wanted to seem so. I sensed no other suspicious*
> *circumstances.*

And here is one more noteworthy case, that of the female Israeli border guard:

REPORT

Budapest, 24 March 1977

MRS PÁPAI reports:

She returned this year on 18 March from visiting
relatives in Israel. At the Tel Aviv airport her
documents were checked by border guard J. J.
When J. J. learned that MRS PÁPAI was Hungarian,
she called her aside and inquired at length about
Hungary. Is it true that there is democracy there,
that the churches are open, that Jews are not
persecuted, and so on? She then explained that she
too is of Hungarian descent. She was born there,
and when she was eight, in 1948, her parents
emigrated to Israel. She is married, has a child, and
her husband is the commanding officer at a small
garrison. She knows of just one relative in Hungary,
whom she hasn't heard of in a long while. That
relative was seriously ill and often hospitalized, and
maybe isn't even alive any more.

She would very much like to see Hungary and meet
her relatives, but she is afraid of travelling there. For
one thing, she doesn't know if she would be allowed
into Hungary; and for another, she is afraid of how

the Israeli authorities would react if they learned that
she had been to Hungary. This could cause problems
for her husband as well.

She asked MRS PÁPAI to assist her in getting news of
her relative. Telephone her or write her a letter and
tell her that she'd like to call her, but that she, J. J.,
can't discuss this with her in a letter. She also asked
MRS PÁPAI that if she does visit Hungary, that MRS
PÁPAI should help her in Budapest, since she doesn't
know the customs, and it would be good if someone
were to help her out.

MRS PÁPAI promised to help. And she also agreed to
travel to Miskolc to find her relative.

An anonymous handwritten note in the margin reveals that
in Sub-department III/I the question arose: is this a clever trap
set for Mrs Pápai? Has the Tel Aviv border guard initiated the
conversation with the aim of ensnaring their agent?

*Interesting information that seems perfectly natural – but it is not
certain it is in fact something so innocent. All the more so because
Mrs P's political affiliation is well known in Israel. We must
inquire through the sub-division in Miskolc at the street in Miskolc,
we must find out who this relative is, and whether J. J. has other*

relatives in Hungary aside from this one. But it seems advisable to
suitably prepare MRS PÁPAI and then send her to Miskolc, but by
then we must lay down a well-thought-out idea of how to proceed.

Lay it down, go ahead and lay it down!

And my mother, my always busy mother, who never has time for anything, is ready to drop everything and travel halfway across the country, to Miskolc, to ensnare the border guard. The story, at least in Bruria's dossier, ends there.

What complicated family relationships she has to disentangle in the course of her tip-off-individual research, and while mapping out the weaknesses of the families she visits! There are relatives, friends and friends of friends, confidential information to be gathered during conversations, and she crams everything of use into her reports:

Another family of Hungarian immigrants: W. (. . .)'s
brother, I. L., is a retired lieutenant colonel who
lives in Budapest. Mrs L. has three sisters who live
in Israel. The most interesting is M.'s family: her
husband [W.] is a big businessman in the import–
export of food products, they are extremely rich.
The man had contacts in Hungary in the past, but I
learned from L. that W. can be classified as a crooked
businessman. The family has two sons, both doing
their compulsory military service. The younger one,

J., is in his first year and is serving in intelligence. His mother, M., asked me in confidence to tell Mrs L. not to write her a letter at any cost, and if she'd like to visit Israel, she should not mention W. and family at all as relatives on her visa application. She should include only the names of her other two siblings. Her reasoning was that her son had learned that another person of Hungarian descent, a young woman born in Hungary who speaks several languages perfectly – including Hungarian, which she learned from her parents – and who would have been well suited in every respect for intelligence service, was rejected because she has relatives in Hungary. So J. resolved this problem by denying that he had any relatives in socialist countries. His mother also told me that J. would like to stay in military intelligence as a career. At the moment he is completing the first of his required three years of service. When I was visiting with W., J. happened to come home from work – he lives at home – in his military uniform, and he was not at all happy to find me there.

Why would he have been happy?

As a professional, my mother is not bothered a bit when she senses that others find her suspicious or disagreeable, that they are wary of her.

*The third Hungarian I spoke to on several occasions
but, for lack of time, not in sufficient depth, was S.,
the secretary of the organization of 'those who refuse
military service for reasons of conscience'. (There
are about 10–15 members.) S. was quite wary of me,
and never did tell me whom he stayed with in Kispest
when he visited Hungary (in summer 1975, as far
as I know). He said he didn't stay with relatives, but
rather with a likewise 'peace-loving' person, one who
objects to military service for reasons of conscience,
and whom the Hungarian authorities do not like and
for example do not permit to travel abroad.*

Bruria nonetheless gets a brownie point from me, a tiny
one, when this certain S. asks her advice on resettling in
Hungary, and Bruria wisely talks him out of it:

*He asked my opinion on whether he should resettle
permanently in Hungary. This question is on his mind
primarily because he has two daughters whom he is
raising in a different spirit than in schools there [in
Israel] – e.g. anti-war, completely vegetarian, against
biblical education. Rather than provide him with
yes or no answers, I posed him several questions
from which he could understand that someone who
'objects to military service for reasons of conscience'*

could face problems in Hungary too, in raising his
daughters, and could find himself at odds with our
educational principles as well.

If only I could ask my mother just what it is she meant by *'our educational principles'*! That all-important question, 'Which homeland would you be loyal to?', also arises in the course of her conversations with this tip-off individual, come to think of it, S. reporting that it was a Shin Bet interrogating officer who put it to him – yes, I'd ask my mother this too. The vigilant observer concludes that the officer identified himself by what was *'probably an assumed name'*. Mum is starting to really learn the ropes of spying. This occurred during what was perhaps Mrs Pápai and S.'s third conversation, when S. *'relaxed a bit'*, and she meanwhile seems not to have been bothered by the fact that S. was a leading member of the Israeli League for Human and Civil Rights, whose president at the time, it so happened, was her father, my grandfather. During the conversation S. divides Hungarian communists into two categories, essentially pointing to one of the key pillars that ensured the stability of the Kádár regime:

S.'s relatives live in Budapest, and in his view some
are 'sincere communists' and others are 'insincere
communists'. Since he himself is an anti-Zionist,
he involuntarily fell into an argument with friends

of his relatives when he arrived in Budapest for
three days to arrange his Hungarian citizenship.
He had a surprisingly positive impression of the
Hungarian police, who were 'kind and obliging' in
their encounters with him. When (perhaps during
our third conversation) S. relaxed a bit, he said
that on returning to Israel he was immediately
summoned to the Tel Aviv office of the Shin Bet [the
Interior Ministry], where one M. Z. (probably an
assumed name) subjected him to a long interrogation,
asking why he had requested citizenship of socialist
Hungary, and what if in Budapest he would be
interrogated about Israeli military secrets? Whom
would he be loyal to then, Israel or Hungary? S. said
his reply was unequivocal: he opposes all military
service, and neither in Israel nor elsewhere does he
speak about this, and what's more, he doesn't even
know a thing about military secrets, so neither in
theory nor in practice can he speak about them. S.
had the sense that perhaps this would not be the last
such interrogation, but months had passed since then.

My mother, that good girl and eager-to-please pupil, had
it in her not only to set up such ostensibly rather incon-
sequential meetings but also to comply with her employers'
every demand in an exemplary manner. *Why* she did so, I

may now be able to answer, for since first opening that fatal dossier a year and a half ago I have racked my brain and have kept racking my brain until answers came, but this is not the moment to unveil them to the reader. My mother probably thought that this would never come to light, but I'm certain she would have accepted responsibility had it come to light while she was alive. Odd though it may seem, she, as an unrelenting foe of Zionism, must have seen something positive in all this clandestine activity. The same thing is also said, and I tend to agree, of the brilliant film director Gábor Bódy, whom I knew personally and who for a time was a friend of mine, and who killed himself in 1985, the year my mother also died. Some see connections between the circumstances of his death and his being an informant. If there were private or career-related motives that led this scintillatingly intelligent man to accept this role, surely his leftist convictions also played their part – at least this is how it seems, judging from his reports and some assessments by his handlers. True, on his second meeting with a handler, in the conspiratorial flat, like some sort of lamenting, lamentable Faust, he would have liked to take back his signature on the recruitment paper. But his handler, whom he found very sympathetic, reassured him with the promise that all this would never wind up in unauthorized hands. To Bódy's great surprise, essayist and screenwriter Yvette Bíró was booted out of her position as editor-in-chief of the magazine

Filmkultura a couple of weeks after Bódy had recommended the measure. Gábor had somehow imagined that he could say all sorts of things without any consequences. What a mistake. Ironically enough, he was then tasked with getting closer to Yvette Bíró. He sought to carry out the assignment to the best of his abilities.

In Israel, my mother persuaded her younger sister, my aunt, to visit a former suitor and fellow comrade of hers, Zvi Elpeleg, who, as revealed by the thorough report she prepared, had climbed high up the Israeli military and civilian ladder. Now, both my aunt and my mother, the Avi Shaul girls, were legendary beauties during the British Mandate in Palestine, so the retired colonel could hardly say no when they phoned him, and he immediately invited them to his house for dinner:

Among my meetings, a particularly interesting one perhaps worth cultivating is that with Zvi Elpeleg, who climbed to a high rank up the Israeli military ladder: he served as the military governor of the Triangle during the 1950s, of Gaza after the 1956 Sinai campaign, and of Nablus after the Six-Day War. Long ago his name was Zvi Alphalug [sic], and in the early 1940s we were members of the 'Working Youth' organization. Later he was a leading member, and his task was to discover and disbar those illegal young communists who had infiltrated the Working Youth. (I escaped this because meanwhile I'd travelled in 1942 to Lebanon.)

El-Peleg is presently in the reserves. He is a graduate of Tel Aviv University and is president of the Israel Oriental Society, which is affiliated with the university.

His articles are sometimes published in New Outlook Middle East Monthly *and in the afternoon tabloid* Maariv. *El-Peleg invited me (at my suggestion) to his home. Our conversation circled around the 1956 counter-revolution and the question of why I had not defected then. Why do I call the events a 'counter-revolution'? This question especially interested him. That evening television broadcast a debate between Hillel, Minister of Police, and some professors concerning preparations for elections in the occupied Arab territories, and more than once, Elpeleg called Hillel an idiot and criticized the entire Rabin government. Their policies in the occupied territories are bad, he said. The conversation lasted until late at night, and my host asked for my opinion on Solzhenitsyn. I promised that we'd speak about this at our next meeting. Unfortunately, lack of time*

didn't allow this to happen. Elpeleg is held to be a
wealthy man: he owns sewage treatment plants.

But Elpeleg had been on his guard: he was not impressed
by feminine charms, and, just as in other cases, there is no
sign that the intelligence service took this any further. And
yet Bruria did have a meeting that proved especially useful,
as we can read in a so-called 'data sheet'.

DATA SHEET

on information received by Department 6

26 April 1977

CHANNEL			HANDLER
Mrs Pápai	*SC*	*Unit 4*	*K. Mercz*

name – code name – qualification – name of
unit – organ

TITLE: *'Zev Zaretsky's Anti-Soviet Activity'*

WRITTEN ASSESSMENT, OBSERVATION,
RECOMMENDATION, SUPPLEMENTARY
INTELLIGENCE NEED

Used for providing intelligence to a friendly
organization

I take for granted that my mother would have transubstantiated into Mrs Pápai during this conversation, indeed she couldn't have even begun chatting with this Zaretsky without taking pains to disguise her feelings.

In a brilliant passage from his previously quoted work, Ottó Szélpál – that enthusiastic disciple of the great actor-pedagogue Stanislavski – draws a firm distinction between living (or experiencing) a role *externally and internally*. Let's just say that this was not my mother's forte. At least not always. But according to Szélpál, who was addressing operations officers handling prospective network individuals, living a role is undoubtedly a learnable skill:

a) Developing the Skill of Living a Role
In carrying out his duties, the network individual
follows a pre-determined behavioural line. This line
must be presented by living the role externally and
internally in a manner acceptable to the hostile
environment.

Mrs Pápai met with no little – and well-founded – criticism for her deficiencies in this regard. Yes, she did adhere to the behavioural line, and was in fact as linear as could be, but when it came to Zionism, she just couldn't contain herself. It was as if someone had pressed a button. Szélpál goes on to say:

> Consequently, the network individual's ability to present the behavioural line well or poorly in hostile circles is no trivial matter. Not even the most meticulously defined, well prepared and thoroughly developed behavioural line will be convincing if the network individual does not represent it in a suitably evocative manner, living the role thoroughly both externally and internally.

My mother certainly wasn't lacking in evocativeness, that I can attest to. She was the firmament, and still is, even if she's clouded over.

> Living a role externally appears in externals, meaning behaviour that aligns itself deliberately to the content. These externals include, for example: physical appearance, dress, gestures, demeanour. Living a role externally is integrally related to inner content. For example, a network individual playing the role of someone beset by serious financial troubles must not dress in the latest fashions and must not seem to be in a wonderful mood.

Surely this would not have presented a problem for my mother, who never took much trouble over how she dressed and was often in a bad mood. With the concept of 'the façade reflecting human traits' Szélpál really is at the top of his literary game in describing, with stunning precision, how my mother's handlers – Lieutenant Colonel Beider, Lieutenant Dóra and perhaps Captain Mercz – imagined her.

Living a role internally refers to the skill whereby the network individual can identify with the façade (reflecting, for example, a worldview, a political or moral orientation, or human traits) defined as within his or her behavioural line, and evocatively convey emotions, thoughts and so on in keeping with this façade.

Szélpál goes on to astutely point out that the network individual 'meets with various persons in various situations'. How nicely put! A whole novel could be written about this! And he sees the consequences right away:

In the course of his work, the network individual meets with various persons in various situations, and so the behavioural line he represents cannot be the same in every situation. It is precisely cultivation of the skill of living a role that guarantees for a network

individual that he can adjust with relative ease and
speed to roles that require different behaviour.

And let us not forget what peerless acting-teachers the
operations officers are:

> The skill of living a role is continually developed
> and refined through both detailed discussions and
> occasional practice sessions of the represented
> behaviour under the direction of the operations
> officer, as well as in the course of the work itself.

Of all the things she heard, those voiced by Zaretsky didn't
sit well with my mother, that's for certain, and she might well
have fallen into a heated, interminable argument with him then
and there. But, presumably, as a good student of sorts, Bruria
knew full well – as Mihály Rapcsák writes in his master-
piece, *Psychological Aspects of the 'Dark' Methods in the System of
Network Building and Intelligence Gathering* – the importance of:

- Selecting a tone suitable to the conversation. For
  this it is imperative to accommodate to the partner
  who is presumably giving the information.
- Practising in advance the forms of courtesy and
  the habits of the subject to be studied, and their
  practical application.

- Acquiring the propensity to listen patiently and actively by displaying a suitable degree of interest.
- Initiating contacts and evoking trust and sympathy with ease.

My mother possessed ease, and she could evoke trust and sympathy in just about anyone. But this in itself is not enough, since one must recognize the other's 'human frailties'; for 'the propensity to pass along secrets' lurks in certain people (or in us all?), and, according to Szélpál, such people need only be suitably *provoked*:

Most important is <u>recognizing and utilizing the chosen individual's human frailties</u>. These may include, for example, the propensity to pass along secrets, which manifests itself especially in those who can be 'provoked' in line with the goal. By exploiting such persons' vanity or over-emphasizing their human dignity, the intelligence officer can get more or less the desired answer. We may also include the pretensions displayed by some when conversing with others in their field whom they deem less capable than themselves.

It is worth also mentioning those human frailties which manifest themselves in individuals given to

talking more than necessary, especially when in an
emotionally charged condition or under the influence
of alcohol. In such cases the intelligence officer
or the secret colleague, or even another member
of the network, may incite the target individual
with well-chosen 'provocative' comments, and that
individual, inadvertently throwing caution to the
wind, provides the desired information.

Much shrewder is the strategy proposed by Rapcsák, the
'art of the opening', which goes beyond the realm of human
frailties:

Initiating a conversation is, for example, often called
the 'art of the opening', since it indisputably embodies
certain elements of art. The ability to break the ice
determines the conversation's entire trajectory and,
later, the result of the dark information-gathering.

The introduction itself plays a positive role in the
'art of the opening' (especially on the occasion
of the first meeting), as does highlighting some
detail of the 'life story' (cover story), shared or
similar experiences, or shared interests. This must
be determined in advance, and then, turning the
conversation in that direction, expressing heightened

interest in the conversation partner's personal life (e.g. circumstances of house/flat residence, books, children, pictures, animals, stamps, fishing, sports, diplomats).

But for Rapcsák, ever the perfectionist, a devotee of the 'dark' method, this isn't enough (italics added by the present author):

The true conversation can be begun only after the proper mood is established. A prominent role is played here by the other's self interest, which is to say, his *feeling that the prospective conversation will be to his (intellectual or financial) advantage.* But other key considerations can also come into play, such as *an occasion for 'telling all', curiosity, or the feeling that rejecting participation would be an indiscretion, an act violating good manners.*

The ideal situation is, however, when the conversation ensues in submission to the intelligence officer's unequivocally sympathetic behaviour.

It may happen that the intelligence officer can bear upon his partner precisely by *making himself out to be less informed in the given topic.* This is especially

342

effective when the intelligence officer has come
to understand that his conversation partner will
probably be given to speak with complete sincerity to
the intelligence officer.

It is appropriate that the intelligence officer should
endeavour through his behaviour to maintain a
friendly, somewhat familiar, back-slapping tone, and
that through his words and gestures should convince
his partner that his person and what he has to say
is at the centre of interest. *If the partner does not
perceive sincere interest in the questions posed to
him, then this behaviour will not motivate him to a
broader providing of information, and indeed might
even lead him to wonder why he is being asked.*

To build up the trust, we too must say something –
something of interest to the partner, hence it is
necessary to know his interests. If possible this
endeavour should not unfold on a give-and-take
basis. When, notwithstanding the multi-faceted
preparations, we find ourselves confronting a question
we must react to but don't yet know how, we can
prepare ourselves for this situation, too, and give
evasive answers: 'I haven't yet thought about this',
'your opinion in the matter is more important than

mine', or perhaps, 'at the end of the conversation we'll return to this', which might even stoke the partner's curiosity and maintain it throughout.

The passionate, unending discussion – in other words, the ceaseless provocation of one person by another – was very much a speciality of our family, a kind of dessert after Sunday lunch. Imagine having lunch with the Kafkas, but in contrast to the Kafka family, where the arguments were generally about the exact day and hour when the family had done this or that, or about who was present and who wasn't, in our home murderous quarrels invariably broke out over the Arabs and the Israelis, the political goals of the Americans and the Soviets, and the whole situation in the Middle East, and they lasted until veins were ready to burst, faces turned purple, throats hoarse. The point was that the two parties should if possible *not* agree on a single thing, and this disagreement, this irreconcilable difference had a value all of its own: perhaps it evoked the drama of the class struggle, modelling itself on the implacable antagonism between the working classes and the bourgeoisie. I can't even guess how my mother persuaded Zaretsky to expound on his views in her presence. Did she appeal to his vanity? Provoke him in some way? Or did it occur in a larger group of people, with Bruria merely an observer, lurking unnoticed, gathering all her strength in order not to respond?

On 9 March 1977, I met with Zev Zaretsky, an
employee of Russian origin of the Israeli Weizmann
Institute, who directs the institute's spectrometry
laboratory. Zaretsky, who is forty-nine years old, left
the Soviet Union in 1971. In Moscow he worked in the
chemistry department of the Academy of Sciences. He
boasted about the important task he was entrusted
with there: maintaining close relations with Zionist
activists of the organization in the Soviet Union.

He vehemently attacked the film *Soul Hunters*, which
had been screened in Moscow. This film was about those
young people who – in the words of the film – 'accepted
money from foreign Zionist organizations'. According to
Zaretsky, it was the first step in Soviet anti-Semitism,
portraying as enemies those fighting for human rights.

Zaretsky said he deplored the protest gestures taken
by the USA (Bukovsky's reception at the White House,
the letter to Sakharov) because they forced the Soviet
authorities to take drastic measures. From Moscow's
perspective it cannot keep making concessions,
because it is faced with newer and newer demands.
If, after this, harder measures follow, it will cut
back even more on emigration, which has dwindled
substantially already.

345

Zaretsky said he and his associates were endeavouring to develop suitable lines of communication towards Zionist activists living in the Soviet Union. One very important channel is regular phone communication. Although the KGB is doing all it can to eliminate telephone conversations, the activists can barely go without them, as it is important for them to feel supported and encouraged. This is now especially necessary because since 1972 Russian-language broadcasts directed at the Soviet Union have been interrupted by counter-intelligence, meaning that even where they can be picked up, only in southern regions, they are hard to receive.

He was sorry to conclude that motivation to emigrate had subsided in the Soviet Union. They are labouring to develop other methods which they anticipate will yield a newer wave of emigration, and for which they need to prepare on time.

According to Zaretsky, it is a big mistake that Jews living in the Soviet Union know too much about the difficulties awaiting them in Israel, which among other things explains why half the emigrants do not wish to settle in Israel.

Now that gets an A+.

Mrs Pápai's employers are so pleased with her that a short time later they entrust her with a task beyond her abilities. They are rather critical of the result:

In the course of her travels MRS PÁPAI succeeded in acquiring valuable documents about the 30th World Zionist Congress, and yet her work as a gatherer of political information leaves much to be desired.

In her reports she answers our questions with generalities, in a journalistic, propagandistic style that does not satisfy the minimal demands of information gathering.

Her statements and conclusions strongly suggest that her own political orientation and commitment does not allow her to remain objective.

Noteworthy, however, is the high level of MRS PÁPAI's Israeli contacts, which can represent fundamental elements of MRS PÁPAI's future operative assignments.

Though Mrs Pápai attempted several times to carry out her assignment, admittedly in a burlesque manner, her labours were in vain: not only could she not get in to the closely guarded 29th and 30th World Zionist Congresses in Jerusalem, she didn't get close to so much as a single delegate. Though I suspect she was secretly happy about this, she did twice, heroically, get an acquaintance to take her there – to whom, in return for the petrol and the favour, she later presented an edition of the works of the great Hungarian naïve painter Tivadar Csontváry Kosztka, a gift she naturally requested the Hungarian secret services buy for her. In the end the scraps of information she paid her employers came from political brochures and the like – she was also tasked with collecting the paraphernalia of the Israeli postal service, including stamps, envelopes and stationery, and did so with ease – but her failure was obvious, even if her handlers didn't say so right away. It turned out that she was unfit for more complex and delicate matters. She simply could not play a role.

The biggest problem: Zionism.

We grouped her tasks in detail under the following categories:

- The most important decisions of the 29th World Zionist Congress brought against the Soviet Union and the other socialist countries in the interest of the Jews residing there.
- The nature and essence of specific anti-Soviet

measures whose implementation was the
responsibility of the Congress.

- What doctrine are they endeavouring to develop to
  enhance the effectiveness of the Zionist ideology?
- What measures and ideas do they intend to
  implement to draw more Jewish youth into the
  Zionist movement.
- Measures and ideas expected to be implemented to
  bolster emigration and to activate Jews living in
  socialist countries.
- Aspects of the Palestinian problem as raised from
  the side of individual delegates.
- The nature of possible conflicts between the World
  Zionist Congress and the World Jewish Congress, as
  well as Israeli and American and other delegations.
- The opinions of various sectors of society and
  various individuals on the special Israeli-Egyptian
  talks on Middle East peace.
- We may be interested in her keeping track of
  measures related to her entry into Israel in the
  course of border and customs inspections, and
  generally during her stay. What changes occur?
  Are they stricter or more favourable?
- Domestic travel restrictions, and the security
  measures introduced to protect the Congress.
- In addition to the above, we request documents

and materials that can provide an understanding of Israel's domestic economic and political circumstances, especially in view of the aftermath of LIKUD's rise to power.

<u>Financial matters:</u>

On the basis of the approved Travel Plan, in return for a receipt, I have given 8,000 forints and 500 US dollars to cover travel and defray other costs. To legalize the latter sum I have also provided her with a foreign currency export permit.

Mrs Pápai knew she was attempting the impossible, and yet she went. As for myself, I can't – and I don't want to – undertake to analyse twentieth-century Middle East developments, Palestinian-Jewish strife and/or the Israeli-Arab wars, and I don't wish to have my say about world politics. No, here and now I wish only to understand my mother. It is impossible that she would not have sensed – as is perfectly evident from certain pronouncements she issued much later (too late!) – that no matter how strong her political convictions, her faith, no matter what great injustice she saw in her homeland (e.g. expelled Palestinians, bulldozed Palestinian villages and Palestinians languishing in refugee camps), and no matter how irresolvable the situation seemed to her, she was engaged in an endeavour to dig up the faults and sins of the Israelis, sometimes employing the contorted, primitive rhetoric of the lead articles in *Pravda*. In this Mrs Pápai had something in common with numerous prominent leftists of Jewish ancestry, the most well known being perhaps Noam Chomsky, but then there's the director Ken Loach and the actress Vanessa Redgrave. My mother took a blind nationalism – this is how she saw Zionism – and confronted it with another sort of blindness, the ideology of the Soviet empire.

It was with the Arab world that Jean Genet confronted the colonizing French and a French culture he hatefully idolized, and when, at the invitation of Yasser Arafat, he spent some time among Palestinian fighters, for him it was primarily an erotic adventure (and he wrote about it as such). Later still, when he spent two hours in the Sabra and Shatila refugee camps in Lebanon and described the sight of massacred Palestinians, even then it was above all the tragic event that concerned him, the description of death, and not necessarily the ideologies facing off against each other, even though he took the side of the vulnerable, not of those in power. At one time Genet even supported the Black Panthers. But all this was, for him, part of his individual mythology, not a thinking rooted in subjugation, subordinate to an authoritarian regime. It just isn't possible that Bruria never sensed that she was constantly and increasingly crossing borders, not just those of nations but also those of ethical norms. True, she could perhaps rationalize their violation by telling herself that the end justifies the means. Her whole life she'd been surmounting barriers, after all, sometimes radically and bravely, but in the end in a morally indefensible way, even if she did perhaps occasionally draw parallels between her courage as a youth partaking in illegal activities, and the help she provided to Department III/I that was rewarded with money. Her border crossings went on and on, their ripple effect affecting the everyday lives of others; not only of unknown strangers but also of friends and relatives, not always directly perhaps, but they undoubtedly buttressed a corrupt and petty bureaucratic dictatorship that served the interests of the Soviet empire and deprived its citizens of their freedom. Certain slips of hers make clear that she sensed that what she supported, the regime here at home, behind the Iron Curtain, was as inane as it was incorrigible. Why, after all, would Jews feel themselves to be *strangers in their own homelands*?

The realization of every such anti-communist, anti-socialist plan could be neutralized if the non-Zionist Jews in the various socialist countries did not feel themselves to be strangers in their own homelands. The Zionists know this feeling of strangeness well and use it to their advantage.

They exploit those cracks that can be found in the
bureaucratic apparatus of the socialist camp. And
so it's not merely a matter of strengthening internal
security and all that is connected with that, but
serious consideration should also be paid to every
step that might nourish international Zionism, so it
might exploit the remaining rigid regulations found
in the socialist camp. Hungary's policies could be
exemplary in this area, though there are still faults
here too. It is much better if the Israeli papers accuse
intellectuals of Jewish descent in socialist countries
of anti-Semitism (for example, on 27 January 1983,
Maariv accused Mihály Sükösd and András Mezei
of being anti-Semitic and also holding 'hair-raising'
opinions) than if they criticize the Hungarian
government or its bureaucratic apparatus.

Then she sends a message, without commentary, to the
eavesdroppers:

This man is a teacher of astrophysics at Tel Aviv
University and just spent a year on sabbatical in the
US. Before that he attended an academic conference in
Budapest. On returning to Israel he recounted having
had pleasant experiences in Budapest, the only thing
he disliked being the fact that in the hotel the radio

*was constantly on, as if on a central system, and
whenever he turned it off, a staff member showed
up to ask what the problem was with the radio. He
thinks there is some connection between this and the
bugging of conversations. He thinks people talking
in hotel rooms are always bugged, as are telephone
conversations.*

And finally the crown jewels, a little snippet on the problem of Judaism that bears witness to my mother's knowledge of the Talmud. This eternal mental back and forth is by no means unfamiliar to the person filing these reports. No, I will now quote her words as close as possible to the form in which they appeared in her hand in her work dossier, and I can't stifle my sense that her turn of phrase *'there probably is such a feeling'* – which is to say, that certain people really do feel themselves to be Jewish, wherever they may live – harbours a touch of irony:

*Let no one delude themselves into thinking that
anti-Israel sentiments have taken root in Jews
living in the diaspora on account of the aggression
committed by Israel. Historical experiences prove
that Jews, if they feel themselves to be Jewish
(for there probably is such a feeling, true or false,
but there is), will find a means to vindicate Israeli*

THE ACTS OF MY MOTHER

*policies. Not even if they do voice criticism or are
repulsed by certain aggressive acts do they turn
away from Israel, from Zionism. Their support, which
manifests itself in sympathy and financial support,
will continue. Many in Israel are concerned that Jews
living in the diaspora will turn away from Israel.
Hence they are trying at breakneck speed to organize
the brainwashing of the diaspora Jewry with better
and better delegates. They organize debating societies
small and large (not only in Jewish circles) in which
the justification of [Israel's] acts unfolds. I brought
material about one of these. True, a depressing mood
prevails in Israel. The right exploits this well for
its continuing ends. There is polarization towards
positive, fair solutions, but for the time being the
aggressive force prevails.*

The pathologist's report is quite sophisticated. Bruria often
fell to arguing with her handlers, and even if she did then
grovel, she would soon start arguing again. She served the
system with her work, whether interpreting or nursing, and
she naturally received remuneration, which she accepted as
what was rightfully due to her. Even so, she had to fight her
handlers every centimetre, every millimetre of the way – yes,
she had to fight the whole system and she didn't enjoy exceptional privileges. Though, truth be told, in the late 1960s, in

the middle of the decades-long Kádár regime, she and my father both received the For the Socialist Homeland Order of Merit, a sort of successor to the Order of Vitez. They received this for their supposed partisan past, and it did indeed come with benefits – and even if they weren't that great, there were benefits nonetheless, and every penny or, rather, fillér, counted.

And so, at the cost of a lot of scurrying about, or, as she liked to say, 'crawling on my bloodied belly', she even managed to procure a flat for the continually expanding Forgács family in a big tower block on Kerék Street, at the other end of town. And in moved the smaller half of the family, because, until then, at our previous address, we'd been living on top of each other, a real clutter, as if in a hovel. My father's attempts as the family provider to buy a larger flat had met repeatedly with failure: occasional freelance translations and articles supplemented his regular pay as a news editor and shift manager at state radio, but they were barely enough to plug the larger holes in our financial affairs. No, my parents were incapable of managing money. They just didn't understand its value, treating it as children might, which explains the refrain 'I'm broke', heard so often at the start of the month.

The main point: Bruria, to ensure the regular visits to far away relatives that she could not do without, procured (by way of compensation for her work) not only a passport for herself but also for the rest of the family – that is, for me, my big brother, and my little sister. That's not to mention inexpensive entry visas for her Israeli friends, relatives and comrades when there happened to be no diplomatic relations between Hungary and Israel, and for quite a while there weren't, and that wasn't Israel's fault. Last but not least, as a heroic mother, as a sort of one-woman human shield, Bruria spread her wings over her brood, who made no effort to act as if they were unfalteringly loyal to the regime, who hung out with all sorts of dubious people, who were part of artistic movements modelled on those in the West, and who regularly popped up in various Interior Ministry reports.

As in ancient Greek theatre, among the tragedy there is always a satyr play, and the case of György Petri and my bugged flat was not the only one. Indeed, Bruria was used cynically and sordidly, cynically and sordidly – yes, cynically and sordidly – by the operations officers of Department III/I, who, it seems, imagined themselves to be apocalyptic horsemen made of Herend porcelain who would bring peace to the world and could thus legitimately do anything they wanted. But I cannot understand why they felt themselves authorized to trick her, screw her over, and lie to her face when my mother was helping them out of inner conviction. The comical dilettantism of the following episode does not excuse the sordidness of their intentions – no, ineptitude does not excuse evil. My mother was instrumental, too, no doubt about that: her conviction that they could do anything they wanted was instrumental, yes, her misguided subservience was instrumental, too, her feeling that these people were fighting the 'good fight', though there is much to suggest that, finally, she didn't believe this unreservedly. Only she didn't yet have the words to express it.

Nonetheless, it is clear that the information in the document I'm about to quote from did indeed originate with her, and that the operations officers blessed with the wisdom of the Buddha, the officers who'd cooked up the plan in their witches' kitchen, were bent on playing with my mother as if this were a game of billiards, setting the ball rolling with their poorly crafted cues, watching it bounce off the cushions, experimenting a little with the human psyche, unconcerned that they were invading other people's family lives, that they were assigning a role to a mother that a mother must not be allowed to play. It is nonetheless irresistibly comical; and it is comical even if this method, in other circumstances, might well have led to tragedy. Evil in miniature, worth crying and laughing about.

MINISTRY OF THE INTERIOR   TOP SECRET!
Sub-department III/III-4-a
Szakadáti e. Sz J., B.

To Comrade ISTVÁN BERÉNYI, police colonel
Director, Ministry of the Interior Department III/I-II

<u>Budapest</u>

In his capacity as an author of texts of hostile content distributed in Hungary, and as the chief organizer of their distribution, we have kept H. Cs., a former director with Hungarian Radio, under surveillance.

In the course of the surveillance we have determined that suspicions have been strengthening in the samizdat-producing group that Cs. is the 'Interior Ministry's stool pigeon'.

An argument he had with [name redacted], a university student, heightened these suspicions. Citing his own experiences, [name redacted] recounted police excesses, which Cs. firmly cast doubt on.

In the wake of this incident [name redacted] was left with practically no doubt concerning her suspicions, as she told her mother too.

On the basis of our oral understanding, Comrade Miklós Beider, police lieutenant – employee of Department III/I-11 of the Interior Ministry – has the opportunity to play back information to the mother, Mrs Marcell Forgács.

In the interest of discrediting H. Cs., to reinforce the suspicions over him, we ask Comrade Beider to notify Mrs Marcell Forgács of the following – clarifying that his information comes from a confidential source:

- It is our understanding that [name redacted] is apt to discredit the police, and at the same time is spreading false rumours about H. Cs.
- Mrs Forgács should seek to persuade [name redacted] to change her behaviour, for she has already raised the attention of the Interior Ministry through other, but similarly destructive activities.

From Comrade Beider's above notification we expect that in this manner more information will filter into the group about Cs.'s 'contacts with the Interior Ministry, his protectors', that his isolation will intensify and that more people may slacken their remaining ties with him. Moreover, it can be expected that [name redacted]'s activity will diminish.

Budapest, 12 December 1978

Dr József Horváth,
Police Colonel
Team Deputy Director

Miklós Esvégh,
Police Captain
Sub-department Head

How was she still capable of co-operating with her 'comrades', one handler after another, allowing them to enter her most intimate domain, parading her embroideries, sharing her fears with them?

Of course they are taught how to achieve this, too:

It may be stated that it is generally the initial stage
of the working relationship that is most amenable
to <u>the development and nurturing of honest, human
ties between the operations officer and the network
individual.</u>

It is advisable to steer this stage of the conversation
in such a way that the network individual may
raise his or her personal problems, including any
professional, family or other difficulties, and find the
opportunity to share with the operations officer all
his or her sorrows and joys.

But things don't always go so smoothly, and, like an eagle-eyed psychologist, the operations officer – Lieutenant Dóra in the following passage – perceives this and records it in his report:

MRS PÁPAI requests our assistance in inquiring, on
behalf of her daughter who is studying in Moscow,

361

how much Waldmann PUVA 180 and PUVA 1200
phototherapy lamps used in dermatology cost in
Vienna.

We agreed to arrange the time of our next meeting by
phone at the beginning of March 1983. We concluded
this meeting, which cost 75 forints, at 12:35.

Assessment:
Mrs Pápai looked very tired at today's meeting,
and yet she was ardent in her oral observations
concerning her written report.

It seems she will be willing to undertake active tip-off
research work in her environment.

She was very awkward in presenting her request for
assistance concerning the therapeutic devices.

Mum presented her request awkwardly, and with that
she gave herself away. Not as a jaunty, confident agent but
rather as an uncertain, anxious mother. Well, we'll take care
of this too. As Ottó Szélpál says in his textbook of the ideal
operation officer's 'honesty' (an oxymoron if there ever was
one):

362

The initiation of such a conversation is not a customary courtesy on the part of the operations officer, but a key aspect, a fundamental element of forging a deeper, sincere human bond. The operations officer's expression of sincere interest in the network individual's problems, expression of empathy, and far-reaching helpfulness invariably yields a positive result. Such a relationship forms the basis of mutual trust and respect. Steering the conversation in this direction is expedient also in the interest of creating the tension-free atmosphere requisite to the taking of reports.

Notwithstanding the above, though, to feel trust towards these gentlemen, these strangers, required not only the chaotic circumstances and emotional disorder of home but also something else: the primitive ideology she'd absorbed since her childhood, and which still resonated in her profoundly. It isn't by chance that Blanche Dubois says to the doctor in *A Streetcar Named Desire*, 'Whoever you are, I have always depended on the kindness of strangers.' It required her oversimplistic explanation for social injustices, her sense of solidarity with those grey Interior Ministry figures, those bureaucrat-warriors of Department III/III she met in offices and sundry meeting places, those characters who, one way or another, were in her eyes knights on some sort of holy crusade. What about Thomas Mann, Goethe, Oscar Wilde and Joseph Conrad? What of Bach, Beethoven, Brahms, Schubert and Tchaikovsky? All of them proved too little, too feeble a counterbalance to that thinking which simplified the world so dangerously, which an irredeemable and yet beautiful human being equipped to help others in this world had a burning need for.

Even if it is alluring to so many, this thinking – which equates the Holocaust, which will disgrace the world for ever, with the tragic injustice that was the fate of Palestinians – surely doesn't hold up logically, it doesn't stand the test; the mirror distorts. But for Bruria, it had by then crystallized into an obsession. She'd locked herself away in ideology just as she could lock herself away in music, even as she continued a family tradition of helping a great many people – she adopted some girls whom she almost loved even more than her own children, with utter selflessness. Yes, even when her own kids didn't have enough, she gave unquestioningly to others all the time, and she didn't notice that sometimes she deprived her own of the attention they needed; for even this sort of self-sacrifice – this nurse and midwife who'd graduated summa cum laude from the American University of Beirut often considered taking off to Africa – helped to perpetuate the disarray her handlers saw as fundamental to her character, a disarray that regularly intensified to the point at which it became intolerable. Not that this bothered them, far from it: they exploited it, deceiving her shamelessly again and again, using her like a tool, a piece of furniture, a mindless *thing*. And yet there was a method to her untidiness, a hidden order to the personal chaos, which she herself needed: she put away every last piece of paper and silk, every official document and postcard – often she didn't even know where, but she threw nothing away, and I'm like this, too, by the way. So then, she really needed this constant or, rather, constantly renewing chaos to avoid coming face to face with her own fundamental problem – namely, that she was nowhere. Nowhere. The word for it in Hungarian echoes the word for hell in Hebrew. *Sehol* and *Sheol*. She was nowhere, she was in hell.

* * *

In 1688 the Swiss physician Johannes Hofer coined the term 'nostalgia', so the story goes – from the Greek nostos ('homecoming') and algos ('pain'), words that occur in the Iliad – when a mysterious disease swept the ranks of Swiss soldiers, mostly mercenaries, who were serving not even so far from home. Their symptoms included neurosis, despair, fits of sobbing, anorexia and suicide attempts. 'Nostalgia' went on to enjoy a brilliant career, and it shouldn't be mistaken for homesickness. Hofer noticed the symptoms even in a young man who had moved from Bern to Basel – just forty kilometres from his hometown. In his dissertation

Hofer characterizes it as 'a cerebral disease of essentially demonic cause' which was produced by 'the quite continuous vibration of animal spirits through those fibres of the middle brain in which impressed traces of ideas of the Fatherland still cling'. In 1732 a compatriot of Hofer's, the scholar Johann Jakob Scheuchzer, wrote that nostalgia was due to a 'sharp differentiation in atmospheric pressure causing excessive body pressurization, which in turn drove blood from the heart to the brain, thereby producing the observed affliction of sentiment'. Back then it was widely accepted that nostalgia was a uniquely Swiss disease, for trusted and well-trained Swiss soldiers served as mercenaries in numerous armies throughout Europe, and certain military physicians speculated that the cause of the disease lay in the serious damage done to the eardrums and brain cells by the constant clanging of cowbells in the Alps. It is also said that in the early nineteenth century, a Russian general happened upon a surprisingly successful treatment for the nostalgia sweeping the ranks of his troops – burying alive those complaining of it.

In Bruria's case, the only treatment would have been for her to move back home, but that was impossible, and so her feelings of nostalgia grew ever stronger every time she returned from Israel to Hungary. But perhaps not even that would have solved matters, her move home, for the obscure object of her desire was a long-lost country, an underwater world called Palestine in which the two peoples had lived side by side – true, they were under the control of a foreign power. The symptoms would abate for a little while only to possess her all the more powerfully. This must have intensified the hayfever that tormented Bruria from spring to autumn to the point at which she gave herself over to suffering, hoping perhaps it would take the edge off the nostalgia that threatened to drive her mad.

At a certain moment in her life, without her having noticed it, she'd been imprisoned in a country she didn't want to live in, though for a while she believed she would want to; a country whose smells were foreign, whose colours were foreign, whose language was foreign; a political system that, she was told, was the world's best, and turned out to be one of its worst. But she made the best of it, acting for a good many years as if this really was what she wanted, living in a country in which she was for ever a foreigner; for if she spoke English or Hebrew on the tram, she was reported to the authorities. This first happened in the Fifties by way of a warning sign, and counting such signs was in vain, because they didn't subside, no, they only multiplied, and how. But there was no turning back.

In 1983 I gave her a postcard I'd purchased in Dahlem, a district in West Berlin, at the Gemäldegalerie, a museum that was home to the city's pre-eminent art collection before German reunification. The famous painting on the card, *Two Monkeys*, was by the Flemish painter Pieter Bruegel the Elder, the Bruegel without an 'h'. In the foreground are two monkeys, sitting in a large, arched window that opens to a view of the port of Antwerp in the background. Both of the monkeys are chained to the same iron ring, one of them gazing at the viewer, the other, face turned away, apparently sulking. Broken peanut shells or walnut shells are scattered on the windowsill beside them. When I handed Bruria that card, she just stared at it as if hypnotized, as if the painter in 1562 had summed up the whole of her life. No less than twice she then embroidered those monkeys, and without ever having seen the actual painting; remarkably enough, in doing so she enlarged the image on the postcard to precisely the dimensions of the original. By then the sky was Bruria's limit when it came to embroidering, and, at the time, she told every visitor who asked her what she was working on that those two monkeys were her and my father.

The two of them were the inhabitants of nowhere – neither Hungarians nor Jews, nor foreigners, nor comrades, nor compatriots. Among comrades they were Jews, among Jews they were communists, among communists they were Hungarians, among Hungarians they were foreigners. Patriots of nowhere land. They were the inhabitants of *Sheol* – the place of darkness to which the dead go; or, rather, of their own personal hell. It is not obligatory, of course, for a wandering Jew to be recruited as an agent of the state; no, it's quite enough of a burden that he or she must wander until the Day of Judgement.

And then came – the icing on the cake – the 'Rapcsány'

case. Bruria and her handler consistently misspell the name of the writer in question – László Rapcsányi – which leads me to conclude that his book never found its way into the hands of Lieutenant Dóra, who didn't even know what he was talking about – no, he was focused solely on ensuring that my mother's letter was never made public. Rapcsányi's book, *Jerusalem*, was, for my mother, the straw that broke the camel's back. And yet what is also clear from the lieutenant's report of 13 April 1984 is how the give-and-take works: they don't support my mother's desire to have her letter be made public, but her Israeli nephew in Canada can get a Hungarian visa, no problem.

REPORT

<u>Budapest, 13 April 1984</u>

I report that at 3 pm on 9 April 1984 I had a meeting in the Ferenc Rózsa Nursing Home with the secret colleague code-named MRS PÁPAI.

At the meeting we set out to discuss the following topics:

• László Rapcsány: his book *Jerusalem*
• The matter of Gregor Zwi Havkin

MRS PÁPAI expressed her deep indignation that Rapcsány's book, whose every page exudes Zionism, was allowed to be published in the Hungarian People's Republic. MRS PÁPAI handed over the draft letter attached, which she wishes to send to Comrade Berecz. (Attachment no. 1)

In the discussion that unfolded concerning the letter and the need to write it I sought to persuade MRS PÁPAI that while I understand her indignation, I would regard it as neither expedient nor useful if she were to send the letter in this form anywhere at all, because doing so could hit back on her own person and also on our operative co-operation.

MRS PÁPAI said she understood the reasons for my concern and said she would abandon the idea of signing the letter herself. But she would like a book review to appear in some form that would set right the value and faults of the 'work'.

We agreed that we will examine what opportunity we see for an appropriate critique of the book.

MRS PÁPAI asked that we make it possible for her relative Gregor Zwi Havkin to visit Hungary. Havkin is an Israeli citizen who has lived for several years in the United States and works in research on animal psychology, and she submitted Havkin's data. (Attachment no. 2)

At the end of the meeting we discussed MRS PÁPAI's children.[1]

Assessment:

I recommend that we contact Department III/III-1 of the Interior Ministry in the matter of the Rapcsány book.

And the handler attaches the ominous letter about the Rapcsányi book, which perfectly sums up that schizophrenic situation, that labyrinth without an exit, in which Mr Pápai and Mrs Pápai, my father and my mother, existed and floundered here and in the big wide world.

Pápai's three dossiers went missing, true enough, but his reports can be found lying low in various other dossiers, such as the media review from 1972 that popped up a couple of days ago, which is obviously one of his last reports. It concerns a monthly magazine published in Italy, *Ha-tikwa* (from *hatikvah*, the transliterated form of the Hebrew word for 'hope', 'Hatikvah' also being the name of the Israeli national anthem). In this report Pápai offers a scintillating analysis that reveals

---

[1] Not that I'm thrilled about this, but nothing can be done about it.

the publication's duplicity: the magazine pretends it isn't Zionist, and yet it is just that. Pápai sees through the ruse. His merciless iron logic (which reads more like a parody – *sorry, Dad, but I had to say it*) rests on a single, imperishable pillar: his own immutable loyalty to the prevailing position of the great Soviet Union. In vain is this seemingly high-minded magazine open to other ideas, for as Papa's, er, Pápai's summary of its contents makes clear, it is nothing but cunning trickery – vile, veiled propaganda. Only one truth is possible. The report is a veritable X-ray image of that labyrinth in which both Mr Pápai and Mrs Pápai had lost their way, in their early youth, and from which, alas, they never would find their way out:

REPORT

Budapest, 26 January 1972

Ha-tikwa is the magazine of the Italian Jewish Youth Federation. Its November edition covers the Federation's 24th congress.

From the resolutions taken it is clear that while the Federation emphasizes its 'independence' from Zionist organizations, it serves Zionist policies and Israel directly and indirectly.

Knowing as it does the leftist orientation of Italian youth, it promulgates a decidedly 'leftist' programme [...] Cunningly it claims to seek that the rights of Palestinian Arabs are ensured and says military installations need not be established in the occupied territories, and yet it does not explain how Palestinians can enforce their rights and it places emphasis on guaranteeing the rights of Israelis.

It undertakes a pointed attack at Syria, Iraq and the Soviet Union for so-called 'anti-Semitism'. And while repeatedly insisting that it is not Zionist, it gives publicity to Israel in myriad ways, runs paid ads for Israeli firms, and organizes Hebrew language courses and seminars on Israel, as well as study trips to Israel.

Under the title 'Open Debate' it communicates the stance of well-known Zionists, interviewing [...] one of the leaders of the World Congress of Jewish Youth, who [...] calls for co-operation between Zionists and non-Zionists. (Of course he is quick to clarify that non-Zionists are not anti-Zionists.)

SC CN PÁPAI, OH

Note:

We will study the magazine *Ha-tikwa* in the framework of the mapping of Zionist organizations in Italy.

János Szakadáti, Police Major

To the lieutenant, the official line was merely a line, which, if drawn elsewhere, would then be, well, elsewhere. To my mother, that 'line' was a matter of life and death, an electrified barbed-wire fence. It would be good to leave the next letter out of the book, but, alas, I can't: even as Bruria, using needles and multi-coloured threads, devotes her nights to recreating Bruegel's painting with astonishing sensitivity, she doesn't notice that the logic of Rapcsányi's *Jerusalem* – which she sees, rightly, I think, as a one-sided and superficial piece of propaganda – is the same as that of her letter. A sentence she finally crossed out, which compared Golda Meir to Rudolf Hess, is precisely the absurd consummation of this mirror logic. And there is another rather interesting sentence – the style and grammar of which suggest that it is the amalgamation of phrases from propaganda publications and newspaper articles read over the decades, and thus reveals the letter-writer's own inner chaos, too:

To skim over that fact does not clarify reality but only stirs helter-skelter in people's minds.

And yet the letter-writer has a point – Rapcsányi's book is indeed one-sided. But the letter is just as one-sided. Yes, the false mirror logic works in reverse, too, because it could be used to argue that the Arabs are all Nazis. When the letter-writer's father, my deeply religious grandfather, arrived in Jerusalem in 1922, he was surprised to find that the country was not empty, as he'd been told – Arabs lived there.

Moreover, those Arabs – Bedouins, that is – lived like biblical Jews, and because of that, following an Arabic custom, he took on the name 'Father of Saul' after his firstborn son, which is how he became Avi Shaul. And the great Soviet Union had barely got off the ground back then, not to mention the Nazis! And yet by the indignant letter-writer's mirror logic, the idea of suffering, which until then – for thousands of years, in fact – the Jews had claimed for themselves, now belonged to the Palestinians, while the terrorists – and there is no appeal against this designation – are the Israelis. It's not even this conclusion that's frightening – this mode of thinking, mechanical in all respects, automatically arrives at it – but rather that Bruria fails to notice, and is unable to notice, what flimsy foundations this reasoning rests on given that every conclusion has been arrived at in advance (even if genuine suffering and a profound knowledge of the city and its inhabitants – the city of her birth –underlies it). Bruria shuts her eyes. After all, she is squirming in the hands of men who write about her like this:

> She undertakes work for us – the gathering of
> information and the processing of individuals – based
> on the information needs we provide.

This, then, was Mum, a 'processor of individuals', Mum, whose gentle hand could make my headache go away? Mum, who, on reading Rapcsányi's book, which had been tacitly supported by the regime, let out the following, virtually inarticulate scream in half-baked Hungarian, addressed to 'Comrade Editor-in-Chief', which was tempered only by her iron discipline as a Party worker:

Most Respected Comrade Editor-in-Chief,

I would be so bold as to make a few critical observations concerning a book published amid much ado: László Rapcsány's 'Jerusalem'.

The author dedicates the book to 'his brethren or god'. The book's contents, however, make clear that the much suffering Palestinian people do not belong among the writer's brethren. I will not address the book's historical assertions through 1948, though what it supposedly says about the Balfour declaration is quite antipathetic, for the Balfour declaration served the interests not of the Jewish people but that of English imperialism, Great Britain's colonization policies. To skim over that fact does not clarify reality but only stirs helter-skelter in people's minds.

The author repeatedly states that he will not politicize – but is not not politicizing also a form a politics? Is there such a thing as an objective historical perspective? Does not a historian or newspaper reporter need to be loyal to the policies of the Hungarian People's Republic to accept a minimal commitment to the policies, the ideology that is ours?

At the same time, the book is biased and tendentious, seeking to smuggle in the notion that Jewry survived through the centuries because it was unified by the 'idea of Jerusalem'. I do not wish to issue rebuttals, though I could. However, if what the writer writes is true – and as Zionist political-ideological books have described before, and has been discussed at numerous Zionist congresses, yielding one declaration after another about magical Jerusalem – then it is an obvious conclusion of this book (first paragraph page 20) – that the Israeli state was justified in occupying the Old City of Jerusalem and the entire West Bank, for God promised this in the Bible to Abraham.

Rapcsány takes this occupation for granted to such a degree (though obliquely indeed, and thus more dangerously) that he even describes the city of Nablus, occupied in 1967, as Israeli: 'One of Israel's most interesting settlements' (p. 147), whereas even the average Hungarian newspaper reader knows that Nablus is a centre of Palestinian resistance to this day. Not long ago a Jewish terrorist group carried out an assassination attempt on the city's mayor in which he lost both his legs. This bloody terror attack was denounced not only by the Arabs and the communists but also by the UN. But Rapcsány doesn't politicise. [. . .]

The university that invited the writer, Bar-Ilan, is a

bigoted religious institution that keeps itself sustained mainly by American money.

Yehuda Lahav, who received and accompanied him, is a renegade who in 1965 left the Israeli Communist Party and since then has been the wildest anti-communist spokesman for instigation against the socialist countries. But the Israeli Communist Party would have a lot more to say about Lahav.

On pp 300–301 the book's enthusiasm for the united (Israeli) Jerusalem becomes completely clear as it nicely describes the enthusiasm of the Jewish leaders. As for the 'bulldozer' action, all it writes is that 'this sparked a sharp reaction from Arab public opinion and the international media' – but was mention made of how many Arab houses, which had likewise stood in their places for centuries and whose inhabitants had likewise been in Jerusalem for centuries, were razed, or that a legion of Jewish progressive, humanist, communist people living in Israel had protested this? No – there is no room for that in a book that doesn't politicize.

The author describes the mayor of occupied Jerusalem as an exceptional cultural scholar. Of course Mr Kolek is that, too, and he loves Jerusalem, but is not the mayor of an occupied city a politician par excellence? Rapcsány didn't even bother to meet residents of occupied Jerusalem, for that would have been to politicize. Indeed, the only Arab he did meet (p. 74) was the owner of an Arab café who told him tales. [. . .]

No, he didn't pay a visit to the former mayor of Arab Jerusalem, Amin Majaj. Descended from an ancient Jerusalem family, this physician and director of Makased Hospital, who lives in an ancient Jerusalem house by Herod's Gate, could have told the writer a lot about his city. But that would naturally have been politicizing, and Mr Kolek is more competent a source, since he was born in Hungary. [. . .]

But is not the author – who certainly travelled to Jerusalem to meet with archaeologists – politicizing by speaking with archaeologists and historians of an occupying power on the occupied territory, people whose work and research is <u>illegal</u>? Of course, had he mentioned this, he would also have had to mention the 1967 <u>occupation</u>, which, it seems, does not exist for the writer, indeed, as he writes, 'it has now become clear to me that it is not a bizarre idea if we seek the reviving continuity of stones and thoughts' (p. 161, cf p. 20).

Thus it is that he smuggles into the whole book that false consciousness that Jerusalem is one and indivisible, moreover, in Israeli hands.

On p. 156 he mentions that the Israeli authorities opened Jaffa Gate and that this 'eases the traffic' – but would the author react the same way if the German Federal Republic attacked the capital of the German Democratic Republic and then opened the wall to ease the flow of traffic?!

[...]

The method the writer uses is to not speak about many things, and so what he does not write about does not exist. The actions of Motta Gur and his soldiers do not exist, the terrorist acts of the occupying forces do not exist, and expelled Palestinians do not exist who live in refugee camps and wait to make good on the several dozen UN decrees in the matter that have been brought since 1947. But that is all politics – what's not is that in the writer's book Golda Meir figures as a 'good grandmother'; that same Golda Meir who initiated several of Israel's wars of aggression. History knows several politicians who loved music, their wives, and indeed even their grandchildren, but history keeps a record not of their acts as grandfathers but of their political actions. ~~*Even Rudolf Hess, commandant of Auschwitz, loved his family.*~~

It is neither my goal nor my responsibility to mention every passage of the book similar to those above – this <u>should have been</u> the responsibility of others. However, I do by all means consider it necessary that the book be read ~~also by competent individuals~~ and that <u>reviews of it be published from a political perspective</u>, which could somewhat clarify that the book does not reflect the thinking of official Hungarian policy – at least I would like to hope so.

Respectfully
Mrs Marcell Forgács
Avi Shaul Bruria
Budapest, 6 April 1984

So there we are, lock, stock, and barrel, Mum's worldview. She is led neither by calculation nor some hidden agenda, but wants only to scream the truth. And then she gives in.

Three weeks later, on 2 May, Lieutenant Dóra reports:

In the matter of the RAPCSÁNY book MRS PÁPAI said that she has spoken with a staff member of the Foreign Affairs Institute, Comrade ENDREFI, who was of the same opinion as we; that is, that she should not send her letter critiquing the book to anyone.

Following through on this thought, I managed to persuade MRS PÁPAI that in this case, the letter – wherever she might send it – would trigger only a negative effect.

The result she seeks can be achieved only with very thorough, slow, persistent work, which, however, falls under our purview.

I thanked MRS PÁPAI for bringing our attention to this dangerous book and assured her that we would do everything to ensure that in the future this sort of thing hopefully will not occur, though this can be realized as the result of a struggle, and so we cannot expect spectacular results right away.

At the close of our conversation PÁPAI's health came up, and then we discussed the May Day festivities.

Our meeting ended at 3:30 pm with us agreeing that I would return P. GAME's letter as soon as possible to MRS PÁPAI.

Assessment:

The effect of reasoning and time seems to have calmed MRS PÁPAI, who will call off her plan to publicly disseminate her critique.

Defeat on the back of defeat. But at least the lieutenant and Mrs Pápai discussed the May Day festivities.

Did my learned grandfather, in giving that very rare and beautiful name, Bruria (a name more or less corresponding to the Latin name Klara: *clear, bright*), to his girl by chance bequeath her with a propensity for tragedy, for catastrophe by

382

way of the fate of another Bruria (spelled Bruria*h* in English), the daughter of renowned Rabbi Haninah ben Teradion (who was burned slowly at the stake by the Romans), who would become the wife of the great Rabbi Meir?

According to legends born centuries after the events, *that* dazzlingly clever Bruriah – who was given to converse with the scholarly rabbis, and whom the Babylonian Talmud quotes in numerous places, and who was possessed of brains and beauty – supposedly died when her husband, Rabbi Meir (who, according to a legend, had to flee to Babylon because he had rescued Bruriah's younger sister, who was, notably, still a virgin, from a brothel established by the Roman occupiers), out of pure scholarly curiosity, sent one of his students to seduce Bruriah. He wished to prove the Talmudic assertion that women are easily swayed; which is to say, a woman who whiles away too much time with the Talmud and is too clever for her own good is more lecherous and susceptible to sin. Bruriah had shown this reasoning to be ludicrous on many occasions. But although she resisted the young student's advances for some time, finally she gave in, and so sad and sorry was she, so the legend goes, that she hanged herself. A number of scholarly commentaries proposed mitigating circumstances. One has Rabbi Meir himself disguised as the student. The commentaries concur that Bruriah need only have said that the Talmud's assertion about women was true, and that she was merely an exception, but that she was unwilling to do this, and so had to be put to shame. Bruriah was in this respect one of the first feminists. 'By which road should we travel to Lod?' a rabbi once asked her. Bruriah berated him, saying that if it were really true, as the same rabbi had said not long before, that learned men should speak as little as possible with women, why then he should have asked 'Which road to Lod?'

From this is it fairly clear to me that it was the intellectual envy of male Talmudic scholars in the centuries to come that cast a shadow over the rabbi's wife who dared to mock them. For Bruriah was said to have learned three hundred *halachot*, or laws, from three hundred teachers in a single day, and she is there in the Babylonian Talmud with her sharp-witted or vitriolic utterances and interpretations. In short, Bruriah was one of the stars of the Talmud. When her husband would gladly have murdered his noisy neighbours for disturbing his meditation, it was Bruriah who explained to him that the psalms said not that sinners must cease from the land, but sin. According to the Midrash Proverbs, even her most famous act was tragic: when her husband was away at a religious festival, both of their sons died unexpectedly of an illness. When her husband returned, she didn't tell him what had happened, but said instead, 'Some time ago a deposit was left with me for safe-keeping, and now the owner has come to claim it. Must I return it?' To which her husband responded: 'Can there be any question about the return of property to its owner?' Bruriah replied, 'I did not want to return it without letting you know of it.' And, taking him by the hand, she led him into a room in which the bodies of their two sons were lying on a bed. When she drew back the cover, Rabbi Meir broke out in tears, to which Bruriah said, 'Didn't you say that the deposit must be given back to the owner?'

* * *

We're pitching pennies in the courtyard of our block of flats, under the chestnut tree, and night is falling fast. To us the game is also called *Schnur*, which in German means 'string' or 'line'. We throw ten-, twenty- and fifty-fillér coins so that they land on a line drawn in the dust, though sometimes we throw them up against a wall. According to the rules, whoever throws the coin that lands closest to the line gets to pick up all the money and toss it in the air, keeping all the coins that land heads-up. Every player wants to throw last, and so, once we've divvied up the winnings according to various rules, someone calls out:

'I'm last!'

'Next t'last!'

'Next t'next t'last!'

'Next t'next t'next t'last!'

'Next t'next t'next t'next t'last!'

'Next t'next t'next t'next t'next t'last!'

At that moment a female figure leans out of a dark window on the second floor and says only this, in a melodious voice:

'But this should really be the last next t'next t'last.'

Looking up at her, I see, by the light that shines from behind her, her shimmering smile.

On this day I have closed the dossier, at 79 pages and 48 lines.

Budapest, 30 September 1985

Lieutenant Dóra

ACKNOWLEDGEMENTS

I want to thank *Tamás Szőnyei*, the excellent researcher of this dark domain of Hungarian history for his selfless and invaluable help, my editor *Boglárka Nagy*, who could make delicate decisions when I lost track and guided me through this thorny bush with a steady hand, my publisher and agent, *Bence Sárközy*, for his empathy, his constant attention and ingenious support during that most difficult year of my life when all this came to light, and my brother *Peter* for his courage and the deep dialogue between us without which this book wouldn't be what it is.

András Forgách

Teach Yourself VISUALLY™

Crochet

Second Edition

Teach Yourself VISUALLY™

Crochet

Second Edition

Cecily Keim and Kim P. Werker

WILEY

Wiley Publishing, Inc.

Library of Congress Control Number: 2010941213

ISBN: 978-0-470-87997-9 (pbk)

ISBN: 978-1-118-00494-4 (ebk)

Printed in the United States of America

10   9   8   7   6   5   4   3

Book production by Wiley Publishing, Inc. Composition Services

Praise for the Teach Yourself VISUALLY Series

I just had to let you and your company know how great I think your books are. I just purchased my third Visual book (my first two are dog-eared now!) and, once again, your product has surpassed my expectations. The expertise, thought, and effort that go into each book are obvious, and I sincerely appreciate your efforts. Keep up the wonderful work!

—*Tracey Moore (Memphis, TN)*

I have several books from the Visual series and have always found them to be valuable resources.

—*Stephen P. Miller (Ballston Spa, NY)*

Thank you for the wonderful books you produce. It wasn't until I was an adult that I discovered how I learn—visually. Although a few publishers out there claim to present the material visually, nothing compares to Visual books. I love the simple layout. Everything is easy to follow. And I understand the material! You really know the way I think and learn. Thanks so much!

—*Stacey Han (Avondale, AZ)*

Like a lot of other people, I understand things best when I see them visually. Your books really make learning easy and life more fun.

—*John T. Frey (Cadillac, MI)*

I am an avid fan of your Visual books. If I need to learn anything, I just buy one of your books and learn the topic in no time. Wonders! I have even trained my friends to give me Visual books as gifts.

—*Illona Bergstrom (Aventura, FL)*

I write to extend my thanks and appreciation for your books. They are clear, easy to follow, and straight to the point. Keep up the good work! I bought several of your books and they are just right! No regrets! I will always buy your books because they are the best.

—*Seward Kollie (Dakar, Senegal)*

Credits

Acquisitions Editor
Pam Mourouzis

Project Editor
Donna Wright

Copy Editor
Marylouise Wiack

Technical Editor
Rita Greenfeder

Editorial Manager
Christina Stambaugh

Vice President and Publisher
Cindy Kitchel

Vice President and Executive Publisher
Kathy Nebenhaus

Interior Design
Kathie Rickard
Elizabeth Brooks

Photography
Matt Bowen

Special Thanks...

To the following yarn companies generously supplied yarn for use in the tutorials and patterns in this book:

- Blue Sky Alpacas
  P.O. Box 387
  St. Francis, MN 55070
  www.blueskyalpacas.com

- Crystal Palace Yarns
  160 23rd St.
  Richmond, CA 94804
  www.straw.com

- Elizabeth Austen, a Division of
  Knitting Fever International
  P.O. Box 336
  315 Bayview Ave.
  Amityville, New York 11701
  www.knittingfever.com

- Fleece Artist
  1174 Mineville Rd.
  Mineville, Nova Scotia
  B2Z 1K8
  Canada
  www.fleeceartist.com

- Hemp for Knitting
  105 Park St.
  Nelson, BC
  V1L 2G5
  Canada
  www.hempforknitting.com

- Lana Grossa Yarn (distributed
  by Unicorn Books & Crafts)
  1338 Ross St.
  Petaluma, CA 94954
  www.unicornbooks.com

- Lion Brand Yarn
  135 Kero Road
  Carlstadt, NJ 07072
  www.lionbrand.com

- Rio de la Plata Yarns
  13603 Marina Pointe Dr.
  Suite D-319
  Marina Del Rey, CA 90292
  www.riodelaplatayarns.com

- Southwest Trading Company
  1867 E. Third St.
  Tempe, AZ 85281-2941
  www.soysilk.com

About the Authors

Throughout **Cecily Keim**'s life, regardless of the type of study or type of job, making things has always been her fascination. Her great grandmother, Mama Mac, taught her to crochet at age 9. She is mesmerized by the endless possibilities of crochet and loves passing on the enthusiasm as a writer, designer, and teacher. If she's not crocheting, you will find her exploring quilting, sewing, weaving, and occasionally attempting to understand circuit boards.

Kim Werker is a writer, editor, blogger, crafter and speaker. In 2010 she launched the Mighty Ugly project, an online and in-person adventure in embracing the possibility and eventuality of ugliness in creativity, art and crafting so it's not so scary. Her passion in life is to live creatively and to work with others to foster creative, crafty fun. She's written or co-authored several crochet books, including *Get Hooked* and *Get Hooked Again* (Watson-Guptill, 2006 and 2007), *Crochet Me: Designs to Fuel the Crochet Revolution* (Interweave, 2007), *Crochet Visual Quick Tips,* with Cecily Keim (Wiley, 2007) and *Crocheted Gifts* (Interweave, 2009). Follow her continuing work and adventures at www.kimwerker.com.

Acknowledgments

This book has come about thanks to the contributions of many people.

I owe enormous thanks to Pam, Donna, and Cindy, who went above and beyond with great patience.

Working on the first edition with Kim was a great adventure and I thank her for supporting my work on this new edition.

Thanks go out to the many yarn companies that supplied us with yarn for the tutorials and patterns. Without your contributions it would be impossible to show off what crochet can do.

Personal thanks go to Rob and Cara.

Table of Contents

Chapter 3 Basic Techniques 48

Table of Contents

Chapter 4   Stitch Variations   66

Chapter 5   Combining Stitches   88

Rows

Stitches

Table of Contents

Chapter 8   More Techniques   132

Table of Contents

Chapter 11   Flowers, Shapes, and Creatures   206

Table of Contents

Chapter 14   Patterns   266

CHAPTER 1

Introduction to Crochet

Crochet is the process of interlocking loops of yarn with a hook. By combining a simple set of basic stitches, you can create an infinite assortment of items, from garments and accessories to home décor. Before you start to crochet, take some time to familiarize yourself with the tools that will help you along the way. This chapter will introduce you to crochet hooks and notions, and you will learn all you need to know to choose the right yarn for your projects. We believe that crochet is both craft and art, and we hope you enjoy crocheting your own creations as much as we do!

Crochet for Knitters

If you know how to knit, you may have encountered crochet in patterns that call for a crocheted edging or motif. Here are some tips that might help you pick up crochet without getting confused by what you already know about knitting.

The Differences

STITCHING

You crochet with only one hook, and you hold the hook in the hand you write with. Right- and left-handed crocheters produce the same fabric, just in opposite directions. Just because you use your hook with one hand does not mean your other hand is idle. Your yarn hand keeps your tension consistent, holds the body of your work, and helps guide your hook into tight places.

If you are a continental knitter (that is, you hold your yarn in your left hand and "pick" stitches with your right-hand needle), you may find it fairly easy to move into crochet because you will continue to hold the yarn in your left hand and maneuver the hook with your right (if you are right-handed). If you're interested in learning how to knit in the continental style, you may find that knowing how to crochet helps you pick it up more smoothly. If you knit in the English style, you may find that your experience holding yarn and keeping tension with your right hand translates easily to doing the same with your left hand.

In knitting, all stitches remain "open" or "active" throughout your project until you bind off at the end. In crochet, you bind off your stitches as you go; in most cases you have just one loop on your hook when you have completed a stitch.

GAUGE

In contrast to knitting stitches, crochet stitches are generally taller than they are wide. Therefore, you crochet more stitches over an inch than you do rows. It might take a bit of experience with crochet before your instincts adjust regarding how many stitches and rows you require to produce an item of certain dimensions.

Crochet stitches can feel denser than knitting stitches. You might find that you are more comfortable using a hook that is larger than the needles you would use for the same yarn, to produce a fabric with good drape.

Crochet stitches use more yarn than knitting stitches, so when you purchase yarn for your first project, get more than you think you need. See the section "Estimate How Much Yarn You Need" on page 47 for more information.

This book gives you the information you need to learn crochet techniques, but you might want to connect with other crocheters for help or to share your passion. The number of crochet resources you can find online is endless. Crocheters are always sharing tips and projects on blogs and in a variety of online communities. Yarn companies and magazines have Web sites with information, instruction, and patterns. And if you can't find what you need from these sites, simply use your favorite search engine.

LOCAL AND ONLINE YARN STORES

If you live in a large town or city, chances are you can find an independently owned and operated yarn store. Owners of yarn stores tend to be friendly, and many encourage crocheters to spend time in the store by having comfortable chairs and establishing a welcoming atmosphere. Yarn stores frequently offer crochet classes as well, so they can serve as a very helpful resource to you as you advance your crochet skills.

If you can't find a yarn store in your area, large craft stores tend to carry a selection of yarns, threads, and hooks and may also offer crochet classes. And given the number of online yarn stores that exist, you're sure to find just the yarn you're looking for.

There are many options out there when you're looking for crochet supplies. Many designers sell patterns and kits directly from their own Web sites. Simply search the name of your favorite designer to find his or her site. Etsy.com is another place to look for patterns and yarn to buy from enterprising crocheters. It's a handmade community full of inspiration.

CROCHET GUILDS, CLUBS, AND MEETUPS

A crochet guild or club might already exist in your area. Such groups meet regularly for social crocheting and organize classes, fashion shows, charity events, and more. If you can't find a crochet guild or club in your area, you can contact the Crochet Guild of America (www.crochet.org) for information on how to start one.

In many communities, informal groups meet regularly for social crocheting. Meeting at a member's home, at a coffee shop, or even at a bar, crochet clutches are a fun and easy way to connect with people who share your interest in crochet. Some yarn stores even organize social gatherings weekly or monthly. For more information, you can ask at your local store or do a search for groups in your area on www.crochet.meetup.com or groups.yahoo.com.

Join the Crochet Community *(continued)*

ONLINE COMMUNITIES AND RESOURCES

The Internet offers an extensive and rapidly expanding amount of information about crochet. From patterns (free and for sale), yarns, and tools to message boards, magazines, and blogs, you can spend hours learning and connecting.

Pioneered by enthusiastic crafters, Web sites devoted to making free craft patterns and related articles available to the public are becoming more and more abundant. You can turn to these online communities for information about techniques, to find that perfect pattern, or to request advice. Members also share photos of their completed crochet projects, information about works in progress, and links to resources they find useful.

Crochet Guild of America
www.crochet.org
Offers tutorials, news, and patterns.

Crochet Me
www.crochetme.com
Includes patterns, forums, blogs, photo galleries, instructional videos, and more.

Crochet Pattern Central
www.crochetpatterncentral.com
An online directory providing links to free patterns, indexed by category.

Crochetville
www.crochetville.org
A message board devoted entirely to crochet.

Ravelry
www.ravelry.com
Offers a number of ways to track projects and supplies, share notes, get advice on questions and problems, and make friends.

Craft Yarn Council
www.craftyarncouncil.com/standards.html
Offers a wealth of resources, from definitions of crochet abbreviations and chart symbols to tables of hook sizes, body measurements for standard sizing, and yarn weights.

General community sites also hold some crochet surprises. Try searching Flickr.com for inspiring photos of crochet projects, to share your own, and to join groups that specifically share crochet-related photos. Look to youtube.com for video instructions made by other crochet enthusiasts.

BLOGS AND CROCHET ALONGS

Many software programs that simplify the blogging process are available for free, which means that anyone with a computer and an Internet connection can have a blog. Many crocheters maintain blogs devoted to their projects, displaying digital photos of their completed projects and works in progress.

Crochet bloggers and communities occasionally organize *crochet alongs,* during which each participant works on producing an item from the same pattern. This allows for a fun, shared experience, and more advanced crocheters can help beginners.

Hooks

Crochet hooks come in many sizes and are made from a selection of different materials. The hook you choose to use depends on the yarn you are using, how big or small you want your stitches to be, and your personal preference.

THE HOOK

Crochet hooks are generally 5 to 7 inches long. There is a hook at one end, which you use to grab yarn or thread and pull it through the stitches of your work. You hold the hook along its shaft, and there may be a flat section of the shaft to serve as a thumbrest or grip.

HOOK SHAPE

Various manufacturers shape their hooks differently, so try out a few different brands until you find the shape that you feel works best. Each brand has its own trademark style. For example, hook A has a round, smooth throat that tapers toward a narrow hook to help yarn loops slide quickly. The point at the top of the hook can aid in inserting the hook into crochet fabric. Hook B has a flat cut in the throat to create a deeper hook. The hook head is also wider, helping to keep loops from slipping off the hook.

HOOK TYPES

Hooks are usually made from plastic, metal, wood, or bamboo. The smallest hooks are made of steel and are used with thin crochet thread to make intricately detailed items, such as doilies. Metal hooks can be very smooth, enabling the yarn to slide freely. Wood or bamboo hooks, on the other hand, provide a bit of friction with the yarn, which comes in handy when you're crocheting with slippery yarns. Plastic hooks are slightly flexible and lightweight.

HOOK SIZES

Hook size is determined by the diameter of the hook's shaft. Sizes range from tiny ($\frac{1}{16}$ inch/0.75 millimeters) to large ($\frac{4}{5}$ inch/20 millimeters). Smaller hooks work with threads and thin yarns and make smaller stitches. Larger hooks accommodate thicker yarn and make larger stitches. Choose your hook size based on the recommended size for your yarn and on how loose or tight you want your stitches to be.

Most yarn labels suggest a hook size to use with the yarn, and patterns also list a recommended hook size. You may need to change the hook size in order to match the gauge listed in a pattern or to achieve a specific drape and feel. It is more important to match the gauge of a pattern than to use the exact hook size listed.

Hook size

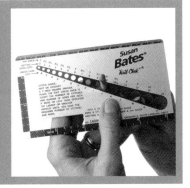

How can I determine a crochet hook's size?

If you are unsure of a hook's size, you can use a hook gauge to measure the size of the hook. Find the smallest hole that the shaft of the hook fits into; the size indicated beside that hole is the size of your hook. Hook gauges usually mark both metric and U.S. sizes.

FAQ

Hooks *(continued)*

Hook sizes are marked differently in the United States and the United Kingdom, although there is a growing interest in standardizing sizes by using metric measurements. Use the following tables to determine your hook size. In some instances, a yarn label provides only a recommendation for knitting needle size. In this case, use a hook of the same or slightly larger metric size. (If you're using U.S. sizing, find the U.S. size equivalent to the metric size given for the recommended knitting needles.)

Hook Sizes		
Metric Size (in mm)	U.S. Size	U.S. Knitting Needle Size
2	A	0
2.25	B	1
2.75	C	2
3.25	D	3
3.5	E	4
3.75	F	5
4	G	6
4.5	—	7
5	H	8
5.5	I	9
6	J	10
6.5	K	10½
8	L	11
9	M/N	13
10	N/P	15
15	P/Q	19
16	Q	—
19	S	35

Steel Hook Sizes	
Metric Size (in mm)	U.S. Size
0.75	#14
0.85	#13
1.0	#12
1.1	#11
1.3	#10
1.4	#9
1.5	#8
1.65	#7
1.8	#6
1.9	#5
2.0	#4
2.1	#3
2.25	#2
2.75	#1
3.25	#0
3.5	#00

In addition to hooks and yarn, there are other tools and notions you will want to keep handy.

MEASURING TAPE AND GAUGE RULER

Use a measuring tape to take body measurements before you embark on crocheting a sweater or other fitted garment. A measuring tape also comes in handy when checking gauge. (See the section "Measure Your Gauge" in Chapter 6.) You may also want a stitch and row gauge (or gauge ruler, which is shown at the bottom of page 9), to help you count how many stitches and rows you have created.

STITCH MARKERS

Stitch markers are useful in many situations. For example, when working in the round (see Chapter 3), you can mark the beginning of the round by placing a marker in the first stitch. You can buy stitch markers designed for this purpose or improvise with scraps of yarn or even earrings. When crocheting a garment, use stitch markers to indicate the placement of increases and decreases for shaping (see Chapter 3).

TAPESTRY NEEDLES

A tapestry needle, also called a yarn needle, has a blunt tip and a large eye to accommodate thick yarns. Use your needle to sew pieces together or to weave in yarn ends when you have completed your project. (See the section "Fasten Off and Weave In Yarn Tails" on page 64.)

Selecting yarn is one of the most exciting parts of starting a new crochet project. The type of material from which a yarn is spun or manufactured has a great effect on your final product. Consider whether your project should be warm, durable, machine washable, and breathe well—the list goes on!

Different Types

NATURAL FIBERS

Natural fibers come from plants or animals. Cotton and wool are perhaps the most common natural fibers, but there are many others.

Plant fibers are usually lightweight, are machine washable, have little stretch, and breathe well. They include cotton, linen, soy, hemp (as shown here), bamboo, and jute.

Animal fibers are very warm (even when wet), have a bit of natural stretch, breathe well, and generally must be washed by hand. They include wool, mohair (as shown here), cashmere, silk, angora, and alpaca.

SYNTHETIC FIBERS

Synthetic fibers are manmade. They include acrylic, nylon, rayon, and polyester. Some synthetics are less expensive than natural fibers, and they tend not to breathe as well. However, as technology advances, synthetic fibers are showing an increasing number of desirable qualities, including durability, softness, and vibrancy of color.

NOVELTY YARNS

Frequently made from synthetic materials, novelty yarns come in a wide variety of textures and shapes. These include eyelash, fun fur, bouclé, ladder, and beaded—the list goes on. Novelty yarns can be used alone or combined with other yarns to create unique crocheted items. It may not be practical to create entire garments or home décor items solely out of novelty yarns, but they are particularly well suited to trims, accents, and accessories.

TIP

Terms

You will encounter the following terms when choosing yarns:

- **Superwash.** This term applies to yarns made from wool, wool blends, and other animal fibers that have been chemically treated to prevent them from *fulling* (shrinking and becoming very dense) when they are agitated in a washing machine or by hand.
- **Mercerized.** This term applies to cotton that has undergone a specific chemical treatment resulting in yarn that is strong, is high in luster, and takes dye extremely well.

Yarn Construction and Packaging

It is important to know a little about the different ways yarn is constructed. Understanding how a yarn is packaged will help you know how to get started.

YARN CONSTRUCTION

Yarn construction can loosely be divided into two categories: traditional and novelty.

- **Traditional yarn** is spun by hand or by machine and is often plied. Plying consists of taking two or more strands of yarn and twisting them together to create a thicker, stronger yarn. These "smooth" yarns show stitches clearly.

- Many types of **novelty yarn** are available, including ribbon, eyelash, bouclé, fun fur, and so on. You can also crochet with twine, raffia, plastic, and strips of cloth.

YARN PACKAGING

Store-bought yarn is packaged in one of two ways:

- **Hank.** The yarn is wound into a circle and twisted onto itself, creating an attractive, compact skein (a). Yarn pulled from a hank tangles easily and is difficult to undo. To avoid this, wind it before use. (See the section "How to Wind Yarn" on page 18.)

- **Center-pull skein.** The yarn is wound into a cylinder. Unwind it from the outside or pull the end out from the inside (b). This results in fewer tangles and prevents the skein from rolling around as you draw yarn from it.

All the information you need to know about yarn is contained on its label. Each skein or hank of store-bought yarn has a label with useful information on recommended hook size, fiber content, care instructions, length, color name, and dye lot.

LENGTH

When it comes time to figure out how many skeins of yarn you're going to need for a particular project, you need to know how many yards each skein contains (for example, 100 yards/4 ounces or 75 meters/50 grams). It's important to buy yarn according to length and not weight. A 4-ounce skein of lace-weight yarn might contain 1,200 yards, while 4 ounces of bulky-weight yarn might contain just 45 yards.

COLOR NAME/NUMBER AND DYE LOT

Yarns are dyed in limited quantities called *dye lots*. This may result in minor variations between lots of the same color. Yarn manufacturers stamp each label with the code for the dye lot of the yarn. To avoid color inconsistencies when you require multiple skeins of the same colored yarn for a project, make sure that you purchase all skeins from the same dye lot.

Yarn Weight and Care Symbols

Although we do consider the weight of a ball of yarn, "weight" is also a type of quality a yarn possesses. **Yarn weight** refers to the thickness, or bulkiness, of a strand of yarn. These categories of yarn weights help us to get a feel for what uses a yarn is traditionally best suited for. You should keep the yarn label after your project is completed, so you'll know how to care for it properly.

YARN WEIGHT SYMBOLS

The Craft Yarn Council has established the following general, industry-accepted standard categories of yarn weights. Use this chart along with the information on a yarn's label to get an even better idea of how best to use the yarn.

Yarn Weight Category Names	Types of Yarn in Category	Crochet Gauge* Ranges in Single Crochet to 4 inches	Recommended Hook in Metric Size Range	Recommended Hook in U.S. Size Range
Super Fine	Sock, Fingering, Baby	21–32 sts	2.25–3.5mm	B–1 to E–4
Fine	Sport, Baby	16–20 sts	3.5–4.5mm	E–4 to 7
Light	DK, Light Worsted	12–17 sts	4.5–5.5mm	7 to I–9
Medium	Worsted, Afghan, Aran	11–14 sts	5.5–6.5mm	I–9 to K–10½
Bulky	Chunky, Craft, Rug	8–11 sts	6.5–9mm	K–10½ to M–13
Super Bulky	Bulky, Roving	5–9 sts	9mm and larger	M–13 and larger

CARE SYMBOLS

Although some yarn labels spell out how to wash and dry items made from that particular yarn, universal yarn care symbols are also frequently used. To avoid accidentally ruining the gorgeous crocheted item you have spent hours creating, refer to the following chart to interpret yarn care symbols.

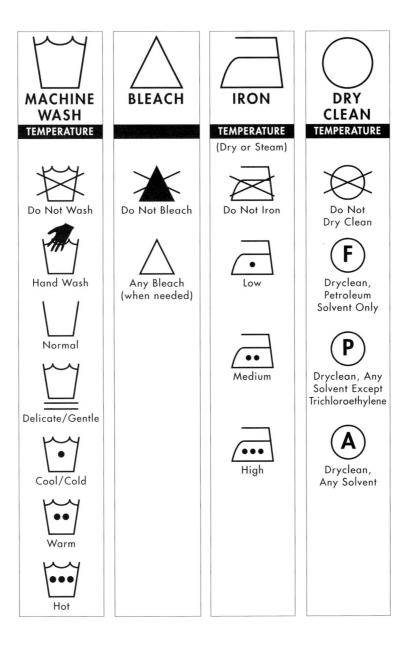

How to Wind Yarn

Whether you have a messy skein or a hank, you can use one of the following methods to wind the yarn into a ball.

Before you begin, you should carefully handle hanks after you remove the ties because the yarn might tangle. Secure the hank before you start winding the yarn.

WIND WITH A SWIFT

A swift resembles an umbrella apparatus; the hank is wrapped around it and it spins freely to enable you to wind the yarn easily by hand or with a ball winder (see below).

WIND WITH A BALL WINDER

Attach the tail to the ball winder according to the winder's manual. If you're using a swift, wind the yarn while ensuring that the swift is spinning freely and the yarn is winding nicely onto the spool. You can use your free hand to control the tension of the yarn as it feeds from the swift to the winder.

WIND WITH A CHAIR

You can either 1) wrap the hank around the chair-back or 2) turn a chair upside down and use the legs to hold the hank. As you wind the yarn by hand, you will need to walk around the chair instead of using a ball winder.

WIND WITH A FRIEND

Slip the untwisted hank onto a friend's outstretched forearms. Cut or untie the strings holding the yarn bundled. Starting with an end of yarn, wind it into a ball.

Once the hank is untwisted and secured, cut the ties holding the yarn in a circle.

Locate the ends of the yarn and choose the one that comes off the hank with ease.

WIND A CENTER PULL SKEIN BY HAND

① Leaving a 6-inch tail, hold the yarn in the crook of your thumb.

2 Wind the yarn in a figure eight around your fingers about a dozen times.

3 Grab the figure eight by the middle and slide it off your fingers.

4 Fold the figure eight over.

5 Lightly wrap the yarn around the figure eight several times.

6 Rotate the figure eight as you wind the yarn around it, starting to create a ball shape.

7 As you wrap the ball, work around the tail so as not to cover it.

NOTE: Remember to wrap loosely; don't stretch the yarn tight. The ball should be soft, not hard.

CHAPTER 2

Getting Started and Basic Stitches

In this chapter, you will learn how to begin a crochet project and how to form simple stitches. From attaching yarn to your hook to working in rows—all the basics will be covered.

Starting with a smooth, simple, light colored yarn will help you concentrate on the stitches as well as the process of crocheting. You will soon become familiar with your stitches and using any type of yarn will be easier.

SELECT YOUR YARN

Starting with a smooth, simple, light-colored yarn will help you concentrate on the stitches and on the process of crocheting.

Use the simplest yarn you can find. It should be smooth and durable. If the yarn frays, unravels, or untwists easily, it won't stand up well to the learning process, during which you will frequently need to pull out mistakes.

Choose a yarn that allows you to see your stitches clearly. Avoid fuzzy, heavily textured yarns. Dark colors make it hard to see the stitches as you're learning, so pick a light color.

SELECT YOUR HOOK

Start with the hook size recommended on the yarn label. If you find that your stitches are too tight, switch to a larger hook. If your stitches are too loose, switch to a smaller hook. You should be able to easily insert your hook into the stitches you make, and you should feel comfortable with the shape of the hook shaft and the hook.

How to Hold Your Hook

There are different ways to hold a crochet hook. It's important that you find a grip that is comfortable and enables you to relax while you crochet.

NOTE: For left-hand instructions and photos, see the section "Notes for Left-Handed Crocheters" on page 27.

The Hook Hand

Hold your hook in the hand you write with. This hand is in charge of controlling the hook and maneuvering it into and out of the stitches as you work.

You can hold the hook like a pencil...

...or like a knife.

Do what comes naturally as long as you can comfortably control the hook. Hold the hook firmly but not too tightly.

How to Hold Your Yarn

Since you control your hook with one hand, you use your other hand to hold your yarn so that it flows freely but maintains an even tension. Although it seems like your hook hand does all the work, your yarn hand performs an essential role.

NOTE: For left-hand instructions and photos, see the section "Notes for Left-Handed Crocheters" on the next page.

The Yarn Hand

The yarn hand is just as important as the hook hand. In fact, the yarn hand does double duty, holding the body of your work and controlling the yarn.

The yarn is attached to the hook with a slip knot. (See the section "Make a Slip Knot" on page 28.)

Your middle finger and thumb hold the tail of yarn that dangles from the hook and hold the fabric you're creating.

Use your index finger to hold and guide the yarn. Gently wrap the yarn once or twice around your index finger to achieve the control you need. The yarn should be taut but should slide easily along the hook as you make stitches.

Another popular way to control the yarn is to wrap the yarn around your pinky finger, then behind your other fingers, and finally over your index finger.

Everyone holds and guides her yarn differently. The guidelines above provide a good place to start. Work from here to see what's best for you. When both hands are relaxed, the stitches move easily on the hook.

Most books and patterns are written from a right-handed perspective. Here's some information for lefties that will come in handy as you progress through this book.

Crochet Left-Handed

Here are some important techniques, illustrated for lefties.

As noted in the section "How to Hold Your Hook" on page 25, the crochet hook can be held like a knife or pencil in your dominant hand or, in this example, your left hand. Referring to the section "How to Hold Your Yarn" on the previous page, wrap the yarn attached to the hook around your index finger (a). Your middle finger and thumb hold both the fabric you're creating and the tail of the yarn that hangs from the hook.

The photo on the right (b) shows a yarn over as performed by a leftie. (See the section "Make a Chain Stitch" on page 30 for more information on yarn overs.) Lefties work crochet stitches from left to right across their rows instead of from right to left.

a

b

> **TIP**
>
> **Lefties Learning from Righties**
>
> When learning from a right-handed crocheter, sit facing each other instead of side by side. Doing so allows you to mirror right-handed actions.
>
> Mirror images of right-handed graphics may also help ease confusion. Hold a small mirror to the side of an image or use a photocopier to create mirror images.
>
> Don't worry if your left-handed stitches look different from the pictures you see. Left-handed stitches slant differently, but that isn't wrong!

Make a Slip Knot

A slip knot is used to attach the yarn to the hook. Making the slip knot is the first step in beginning any project. There are many methods and tricks for making a slip knot. Try both options shown here and see what works best for you.

Slip Knot, Pretzel Method

1 Create a loop with your yarn, leaving at least a 6-inch tail.

2 Place the loop on top of the tail.

3 Insert the hook into the loop and under the tail.

4 Hold both ends of the yarn and pull gently to tighten.

The slip knot should be tight enough on the hook that there is no space between the yarn and the hook, but loose enough that the knot slides easily.

Slip Knot, X Method

① Place the yarn tail in the crook of
your thumb.

② Wrap the long end of the yarn over
the back, up, and around your
index and middle fingers.

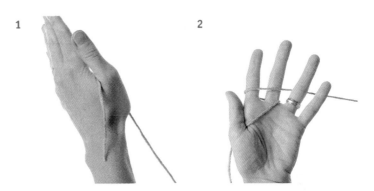

③ Wrap the yarn again, this time making an X.

④ Use a hook, or your fingers, to pull the top left part
of the X through the X.

⑤ Slip the knot off your fingers, adjust the size, and
place it on the crochet hook.

Make a Chain Stitch

The chain stitch is used to create a foundation for most crochet work as well as to create space between other stitches in lace patterns.

Pattern abbreviation: CH or ch.

Chain Stitch

① Start with a slip knot on the hook.

NOTE: See the section "Make a Slip Knot" on page 28 for more information.

② Yarn over.

To do a yarn over, wrap the yarn over your hook from back to front so that the yarn is coming toward you.

③ Draw the yarn through the first loop on your hook (the slip knot).

You've made 1 chain stitch. There is also 1 loop left on the hook.

④ Yarn over. Draw the yarn through the loop created by the last chain stitch made.

⑤ Repeat step 4 until you have made the desired number of chain stitches. (Do not count the slip knot as a chain. Also, do not count the loop on the hook.) Adjust your hold on the chain as it grows so that you're always holding it near the hook.

Keep the chain hanging down from the hook. Do not let the stitches you've made twist around on the hook.

TIP

After each stitch, do not tighten the chain you've just made. Resist the urge to control your stitches by pulling them tight. If your chain is too tight, it will be difficult to work stitches into it later. You should have enough room to poke your hook through each chain stitch.

Too tight

Perfect

Make a Foundation Chain

To begin a crochet project, most patterns call for a foundation chain into which you will work your first row of stitches. The pattern will specify how many chain stitches you will need.

Foundation Chain

Chain 12. Now take a close look at your chain.

The side facing you as you work the chain stitches looks like a braid.

The back of the chain has a ridge down the middle, almost like a spine. There should be 12 chain stitches. Never count the loop on the hook or the slip knot.

For most patterns and swatches, you work a chain for every stitch you plan to have in the first row, plus additional chains to serve as your first turning chain.

NOTE: See the section "Make a Turning Chain" on page 34 for more information.

Work your stitches into whichever part of the chain you are most comfortable with. The examples in this book work into one loop of the chain.

One loop of the braid

Both loops of the braid

The ridge in the back

The ridge and a loop of the braid

Make a Turning Chain

rochet stitches can be quite tall. You use chain stitches at the beginning or end of a row to create the height required by the stitches you are making. These **turning chains** (so called because you make them before or after turning your work at the end of a row) also keep the edges of your work neat and even.

The number of stitches required for the turning chain is added to the number needed in the foundation chain for the stitch pattern.

For example, for a row of 5 single crochet stitches, the foundation row is 6 chains. For a row of 5 double crochet stitches, the foundation row is 8 chains.

Each stitch requires a specific number of turning chains at the beginning or end of a row:

Stitch	Number of Turning Chains
Slip stitch	0
Single crochet	1
Half double crochet	2
Double crochet	3
Treble crochet	4

NOTE: See the sections on specific stitches for more information on the number of turning chains required.

TIP

- This chart is only a guide. With experience, you may find that you prefer to use fewer chains to create a turning chain.
- A turning chain can be made at the end or beginning of a row. Crochet patterns may specify how to make the chains; if your pattern does not, follow your personal preference.

The slip stitch creates the tightest, shortest, and stiffest crochet stitch and is frequently used to stitch squares or panels together when assembling an afghan or other large piece.

Pattern abbreviations: SL ST, sl st, Sl st, or SS.

Slip Stitch

To begin a project with a row of slip stitch, create a foundation chain (see the section "Make a Foundation Chain" on page 32) equal to the number of slip stitches you require. Work your first slip stitch into the second chain from your hook.

1   2

❶ Insert the hook into the next stitch.

❷ Yarn over and draw the yarn through the stitch and through the loop on the hook.

    You have created one slip stitch.

❸ Repeat steps 1 and 2 until you have completed your first row of slip stitch.

❹ Turn the piece. Insert your hook through both loops at the top of the first stitch from the previous row. Follow steps 1 and 2.

NOTE: Slip stitches are very tight when worked in full rows. Take care to keep your tension loose, or use a hook that is larger than recommended.

Make a Single Crochet

The single crochet stitch is the basic foundation of crochet. Most other stitches are variations on this stitch.

Pattern abbreviation: SC or sc.

Single Crochet

To begin a project with a row of single crochet, create a foundation chain (see the section "Make a Foundation Chain" on page 32) equal to the number of single crochet stitches you require, plus 1. Work your first single crochet into the second chain from your hook. Continue to the end of the chain. Turn.

1. Insert your hook into the next stitch, and then yarn over by wrapping the yarn around the hook from back to front.

2. Draw the yarn through the stitch.

   There are now 2 loops on the hook.

3 Yarn over and draw the yarn through both loops on
the hook.

There is now 1 loop on the hook.

You have created 1 single crochet.

4 Repeat steps 1–3 until you have
completed your first row of single
crochet. Chain 1 to create a turning chain.

NOTE: For more on turning chains, see
the section "Make a Turning Chain" on
page 34.

5 Turn the piece. Insert your hook
through both loops at the top of
the first stitch from the previous
row. Follow steps 1–3.

4

5

Make a Half Double Crochet

Half double crochet is a versatile stitch that is commonly used to make garments, hats, and other accessories.

Pattern abbreviation: HDC or hdc.

Half Double Crochet

To begin a project with a row of half double crochet, create a foundation chain (see the section "Make a Foundation Chain" on page 32) equal to the number of half stitches you require, plus 2. Work your first half double crochet into the third chain from your hook. Continue to the end of the chain. Turn.

1 Yarn over once.

2 Insert your hook into the next stitch, yarn over, and draw the yarn through the stitch.

There are now 3 loops on the hook.

3 Yarn over and draw the yarn through all 3 loops on the hook.

One loop remains on the hook. You have created 1 half double crochet.

2

3

4 Continue to follow steps 1–3 until you have completed your first row of half double crochet. Chain 2 to create a turning chain.

5 Turn the piece. Skip the first stitch at the beginning of the row. The turning chain is counted as the first half double crochet of the row. Follow steps 1–3 to create a half double crochet in the second stitch of the row.

NOTE: For more on turning chains, see the section "Make a Turning Chain" on page 34.

Remember to insert the hook through both loops at the top of the stitch from the previous row.

TIP

Because the turning chain counts as the first half double crochet at the beginning of a row, you work into it as though it were a half double crochet.

Make a Double Crochet

Like half double crochet, you make a double crochet stitch by doing a yarn over before inserting your hook into the next stitch.

Pattern abbreviation: DC or dc.

Double Crochet

To begin a project with a row of double crochet, create a foundation chain (see the section "Make a Foundation Chain" on page 32) equal to the number of double crochet stitches you require, plus 3. Work your first double crochet into the fourth chain from your hook. Continue to the end of the chain. Turn.

1 Yarn over once.

2 Insert your hook into the next stitch, yarn over, and draw the yarn through the stitch.

There are now 3 loops on the hook.

3 Yarn over and draw the yarn through the first 2 loops on the hook.

There are now 2 loops on the hook.

40

4 Yarn over and draw the yarn through the 2 remaining loops on the hook.

You have created 1 double crochet.

5 Continue to follow steps 1–4 until you have completed your first row of double crochet.

4

5

6 Chain 3 to create a turning chain (a). Turn the piece. Skip the first stitch at the beginning of the row. The turning chain counts as the first double crochet of the row. Follow steps 1–4 to create a double crochet in the second stitch of the row.

NOTE: For more on turning chains, see the section "Make a Turning Chain" on page 34.

Remember to insert the hook through both loops at the top of the stitch from the previous row (b).

6a

6b

Because the turning chain counts as the first double crochet at the beginning of a row, you work into it as though it were a double crochet.

Make a Treble Crochet

Treble crochet (also called triple crochet) is a very tall stitch, which you create by making two yarn overs before inserting your hook into the next stitch. The tall stitches create a fabric with more drape than the single crochet or half double crochet stitches.

Pattern abbreviation: TR or tr.

Treble Crochet

To begin a project with a row of treble crochet, create a foundation chain (see the section "Make a Foundation Chain" on page 32) equal to the number of treble crochet stitches you require, plus 4. Work your first treble crochet into the fifth chain from your hook. Continue to the end of the chain. Turn.

① Yarn over twice.

② Insert your hook into the next stitch, yarn over, and draw the yarn through the stitch.

There are now 4 loops on the hook.

③ Yarn over and draw the yarn through the first 2 loops on the hook.

There are now 3 loops on the hook.

④ Yarn over and draw the yarn through the next 2 loops on the hook.

There are now 2 loops on the hook.

5 Yarn over and draw the yarn through both loops on the hook (a).

You have created 1 treble crochet (b).

5a 5b

6 Continue to follow steps 1–5 until you have completed your first row of treble crochet. Chain 4 to create a turning chain.

NOTE: For more on turning chains, see the section "Make a Turning Chain" on page 34.

7 Turn the piece. Skip the first stitch at the beginning of the row. The turning chain counts as the first treble crochet of the row. Follow steps 1–5 to create a treble crochet in the second stitch of the row.

Remember to insert your hook through both loops at the top of the stitch from the previous row.

6 7

Because the turning chain counts as the first treble crochet at the beginning of a row, you work into it as though it were a treble crochet.

Count Your Stitches

You need to count the number of stitches in each row or round of your work to determine whether you are achieving the correct gauge for the pattern you've chosen. It's also important to keep track of how many stitches are in a working piece—often, counting stitches is the best way to diagnose mistakes.

IDENTIFY YOUR STITCHES

There are two easy ways to identify an individual stitch in your work:

- Examine the tops of the stitches. The top of each crochet stitch looks like a braid or a V. Each braid or V corresponds to one stitch.

- Examine the post of the stitch. The post (a) is the "body" of the stitch. Just count the posts to see how many stitches you have made (b).

a

b

1 2 3 4 5

HOW HOOK SIZE AFFECTS STITCHES

The hook size you use affects the size of the stitches you create; a large hook creates large stitches, while a small hook creates small stitches. The hook size you choose affects the fabric you create just as much as your choice of yarn, stitch, and pattern.

RECOMMENDED HOOK SIZE

Most yarn labels indicate the hook size recommended for that particular weight of yarn (see the section "Yarn Weight and Care Symbols" on page 16), and patterns indicate the hook size used by the designer. Using a hook that is close to the yarn label's recommended hook size results in a solid fabric that is neither too tight nor too loose, as you can see in the middle swatch. If you crochet tightly, you may need to use a hook that is one or two sizes larger than the recommended size to obtain the required gauge. If you crochet loosely, you may need to use a hook that is one or two sizes smaller to achieve the required gauge.

MUCH LARGER HOOK SIZE

Crocheting with a hook much larger than the recommended size for your yarn, like the bottom swatch, results in loose, open stitches that appear lacy and have excellent drape. Experiment with large hooks for making items such as scarves, shawls, and lacy cardigans.

NOTE: *Drape* refers to how well the fabric "flows." Fabrics with good drape are flexible and move freely when worn; fabrics with little drape feel stiff and boxy.

MUCH SMALLER HOOK SIZE

Crocheting with a hook much smaller than the recommended size for your yarn results in tight stitches and an overall stiff fabric, as you can see in the top swatch. Experiment with small hooks for making items such as baskets, bags, and bowls.

Plan Your Crochet Project

It's easy to determine how many stitches and rows you need for a project, and this information enables you to estimate how much yarn you require. You should purchase all the yarn you need at the beginning of your project.

Estimate Stitch and Row Count

First, do a little math to figure out how many stitches and how many rows are required.

Sample Project: Scarf

Size: 6 inches wide x 60 inches long

1 With the yarn you plan to use, work a 10 stitch x 10 row swatch. Measure and count how many stitches are in an inch.

2 Multiply the number of stitches in an inch by the inches of width in the intended project.

For example, if your swatch has 4 stitches to an inch and your finished piece needs to be 6 inches wide, you'll need 24 stitches.

3 Measure and count how many rows are in an inch.

4 Multiply the number of rows in an inch by the inches of length in the intended project.

For example, if your swatch has 4 rows to an inch and your finished piece needs to be 60 inches long, you'll need to complete 240 rows.

Estimate How Much Yarn You Need

There is such a wide variety of crochet stitches that figuring yardage for a project can be intimidating. Whatever the stitch pattern you choose, figuring out how much yarn you need isn't as hard as you may think.

Using the swatch you created on the preceding page:

① Unravel the number of stitches equal to an inch. Measure the unraveled yarn.

For example, 4 stitches in the swatch = 4 inches of yarn.

② Multiply this yarn length by the number of inches in the desired finished width of your project. This number is the length of yarn required to make 1 row.

For example, 4 inches of yarn x 6 inches of width in a row = 24 inches of yarn needed for 1 row.

③ Multiply the number of rows needed by the number of inches in a row.

For example, 24 inches x 240 rows = 5,760 inches.

④ Convert the inches to yards (36 inches = 1 yard). That's how much yarn you need.

When in doubt, purchase more yarn than you think you'll need. Keep in mind that your gauge may vary slightly throughout a project. You must also remember to account for the yarn tails you leave at the beginning and end of your work and every time you change color or add a new ball of yarn.

CHAPTER 3

Basic Techniques

Now that you know the basic stitches, you're ready to move on to more adventurous crochet. In this chapter, you will learn how to shape your crochet pieces, work in the round, change colors, and finish off a project.

Increase

You use increases to add one or more stitches to a round or row.

Pattern abbreviation: INC or inc.

Increase at the Edge of a Row

You use extra chains to provide room for more stitches at the edge of a row.

1 At the end of the row before the increase: Work a chain stitch for each increase, plus the turning chain.

NOTE: Refer to "Make a Turning Chain" on page 34 for more information.

2 Turn your work. Skip the number of chains necessary for the turning chain. Work stitches into the extra chains.

3 Finish the row as usual.

NOTE: To avoid mistakes, it's important to count the number of stitches in your rows. Doing so is especially critical when increasing or decreasing.

Increase within a Row or Round

Work multiple stitches into 1 stitch to create an increase within a row or round.

To increase by 1 stitch, work 2 stitches into a single stitch from the previous row.

To increase by 3 stitches at once, work 4 stitches into a single stitch from the previous row.

For a more subtle increase of 2 or more stitches, spread the increases out over multiple stitches. (This example shows an increase of 2 stitches.)

1. Work 2 stitches into the stitch from the previous row.

2. Work 1 stitch into the next stitch from the previous row.

3. Work 2 stitches into the next stitch from the previous row.

4. Work even across the rest of the row.

NOTE: "Work even" means to complete the row without changes in stitch pattern and without increasing or decreasing.

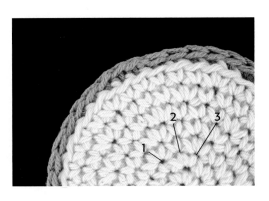

You use decreases to reduce the number of stitches in a row or round. Doing so is useful in shaping crocheted fabric. There are several methods for decreasing by leaving stitches unworked; three methods are described here.

Pattern abbreviation: DEC or dec.

SKIP A STITCH

Skip the next stitch and work into the stitch after it as usual. This method decreases a row by 1 stitch but also creates a small hole. Many patterns use this method to create decorative holes in the fabric.

BEGINNING OF A ROW

Do not make a turning chain. Work a slip stitch (see page 35) into each of the stitches from the previous row to be decreased (a). Make a turning chain that is necessary for the height of the row, but do not turn. Continue with the row as usual. This creates a sharp decrease on one side. On the next row, do not work into the slip stitches (b).

END OF A ROW

At the end of a row, do not work the final number of stitches equal to the number to be decreased. Leave the proper number of stitches unworked, create your turning chain, and proceed to the next row.

NOTE: To decrease by 3 stitches, complete the row by working into the fourth stitch from the end.

You create a gradual decrease by working stitches together. You can use this flexible decrease method anywhere in a row. Any number of stitches can be worked together, depending on the shaping effect you want. You can use any kind of stitch for this type of decrease. We've used double crochet as an example here.

Pattern abbreviation: #TOG (replace # with the number of stitches to be worked together, as in 2TOG).

Work Stitches Together

1 Work the stitch as usual until the final step, when 2 loops remain on the hook. Do not complete the stitch.

2 Insert the hook into the next stitch and work to the same point. There are now 4 loops on the hook. Yarn over and draw the yarn through all 4 loops.

The decrease you have created will look like 2 stitches sharing a top.

For a gradual decrease, use one or more 2TOGs worked over the course of a row or round. For a sharper decrease, use a 3TOG or 4TOG by repeating step 2 until 4 or 5 loops remain on the hook, respectively.

Create a Ring Using the Chain Stitch

You can use the chain stitch to create a ring as a foundation for working in the round. This method is easy to work and creates a strong center, but will likely leave a hole in the center of your piece.

Chain Stitch

1 Chain 5.

NOTE: We're using 5 chains as an example. You can use this technique with any number of chains greater than 3. See the section "Make a Chain Stitch" on page 30 for more on chains.

2 Slip stitch in the fifth chain from the hook (the first chain you made).

NOTE: See the section "Make a Slip Stitch" on page 35 for more on slip stitch.

TIP

There are different ways to work into the ring:

1. Work into each chain stitch as you would work into a foundation chain.

2. Ignore the individual chain stitches and work around the chain, through the center of the ring. To do so, insert your hook through the center of the ring, yarn over, and draw the yarn around the chains. Complete the stitch as usual.

Using a loop to form your foundation for working in the round creates an invisible, adjustable ring. The first round of stitches is worked into the loop.

Loop

① Begin with a slip knot on your hook, leaving a longer tail than usual.

② Wrap the yarn tail twice around your 2 middle fingers to create a loop.

③ Insert your hook into the ring. Yarn over.

④ Draw the yarn through, and continue to draw it through the loop on the hook (the slip knot; see photo on the right). This makes one slip stitch.

⑤ Work the appropriate number of chains to create the turning chain for the stitch you're using. Proceed by making the required number of stitches into the ring.

NOTE: This image shows how to work a single crochet into the loop ring.

⑥ Pull the tail gently but firmly to tighten and close the ring.

FAQ

It is important to have a long tail to weave in at the center. Weave through the entire first round before cutting. This makes the center stronger.

You can make hats, baskets, flowers, and garments by working in the round. Use rows to create a round piece with an even, finished edge. The following instructions use single crochet, but you can use any stitch.

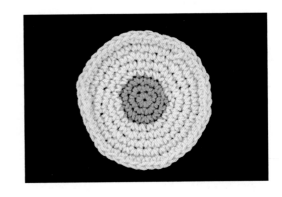

Rounds

To get started, choose one of the ring methods from the preceding sections.

1 Chain 1 to create a turning chain. Do not turn.

NOTE: Just as you do when working in straight rows, you use turning chains at the beginning or end of a round to accommodate the height of your stitches. Unlike when working in rows, you do not turn your work at the end of a round unless instructed to do so. Make a turning chain and continue working in the same direction.

2 Work 6 single crochets into the ring.

3 Slip stitch into the top of the first single crochet of the round to join.

④ Chain 1. Work 2 single crochets into the first single crochet from the previous round.

⑤ Work 2 single crochets into each stitch in the round.

⑥ Slip stitch into the top of the first single crochet of the round to join.

There will be 10 single crochets in this round.

Spiral Method

Work in the round without joining rows or making a turning chain simply by building on top of the last round without a turning chain. The following instructions use single crochet, but you can use any stitch.

To get started, choose one of the ring methods from the preceding sections.

1. Work 6 single crochets into the ring.

2. Work 2 single crochets into each single crochet of the previous round. Mark the first single crochet in this round with a stitch marker or a scrap piece of yarn to help you keep track of where the round started. Move the marker with each new round.

3. Continue to work 2 single crochets into each stitch of the round.

4. Work each round without joining with a slip stitch or creating a turning chain.

Shape in the Round

Working in the round from the center out often involves creating a flat circle. In order to accomplish this, increases are made evenly throughout each round. The table on the next page displays the distribution of increases for several common stitch counts.

Gradual, Spaced Increases

Continue from the final step from one of the methods from the preceding section.

Increasing each row by the same number of stitches you started with is a good general rule for creating gradual increases. You achieve this by interspersing increases with even work so that the number of increases you make are evenly distributed throughout the round.

The following example is for a piece that starts with 6 stitches in the first round.

Gradual, Spaced Increases				
Round 1:	5 stitches	6 stitches	7 stitches	8 stitches
Round 2. Increase in every stitch for a total of:	10 stitches	12 stitches	14 stitches	16 stitches
Round 3. Increase in every other stitch for a total of:	15 stitches	18 stitches	21 stitches	24 stitches
Round 4. Increase in every third stitch for a total of:	20 stitches	24 stitches	28 stitches	32 stitches
Round 5. Increase in every fourth stitch for a total of:	25 stitches	30 stitches	35 stitches	40 stitches
Round 6. Increase in every fifth stitch for a total of:	30 stitches	36 stitches	42 stitches	48 stitches
Round 7. Increase in every sixth stitch for a total of:	35 stitches	42 stitches	49 stitches	56 stitches
Round 8. Increase in every seventh stitch for a total of:	40 stitches	48 stitches	56 stitches	64 stitches

TIP

Notice that each round contains a number of evenly spaced increases equal to the number of stitches in Round 1. Distributing the increases as directed creates a polygon instead of a true circle (this is especially noticeable when you have worked several rounds). To create a true circle, work the same number of increases in each round but stagger where you place the first increase so that you're not placing the increases in the same place on each round.

Whether it's time to switch to a new ball of yarn because you're running out or because you want to change to a different color or texture, you can make the switch at any point in your work. This method creates a secure and nearly invisible yarn change, whether you are continuing in the same color or switching to a new color. It's excellent for crocheting stripes.

Change to a New Color or Ball of Yarn

1 Work the final stitch of the row with the original yarn until only 2 loops remain on the hook. Do not complete the stitch.

2 Yarn over with the original yarn and the new yarn held together. Leave a 6-inch tail of new yarn hanging off the back of the hook.

③ Draw both yarns through the loops on the hook to complete the stitch.

④ Drop the old yarn. Continue crocheting as directed with the new yarn only.

3

⑤ If you've changed yarn at the end of a row, make a turning chain with the new yarn and turn.

If you've changed yarn in the middle of a row (see the photo below), continue to work across the row as normal.

NOTE: You'll need to weave in the tails left by the old and new yarns. See the section "Weave In Yarn Tails" on page 65.

4

TIP

The stitch where two yarns are combined may be a bit fragile, which makes weaving in the ends important. Weave in the ends securely and the stitch will stay put.

5

Fasten Off and Weave In Yarn Tails

Even though you have completed all the crochet stitches for your project, you still have some work left to do. These finishing techniques will help you create a neat, finished-looking item.

Fasten Off

To secure your yarn so that your stitches don't unravel after you've completed your project, you need to fasten off.

1 Complete the last stitch.

2 Cut the yarn, leaving a tail that's at least 6 inches long.

3 Yarn over, draw the entire tail through the loop, and pull tight.

Now you're ready to weave in the tail or add a decorative edging. (See Chapter 13 for more on edgings.)

TIP

Sometimes a knot is necessary to keep the yarn securely fastened. Tie a simple knot before weaving in the tail.

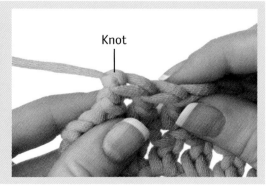

Knot

Weave In Yarn Tails

Every project involves at least two yarn tails: one created when you make your slip knot or beginning loop, and one left when you fasten off. You also leave yarn tails when you join new yarn or change colors. Weave the tails into your work to avoid unsightly, bumpy knots and to prevent your stitches from unraveling.

Use a tapestry needle to weave yarn tails through the stitches on the wrong side of the fabric to secure them and hide them from view. The *wrong side* is the side that will not face out when the piece is completed (on a garment, the side worn against the skin).

To make sure that the tail remains secure, create a *U, C,* or *Z* shape as you sew the yarn into the crochet stitches. The more zigzags there are, the less likely the yarn will come out.

2

3

① Insert the needle into the body of the first stitch and draw the needle through.

② Insert the needle into the next stitch.

③ Insert the needle into the next row.

④ Insert the needle into the next row.

⑤ Continue weaving in the tail, creating a horseshoe or zigzag shape. Take care to make the tail as inconspicuous as possible on the side of the work that will show (the right side).

⑥ When you're sure you've woven in enough that the tail won't slip out, tug on the crochet fabric in all directions to settle the tail in place. Cut the end of the tail if necessary.

CHAPTER 4

Stitch Variations

Building on the basic crochet stitches opens up infinite possibilities for texture, structure, lace, and beyond. Slight variations in how you make your stitches can create subtle differences in the look and feel of your crocheted fabric.

Make a Double Treble Crochet

The double treble crochet stitch (also known as quadruple crochet) is very tall. It is frequently used in combination with other stitches to create dramatic stitch patterns.

Pattern abbreviation: DTR or dtr.

Double Treble Crochet

Foundation chain: Create a chain equal to the number of stitches you require, plus 5. (See the section "Make a Foundation Chain" on page 32 for more information.) Work your first double treble crochet into the sixth chain from your hook.

1 Yarn over 3 times.

2 Insert the hook into the next stitch, yarn over, and draw the yarn through the stitch.

There are now 5 loops on the hook.

3 Yarn over and draw the yarn through the first 2 loops on the hook.

There are now 4 loops on the hook.

4 Yarn over and draw the yarn through the next 2 loops on the hook.

There are now 3 loops on the hook.

5 Yarn over and draw the yarn through the next 2 loops on the hook.

There are now 2 loops on the hook.

6 Yarn over and draw the yarn through both loops on the hook (a).

You have created 1 double treble crochet (b).

6a   6b

7 Repeat steps 1–6 until you have completed your first row of double treble crochet. Chain 5 to create a turning chain.

8 Turn the piece. Skip the first stitch at the beginning of the row. The turning chain counts as the first double treble crochet of the row. Follow steps 1–6 to create a double treble crochet in the second stitch of the row and in each stitch thereafter.

TIP

Because the turning chain likely counts as a double treble crochet in your pattern, work into the top chain as though it were a proper stitch, unless your pattern tells you otherwise.

Some patterns call for even taller stitches. Triple treble starts with four yarn overs and follows the same progression of steps: continue to work the stitch as you would the double treble, until one loop remains on the hook.

The extended single crochet stitch is taller than the single crochet stitch. (See the section "Make a Single Crochet" on page 36.) It creates an interesting texture that adds a change of pace to any project.

Pattern abbreviation: ESC or esc.

Extended Single Crochet

Foundation chain: Create a chain equal to the number of stitches you require, plus 2. (See the section "Make a Foundation Chain" on page 32 for details.) Work your first extended single crochet into the third chain from your hook.

1 Insert the hook into the next stitch, yarn over, and draw up a loop.

There are now 2 loops on the hook.

2 Yarn over and draw the yarn through the first loop on the hook.

There are now 2 loops on the hook.

NOTE: Add step 2 to any basic stitch to make an extended crochet stitch.

③ Yarn over and draw the yarn through both loops on the hook. There is now 1 loop on the hook.

You have created 1 extended single crochet.

④ Repeat steps 1–3 until you have completed your first row of extended single crochet. Chain 2 to create a turning chain.

⑤ Turn the piece. Insert your hook through both loops at the top of the first stitch from the previous row. Repeat steps 1–4.

The extended double crochet stitch is a taller variation of standard double crochet. (See the section "Make a Double Crochet" on page 40 for more information.)

Pattern abbreviation: EDC or edc.

Extended Double Crochet

Foundation chain: Create a chain equal to the number of stitches you require, plus 3. (See the section "Make a Foundation Chain" on page 32.) Work your first extended double crochet into the fourth chain from the hook.

1

① Yarn over. Insert the hook into the next stitch, yarn over, and draw the yarn through the stitch.

There are now 3 loops on the hook.

② Yarn over and draw the yarn through the first loop on the hook.

There are now 3 loops on the hook.

③ Yarn over and draw the yarn through 2 loops on the hook.

There are now 2 loops on the hook.

2

3

④ Yarn over and draw the yarn through the 2 remaining loops on the hook (a).

You have created 1 extended double crochet (b).

4a

4b

⑤ Repeat steps 1–4 until you have completed your first row of extended double crochet. Chain 3 to create a turning chain.

⑥ Turn the piece. Skip the first stitch at the beginning of the row. The turning chain counts as the first extended double crochet of the row. Repeat steps 1–5 to create an extended double crochet in the second stitch of the row and in each stitch thereafter.

NOTE: Because the turning chain counts as the first extended double crochet at the beginning of a row, work into it as though it were an extended double crochet stitch.

The extended half double crochet is a bit taller than the standard half double crochet stitch.

Pattern abbreviation: EHDC or ehdc.

Extended Half Double Crochet

Foundation chain: Create a chain equal to the number of stitches you require, plus 2. (See the section "Make a Foundation Chain" on page 32.) Work your first extended half double crochet into the third chain from your hook.

1 Yarn over. Insert the hook into the next stitch, yarn over, and draw the yarn through the stitch.

There are now 3 loops on the hook.

2 Yarn over and draw the yarn through the first loop on the hook.

There are now 3 loops on the hook.

3 Yarn over and draw the yarn through all 3 loops on the hook.

One loop remains on the hook.

1

2

3

You have created 1 extended half double crochet.

④ Repeat steps 1–3 until you have completed your first row of extended half double crochet. Chain 3 to create a turning chain.

⑤ Turn the piece. Skip the first stitch at the beginning of the row. The turning chain counts as the first extended half double crochet of the row. Repeat steps 1–4 to create an extended half double crochet in the second stitch of the row and in each stitch thereafter.

4

5

TIP

Because the turning chain counts as the first extended half double crochet at the beginning of a row, you work into it as though it were an extended half double crochet stitch.

Crab stitch (also known as shrimp stitch, reverse single crochet, or corded reverse edging) is simple and decorative. Worked in reverse direction (from left to right if you are right-handed or right to left if you are left-handed), crab stitch is easy to make. It does not have a pattern abbreviation but is frequently referred to as rev sc or rsc.

Crab Stitch

Because crab stitch is worked in reverse, begin with a foundation row of any stitch. Here, we used single crochet. (See the section "Make a Single Crochet" on page 36.) These steps are for right-handers. Lefties can reverse the direction.

1 At the end of a row of any stitch, do not turn your work or make a turning chain. Insert your hook into the next stitch *to the right.*

2 Yarn over and draw the yarn through the stitch.

There are now 2 loops on the hook.

2

3 Draw the yarn through the 2 loops on your hook, the same way you would if you were working a single crochet.

You have made 1 crab stitch.

4 Continue to make crab stitches by inserting your hook into the next stitch to the right. When you reach the end of the row, do not turn your work.

3

4

Using texture in your crochet work creates variety and visual interest. In this section, you will learn the simplest technique to add a subtle texture to your basic stitches by working into only the front loops or back loops of stitches from the previous row.

Pattern abbreviations: FLO and BLO.

Front Loop/Back Loop Texture Changes

Throughout this book, we instruct you to create stitches by inserting your hook into both loops of the stitch from the previous row, as shown here. You can also insert your hook into only the back or front loop when you work a stitch. Working into only one of the loops creates a subtle change in texture.

The *front loop* is the loop closer to you when you are holding your crochet work in front of you. Working into the front loop only is also referred to as a *front porch stitch*.

The *back loop* is the one farther from you. Working into the back loop is also known as a *back porch stitch*.

Crochet a swatch using any stitch. After working a few rows using both loops, crochet an entire row working into the front loop only. Note the slight ridge on one side of the fabric created by that unused back loop. Make another swatch by working the back loop only.

Alternating between working stitches into the front and back loops of the same row creates a rumpled texture.

Working into only one loop in every row for an entire piece creates a fabric with gentle drape. The fabric feels less dense than when you work both loops.

NOTE: Patterns indicate whether to work in the front loop or back loop only; if no mention is made, work in both loops.

Make a Spike Stitch

You can use spike stitches in a number of ways to add elaborate-looking details to crocheted fabric. Just work into any space below the top loops of the stitches from the previous row; this results in a "spike" of yarn connecting the stitch you have chosen to the current working row.

You can work a spike stitch into fabric composed of any crochet stitch. This example uses single crochet. Begin with at least 2 rows of single crochet.

Spike Stitch

① Instead of inserting your hook into the top loops of the next stitch, insert your hook into the space directly below the next stitch from the previous row.

② Yarn over and draw up a loop. Pull this loop up to the working row, taking care not to pull the stitch too tight.

③ Yarn over and draw the yarn through both loops on the hook.

You have created one single crochet spike stitch.

Use a Spike Stitch

You can use spike stitches in a variety of ways to add interest to your crochet work. Any of the following simple combinations can be used as a border or inside a piece.

WORK ALTERNATING SINGLE CROCHETS AND SPIKES

Alternate single crochets and spikes in the same row. This effect is striking as a border.

WORK LONG SPIKES

Form longer spikes by working into a space several rows below the working row. When drawing up a loop, be sure to make it nice and long (a). Doing so prevents the fabric from buckling.

Combine single crochets with long spikes to add dramatic detail (b).

Work * 1 single crochet, 1 long spike. Repeat from * to the end of the row.

a

b

EXPERIMENT WITH COLOR

Changing color with each row, alternate working the following 2 spike rows with rows of single crochet between them. (See the section "Join New Yarn" on page 62 for more on changing colors.)

Spike row 1: 1 single crochet, 1 spike, * 3 single crochet, 1 spike. Repeat from * to the end of the row.

Spike row 2: * 3 single crochet, 1 spike. Repeat from * to the end of the row.

Make Crossed Stitches

You create crossed stitches by working pairs of stitches in backward order, creating a pattern of Xs. Using treble crochet as an example, this section shows you a method for crossing stitches that you can use with any crochet stitch.

Make Rows of Crossed Treble Crochet

You can work this stitch directly into a foundation chain or into any row of stitches. To make crossed treble crochet, start with a foundation chain of an odd number of stitches, plus a turning chain of 4.

1 Work a treble crochet into the sixth chain from the hook.

2 Tilt the piece toward you and work a treble crochet into the chain preceding the last stitch made.

You have created a pair of crossed stitches.

3 Skip 1 stitch and work a treble crochet into the next stitch.

4 Work a treble crochet into the skipped stitch preceding the last treble crochet made.

5 Repeat steps 3 and 4 until you have reached the last chain. Work a treble crochet into the last chain. Chain 4 and turn.

6 Skip the first stitch at the beginning of the row. The turning chain counts as a treble crochet. Repeat steps 3 and 4 until you reach the last stitch. Work a treble crochet into the turning chain of the previous row. Chain 4 and turn.

TIP

Any pair of crochet stitches can be crossed. You can also try placing chain stitches between each set of crossed pairs.

Work Double Crochet Post Stitches

Working around the front or back post of a stitch from the previous row creates stitches in relief. This technique is often used to form ribs or cables. A post stitch is also known as a raised stitch.

Pattern abbreviations: FLO and BLO.

Front Post Double Crochet

Post stitches can't be worked into the foundation chain; you must begin with a foundation row of tall stitches (for instance, double crochet, as in this example). At the end of this foundation row, chain 2 for the turning chain and turn.

NOTE: Because a post stitch is shorter than a stitch worked into the top of another stitch, the turning chain for a post stitch is shorter by 1 chain.

1 Yarn over. Insert the hook from front to back to front around the post of the stitch in the previous row.

2 Yarn over and draw the yarn around the post to pull up a loop (a). Complete the double crochet (b).

2a

2b

Back Post Double Crochet

For this example, start with a row of double crochet. At the end of this foundation row, chain 2 for the turning chain and turn.

1 Yarn over. Insert the hook from back to front to back around the post of the stitch in the previous row.

2 Yarn over and draw up a loop. Complete the double crochet.

TIP

To create ribbing, use an even number of stitches. Begin by working a FLO double crochet into the first stitch and a BLO double crochet into the next stitch. Continue alternating front and back post stitches across the row. Make a turning chain and turn. Repeat this row to create a ribbed pattern.

Work a Treble Crochet Post Stitch

Work a treble crochet around the front or back post of a stitch from the previous row to create ribbing or other raised textures.

Pattern abbreviations: FPTR and BPTR.

Front Post Treble Crochet

You can't work post stitches into the foundation chain; for this example, begin with 1 row of treble crochet.

① Yarn over twice. Insert the hook from front to back to front around the post of the treble crochet stitch from the previous row.

② Yarn over and draw the yarn around the post. Complete the treble crochet.

Back Post Treble Crochet

For this example, start with a row of treble crochet.

1 Yarn over twice. Insert the hook from back to front to back around the post of the stitch from the previous row.

2 Yarn over and draw up a loop (a). Complete the treble crochet (b).

2a

2b

CHAPTER 5

Combining Stitches

Now you're ready to combine the stitches you've learned to add another dimension to your crochet. Stitches can be combined, worked into the same space, or joined at their tops to create juicy 3-D stitches. In this chapter, you can also try your hand at some step-by-step patterns as you learn.

Clusters

Clusters are in a category that includes a variety of stitch combinations, such as those worked together to create bobbles and puffs. The stitches in a basic cluster are joined at the top, similar to a decrease, and can be worked into one space or over several spaces. This example uses treble crochet (see the section "Make a Treble Crochet" on page 42 for more information) but you can make clusters with any stitch.

See Chapter 3 for more on how to work stitches together to decrease.

Make a Cluster with Treble Crochet

1. Work a treble crochet until the final step, when 2 loops remain on the hook. Do not complete the stitch (see photo).

2. Insert the hook into the next stitch and work another treble crochet to the same point. There are now 3 loops on the hook.

3. Repeat step 2 to create a partial treble crochet stitch in the next stitch. There are now 3 partial treble crochets (4 loops on the hook).

4. Yarn over (a) and draw the yarn through all 4 loops (b).

4a

4b

Work a Simple Treble Cluster Pattern

NOTE: The foundation chain for the simple cluster pattern should consist of a multiple of 3 stitches plus 4, plus 1 for the turning chain (for example, 12 + 4 = 16 + 1 = 17).

1 Row 1: Work 1 single crochet into the second chain from the hook. Work 1 single crochet into each chain across the row, chain 4, and turn.

2 Row 2: Skip the first stitch. The turning chain counts as the first treble crochet of the row. Work 1 treble crochet into the next stitch. * Chain 2 and work 1 cluster of 3 treble crochets over the next 3 stitches (a). Repeat from * until there are 2 stitches left to work in the row. Chain 2. Work 1 treble crochet into each of the last 2 stitches, chain 1, and turn (b).

3 Row 3: Work 1 single crochet into each of the first 2 stitches. * Work 2 single crochets into the chain space; work 2 single crochets into the space between the clusters. Repeat from * until there are 2 stitches left to work in the row. Work 1 single crochet into each of the last 2 stitches, chain 1, and turn (see photo).

4 Row 4: Work 1 single crochet into each stitch across the row, chain 1, and turn.

5 Row 5: Work 1 single crochet into each stitch across the row, chain 4, and turn.

6 Repeat rows 2–5.

2a

2b

Bobbles

Acluster of tall stitches is worked into the same space and joined together at the top, creating a bobble that stands out. The bobble is a popular way to create a playful texture.

Make a Bobble with Double Crochet

To create a bobble, you work stitches together in the same manner as when making a decrease. (See the section on decreases on page 53 for more information on how to decrease.)

1 Work a double crochet as usual until the final step, when 2 loops remain on the hook. Do not complete the stitch.

2 Insert the hook back into the same stitch and work another double crochet to the same point. There are now 3 loops on the hook.

3 Repeat step 2 to create 2 more partial double crochet stitches. There are now 4 partial double crochets (5 loops on the hook).

4 Yarn over and draw the yarn through all 5 loops.

5 Chain 1 to complete the stitch. You have made a bobble.

1

2

3

5

Work a Simple Bobble Pattern

The foundation chain for this pattern should consist of an even number of stitches, plus 1 for the turning chain (for example, 14 + 1 = 15).

2a

2b

① Row 1: Work 1 single crochet into the second chain from the hook. Continue to work 1 single crochet into each chain across the row. Chain 1 and turn.

② Row 2: Work 1 single crochet into the first stitch. * Work 1 single crochet into the next stitch; work 1 bobble into the next stitch (a). Repeat from * until 1 stitch remains. Work 1 single crochet into the last stitch. Chain 1 and turn (b).

③ Row 3: Work 1 single crochet into each stitch across the row, chain 1, and turn.

Skip
Work into

NOTE: When working into the tops of bobble stitches, it looks like there are 2 stitches to work into. Skip the chain from the top of the bobble and work into the next stitch (see photo).

④ Row 4: Work 1 single crochet into the first stitch. * Work 1 bobble into the next stitch; work 1 single crochet into the next stitch. Repeat from * until 1 stitch remains. Work 1 single crochet into the last stitch. Chain 1 and turn.

4

6

⑤ Row 5: Repeat row 3.

⑥ Repeat rows 2–5.

93

Puffs

Puff stitches are bobbles worked with a half double crochet instead of a taller stitch. (See the section "Make a Half Double Crochet" on page 38 for more information.) This results in the puff being shorter and puffier than a bobble.

Make a Simple Puff

❶ Yarn over. Insert the hook into the next stitch, yarn over, and draw a loop through the stitch. This loop should be looser than the loop you normally create when working a half double crochet.

❷ Repeat step 1 in the same stitch 3 more times to create 3 more partial half double crochets (4 partial half double crochets in total).

There are now 9 loops on the hook.

❸ Yarn over and draw the yarn through all 9 loops on the hook.

❹ Chain 1 to complete the stitch. You have created 1 puff stitch (see photo).

NOTE: When working from a pattern with a symbol chart, the symbol for a given cluster, bobble, puff, or popcorn will reflect the type and number of stitches used in that specific pattern.

Work a Simple Puff Pattern

Try your hand at this simple puff pattern. Begin with a foundation chain with an odd number of stitches, plus 2 (for example, 13 + 2 = 15).

1 Row 1: Work 1 half double crochet into the third chain from the hook. Continue to work 1 half double crochet into each chain across the row, chain 1, and turn.

2 Row 2: Work 1 single crochet into the first stitch of the row. * Work a puff into the next stitch. Work 1 single crochet into the next stitch. * Repeat from * to * until 1 stitch remains. Work 1 single crochet into the last stitch (see photo). Chain 2 and turn.

3 Row 3: Work 1 half double crochet into the first stitch. * Skip the next stitch (the chain from the top of the puff stitch—see photo). Work 1 half double crochet into each of the next 2 stitches. * Repeat from * to * to the end of the row. Chain 1 and turn.

4 Repeat rows 2 and 3.

TIP

The texture and height of a simple puff stitch are determined by the length of the long loop in step 1. Pulling the long loops can become more difficult as you begin to make the third partial half double crochet. Use your finger to pull it loose enough to match the other loops.

Popcorns

A popcorn consists of several tall stitches worked into the same space. Unlike a bobble, each stitch in a popcorn is worked to completion, and then all are gathered together in the final step.

This example uses double crochet. See the section "Make a Double Crochet" on page 40 for more information.

Make a Popcorn Using Four Double Crochets

① Work a double crochet into the next stitch.

② Work 3 more double crochet stitches into the same stitch.

Four double crochets have now been worked into 1 stitch.

③ Slip your hook out of the remaining loop.

④ Insert your hook into the top of the first double crochet from this group and then into the empty loop.

⑤ Draw the empty loop through the top of that stitch and chain 1 to finish the popcorn.

Work a Simple Popcorn Pattern

Try your hand at this simple popcorn pattern. The foundation chain should be a multiple of 3 stitches, plus 1 for the turning chain (for example: 12 + 1 = 13).

2a

2b

❶ Row 1: Work 1 single crochet into the second chain from the hook. Continue to work 1 single crochet into each chain across the row. Chain 3 and turn.

❷ Row 2: Skip the first stitch. (The turning chain counts as the first double crochet of the row.) Work 1 double crochet into the next stitch; work 1 popcorn into the next stitch (a). * Work 1 double crochet into each of the next 2 stitches; work 1 popcorn into the next stitch. Repeat from * until there are 3 stitches left to work in the row. Work 1 double crochet into each of the last 3 stitches. Chain 3 and turn (b).

3

❸ Row 3: Skip the first stitch. (The turning chain counts as the first double crochet of the row.) Work 1 double crochet into the next stitch; work 1 popcorn into the next stitch. * Work 1 double crochet into each of the next 2 stitches; work 1 popcorn into the next stitch. Repeat from * until 1 stitch remains. Work 1 double crochet into the last stitch. Chain 3 and turn.

4

❹ Repeat rows 2 and 3.

Bullions

The bullion stitch breaks from the standard format of most crochet stitches. This stitch involves making many yarn overs (from 6 to 10, depending on the pattern) and has a texture all its own.

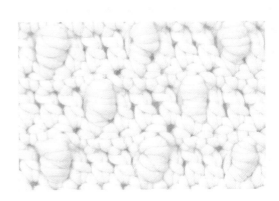

Make a Bullion Stitch

❶ Yarn over 8 times. Insert the hook into the next stitch, yarn over, and draw up a loop.

❷ Yarn over and draw the yarn over through all the loops on the hook.

This can be tricky. Keep the yarn overs loose, and use your fingers to ease loops through one by one.

1

❸ Yarn over and draw the yarn through the remaining loop on the hook. You have completed 1 bullion stitch.

2

3

Work a Simple Bullion Pattern

1 Row 1: Work 1 single crochet into the second chain from the hook. Continue to work 1 single crochet into each chain across the row. Chain 3 and turn.

2 Row 2: Skip the first stitch. (The turning chain counts as the first double crochet of the row.) * Work 1 double crochet into each of the next 2 stitches; work 1 bullion into the next stitch (a). Repeat from * until you reach the last 3 stitches of the row. Work 1 double crochet into each of the last 3 stitches (b).

Repeat rows 1 and 2.

2a

2b

Follow a Pattern

Crochet patterns can look intimidating, but the information in this chapter will teach you how to navigate them with ease. You will learn how to read crochet shorthand and how to figure your stitch and row gauge.

Knowing how to read a crochet pattern enables you to make any project accurately. In this section, you will learn about common pattern conventions.

Understand Pattern Conventions

ABBREVIATIONS

A crochet pattern is essentially a set of step-by-step instructions for how to construct a finished piece. In the interest of fitting the greatest amount of instruction onto one page, a fairly standard set of abbreviations is used for frequently occurring terms like stitch names and techniques. Becoming familiar with these abbreviations enables you to effortlessly make sense of crochet shorthand. See the next page for a list of commonly used abbreviations.

Gauge

12 stitches and 14 rows = 4 inches (10cm)

1. Start with an adjustable ring.
2. Round 1: Work 6 SC into ring, Sl st in 1st SC to join roun
3. Round 2: * 1 SC and 1 DC in next SC, rep from * across round (12 sts total).
4. Round 3: * 2 SC in next st, 1 SC in next st, rep from * across round (18 sts total).

SYNTAX

In the interest of brevity, crochet patterns often utilize the following devices to organize steps. With a bit of practice, you'll find that these devices make intricate patterns less wordy and easier to follow.

Parentheses ( ) and brackets [ ] are used to group sections of instructions. Often, these symbols indicate a certain number of stitches that are to be worked into the same stitch, as in:

Work [SC, ch 2, DC, ch2, SC] into next st.

Asterisks (*) are also used to group instructions. They indicate a set of instructions to be repeated a certain number of times, as in:

SC in first st, * DC in next st, ch 1, skip 1 st, SC in next st. Repeat from * to end of row.

In this case, you would continue to repeat the "double crochet in the next stitch, chain 1, skip 1 stitch, single crochet in the next stitch" until you completed the row.

As we have mentioned, professionally produced crochet patterns typically use a set of fairly universal shorthand abbreviations to conserve space. The following is a list of commonly occurring abbreviations and what they stand for.

Crochet Abbreviations	
Abbreviation	**Meaning**
beg	beginning
bet	between
bl	back loop
blo or BLO	work through the back loop only
BPdc or BPDC	back post double crochet
BPtr or BPTR	back post treble (or triple) crochet
CC	contrasting color
ch or CH	chain
ch-sp or CH SP	chain space
cont	continue
dc or DC	double crochet
dec	decrease
dtr or DTR	double treble
edc or EDC	extended double crochet
ehdc or EHDC	extended half double crochet
esc or ESC	extended single crochet
Est	established
Fl	front loop
flo or FLO	work through the front loop only
FPdc or FPDC	front post double crochet
FPtr or FPTR	front post treble (or triple) crochet
hdc or HDC	half double crochet

Crochet Abbreviations (continued)	
Abbreviation	**Meaning**
hk	hook
inc	increase
lp	loop
MC	main color
patt st	pattern stitch
pm	place marker
prev	previous
rem	remaining
rep	repeat
rev sc	reverse single crochet
rnd	round
RS	right side
sc or SC	single crochet
sk	skip
Sl st, sl st, SL ST, or SS	slip stitch
sp or SP	space
st or ST	stitch
tch or TCH or TC	turning chain
Tks	Tunisian knit stitch
Tog or TOG	together
Tps	Tunisian purl stitch
tr or TR	treble (or triple) crochet
Tss	Tunisian simple stitch
WS	wrong side
yo or YO	yarn over

TIP

Our discussion in this chapter focuses on how to read and make sense of crochet shorthand in patterns. Some patterns, however—especially those published in Europe and Asia—utilize symbols to convey crochet instructions. Each stitch or stitch cluster is represented by a symbol. See Chapter 9 for more information on crochet symbols.

Crochet patterns aren't as complicated as they might seem at first. This section gives you some tips for making sense of the shorthand and gaining the confidence to decipher even the most complicated patterns.

At the top of a pattern, you will find information about sizing, materials, gauge, and stitch notes.

Pattern Information

SIZING

The sizing of a garment is indicated with the smallest size followed by larger sizes in parentheses, as in:

Size: small (medium, large)

Chest measurement: 32–36 (38–42, 44–48) inches

When a pattern calls for different instructions depending on size, those instructions are given in a similar fashion, with instructions for the first measurement followed by instructions for larger measurements in parentheses, as in:

Work 18 (20, 22) SC. CH 39 (39, 45)

Sizing might not be indicated for some patterns, such as bags and scarves.

Cozy, Webby Sweater

This sweater is as cozy as it is contemporary. You use a large hook with two strands of DK-weight yarn to make a simple, webby fabric. The body is worked in one piece, reducing the amount of seaming necessary. You add the collar along the front and neck after the body is complete.

Specifications

Materials
10 (10, 12) balls South West Trading Company *Optimum DK* (100% wool, 154 yd./50g) in Silver

Techniques used
Ch   Chain
SC   Single crochet
FLO   Front loop only
Increasing and decreasing

Finished size
Bust/Chest circumference S (M, XL): 32–36 (38–42, 44–48) inches

MATERIALS

Patterns specify which yarn is called for and how much of the yarn you need. They also tell you which hook size is recommended and what notions and embellishments you need, such as yarn needles, stitch markers, or buttons.

GAUGE

Every pattern for which size is important (such as sweaters, slippers, and hats) includes information about the gauge on which the pattern is based. Always make a gauge swatch (see page 108) before beginning to work on such patterns so that you're sure to end up with the correct size. If your swatch is under or over gauge, adjust your hook size so that you obtain the correct gauge. Use the gauge information given in the pattern to choose a yarn to substitute if you prefer not to use the yarn specified.

STITCH NOTES

Some patterns utilize complex or unique stitch combinations. Notes at the top of a pattern define the abbreviations that refer to these stitch combinations and give you the instructions once so that they don't have to be repeated throughout the pattern, as in:

> Crossed DC: Skip 1 st, work 1 DC into the next st, work 1 DC into the skipped st.

TIP

A crochet pattern is like a recipe: just follow the instructions one step at a time. You might find it helpful to read through the whole pattern before you begin so that you gain a better understanding of the project before you start. On the other hand, you might find the pattern less intimidating if you focus on one step at a time. Whichever way you choose, remember that the pattern is there to help you create something beautiful!

For some projects, crocheting to an exact size is not crucial. For many other projects, however, exact size is imperative. An afghan can be a few inches off, but a few inches off in a sweater creates a garment that is neither useful nor flattering. A little bit of simple math is involved in making sure your finished garments will fit properly. Taking the time to ensure that your gauge is correct will save you from headaches and disappointment down the road.

Gauge

In crochet, *gauge* refers to the number of stitches or rows in a given length of fabric. For example, working a chunky-weight yarn with an 8mm hook might yield 9 single crochet stitches over 4 inches (10cm). For another crocheter, it might yield 6 rows over 4 inches (10cm).

It's important to work up a *gauge swatch* (see the next page) before you begin a crochet project. If your swatch has too many rows or stitches within an area specified in the pattern, use a larger hook or adjust the number of stitches and/or rows you work. If your swatch has too few rows or stitches within an area, use a smaller hook or adjust the number of stitches and/or rows you work. Continue to adjust your hook size until you attain the required gauge.

Every pattern you use should indicate the gauge required to create a finished piece of the proper dimensions. This information is located toward the beginning of the pattern.

Gauge

12 stitches and 14 rows = 4 inches (10cm)

1. Start with an adjustable ring.
2. Round 1: Work 6 SC into ring, Sl st in 1st SC to join roun
3. Round 2: * 1 SC and 1 DC in next SC, rep from * across round (12 sts total).
4. Round 3: * 2 SC in next st, 1 SC in next st, rep from * across round (18 sts total).

Knowing the number of rows that fit in a given length of fabric is extremely important. If your row gauge is off from the required gauge in the pattern you are following, add or subtract rows to ensure a proper fit.

Knowing the number of stitches that fit in a given length of fabric is important, too. In this section, you will learn how to use this information to ensure that your finished project will be the proper size.

Use a Gauge Swatch to Measure Gauge

MAKE A SWATCH

The following instructions are for sport-weight (DK, worsted, bulky, super-bulky) yarn.

1 Using the same yarn and hook you plan to use for your project, chain 28 (24, 20, 16, 12) stitches.

2 Work 24 (22, 18, 14, 10) rows in the same stitch or stitch pattern mentioned in the gauge section of your pattern. Fasten off.

You should end up with a swatch that's approximately 4 inches square. Don't worry if your swatch isn't exactly this size.

NOTE: If you're using a natural-fiber yarn, wash and block your swatch before measuring your gauge. Doing so ensures that your finished project will be the proper size after it's washed. (See the section "Block Your Finished Project" on page 203.)

COUNT THE ROWS

1 Using a ruler, measuring tape, or gauge tool, count the number of rows in 4 inches.

Do not round up or down. If a row is cut off at the 4-inch point, count it as half a row.

2 Make a note of this number.

NOTE: It's common for crocheters to be more concerned about attaining the proper stitch gauge, because adjusting a pattern to accommodate a different stitch gauge is generally more complicated than adjusting for a different row gauge. If your row gauge is off by a small amount, you can adjust by crocheting slightly more or fewer rows in your piece.

COUNT THE STITCHES

1 Using a ruler, measuring tape, or gauge tool, count the number of stitches in 4 inches.

Do not round up or down. If a stitch is cut off at the 4-inch point, count it as half a stitch.

2 Make a note of this number.

ADJUST IF NECESSARY

- If the number of stitches you crocheted over 4 inches is higher than the number required by the pattern you're following, use a larger hook to make a new swatch. Continue to increase your hook size until you create a swatch with the proper gauge. If you need to go up more than a couple of hook sizes, you might want to consider switching to a yarn of a heavier weight.

- If the number of stitches you crocheted over 4 inches is lower than the number required by the pattern, use a smaller hook to make a new swatch. If you need to go down more than a couple of hook sizes, you might want to consider using a lighter-weight yarn.

Whether you are following a pattern or designing your own crocheted garment, you need to start with the measurements of the person who will wear the piece when it is completed. Having correct measurements enables you to create a garment that fits properly and is flattering.

MEASURE YOUR BUST/CHEST

Standing tall, wrap a tape measure around your bust or chest at the fullest part, taking care not to wrap it too tightly. Use this measurement when deciding how much ease you would like your crocheted top to have. *Ease* is how snugly or loosely a garment fits.

If you always wear a bra under a sweater, take your measurements while wearing a bra so that your sweater will fit properly.

MEASURE YOUR WAIST

Standing tall, wrap a tape measure around the narrowest part of your natural waist, taking care not to wrap it too tightly. Use this measurement to figure how much to increase or decrease to shape your top at the midsection.

MEASURE YOUR HIPS

Wrap the tape measure around your hips, over the widest part of your behind. Take care not to wrap the tape measure too tightly. Use this measurement to determine how wide the bottom sweater hem should be if it is going to be long enough to cover your hips.

MEASURE YOUR ARM LENGTH

Hold the tape measure from your armpit to your cuff, with your arm slightly bent. Use this measurement to determine sleeve length.

MEASURE THE WIDTH OF YOUR BACK

Hold the tape measure from the outside of one shoulder to the outside of the other shoulder, across your back. Use this measurement to determine how wide the back of your sweater should be.

MEASURE YOUR TORSO

Hold the tape measure beginning at the most prominent bone at the base of your neck, and extend it to your natural waistline. This measurement helps you determine where to place waist-shaping in relation to the neckline.

MEASURE YOUR HEAD

Wrap the tape measure across your forehead and around the circumference of your head, keeping the measuring tape snug. Use this measurement to determine what size to make a hat.

TIP

The Craft Yarn Council has a list of standardized sizing charts on their Web site www.craftyarn council.com. Click on "Standards" and then "Standard Body Measurements/Sizing" in the left column to see the list of charts.

To ease into your introduction to reading patterns, here are two versions of the same mesh pattern. The first is written in abbreviated form, and the second is in "Plain English."

Mesh is the simplest form of crocheted lace. You use chains connected by single crochet stitches to create an open, versatile piece.

The Pattern

Row 1: SC into 4th ch from hook. * Ch 3, skip 2 chs, and SC into next ch. Rep from * to end of row. Ch 3 and turn.

Row 2: SC into next ch space. * Ch 3 and SC into next ch space. Rep from * to complete row.

Rep row 2 to desired length.

TIP

Also known as a trellis pattern, this simple format makes it easy to create a loose, mesh fabric. You can vary the type of mesh you create by changing one or more aspects of this pattern:

- Increase the number of chains in each arch, but don't increase the number of skipped stitches.
- Increase the number of chains and skipped stitches.
- Use a taller stitch in place of the single crochet.

The Pattern in Plain English

Create a foundation chain that is a multiple of 3 stitches, plus 1.

1 Row 1: Work 1 single crochet into the fourth chain from the hook. (The first 3 chains count as the first arch.)

2 * Chain 3. Leaving the next 2 chains unworked, make a single crochet into the next chain.

3 Repeat from * to the end of the row. When the row is complete, chain 3 (see photo) and turn.

4 Row 2: Work 1 single crochet into the first space created by chains from the previous row. To work into a chain space, insert your hook into the space, yarn over, and draw the yarn through the space (see photo), yarn over, draw the yarn through both loops (one single crochet completed).

5 * Chain 3 and work 1 single crochet into the next chain space. Repeat from * until you have worked a single crochet into the last chain space of the row. Chain 3 and turn.

2

3

CHAPTER 7

Stitch Patterns

In the previous chapter, you learned how words and abbreviations can be used in a crochet pattern. This chapter contains several simple stitch patterns and also introduces how to crochet using only a diagram composed of symbols.

You can use these patterns in any of your projects to add texture and visual interest. Use them as inspiration to experiment with stitch patterns of your own. Play with fibers and colors to create truly unique fabrics.

Alternating a short stitch with a tall stitch creates a soft, slightly rumpled texture. Use this stitch pattern to add style to a simple project.

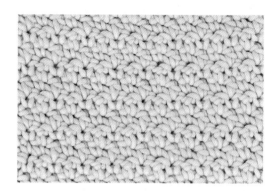

Row 1: SC into 2nd ch from hook. * DC into next ch and SC into next ch. Rep from * to last ch of row. DC into last ch, ch 1, and turn.

Row 2: SC into 1st st. * DC into next st and SC into next st. Rep from * to last st of row. DC into last st, ch 1, and turn.

Rep row 2.

Combining half double crochets with slip stitches creates a dense fabric with an interesting texture. Try using this stitch pattern for hats or purses.

The Pattern

Row 1: Sl st into 2nd ch from hook. * HDC into next ch. Sl st into next ch. Rep from * to last ch of row. HDC into last ch, ch 1, and turn.

Row 2: Sl st into 1st st. * HDC into next st. Sl st into next st. Rep from * to last st of row. HDC into last st, ch 1, and turn.

Rep row 2.

NOTE: You'll work slip stitches into the half double crochet stitches of the previous row and vice versa.

Crunchy Dots Pattern

Placing a tall treble crochet stitch between two single crochet stitches forces the tall stitch to fold on itself and pouf out. This pattern creates a fun, three-dimensional fabric.

The Pattern

Row 1: SC into 2nd ch from hook. * SC into next ch and TR into next ch. Rep from * across to last ch. SC into last ch, ch 1, and turn.

Row 2: SC into 1st st. * SC into next st and TR into next st. Rep from * to last st of row. SC into last st, ch 1, and turn.

Rep row 2.

Alternating chain stitches with single crochet stitches results in a woven effect that makes a lovely fabric with excellent drape.

The Pattern

The foundation chain for this pattern consists of an even number, plus 1 for the turning chain.

Row 1: SC into 2nd ch from hook. * SC, ch 1, and skip 1 ch. Rep from * to last 2 chs. Ch 1 and skip 1 ch. SC into last ch. Ch 1 and turn.

Work 1 SC into next ch

Skip 1 ch

Row 2: SC into 1st st. * SC into ch space, ch 1, and skip 1 st. Rep from * to last 2 sts of row. Ch 1, skip 1 st, and SC into last st. Ch 1 and turn.

Rep row 2.

Use the trinity cluster stitch to create an elegantly textured fabric that you can use either for the body of a work or as a decorative detail. First we explain how to make the stitch, and then follow it with the instructions to create the pattern.

The Trinity Cluster Stitch

1. Insert the hook into the same space as the last stitch, yarn over, and draw the yarn through.

2. Insert the hook into the next stitch, yarn over, and draw the yarn through. Then insert your hook into the next stitch, yarn over, and draw the yarn through.

3. Yarn over and draw the yarn through all 4 loops.

The Pattern

Row 1: SC into 2nd ch from hook. SC into each ch across, ch 1, and turn.

Row 2: SC into 1st st. Work 1 trinity cluster, * ch 1, and work 1 trinity cluster (working 1st st of cluster into same space as prev st). Rep from * across row. Work 1 SC into space of last trinity cluster, ch 1, and turn.

Rep row 2.

Chevrons create a wavy fabric that's especially popular in baby blankets, afghans, and scarves. You shape this chevron by working three stitches into one stitch to create a chevron point.

The Pattern

The foundation chain for this pattern consists of a multiple of 10 plus 1, plus 1 for the turning chain (for example, 30 + 1 + 1 = 32).

Row 1: 2 SC into 2nd ch from hook. * 1 SC into each of the next 3 chs. Skip next 3 chs (a). 1 SC into each of the next 3 chs (b). 3 SC into next ch and 1 SC into each of the next 3 chs. Rep from * to end of row. 2 SC into final ch. Ch 1 and turn.

Row 2: 2 SC into 1st st. * 3 SC, skip 2 sts, 3 SC, and 3 SC into next st. Rep from * to end of row. 2 SC into last st. Ch 1 and turn.

Rep row 2 to desired length.

a
b

TIP

This pattern uses three single crochets after each curve. To vary this chevron pattern, simply add more single crochet stitch spaces between the curves. Adjust the length of your foundation chain accordingly.

For example, to change the pattern to 6 single crochets after each curve, you need a foundation chain with a multiple of 16 plus 1, plus 1 for turning chain.

By working several stitches into one space, you can create a shell or fan. There are infinite varieties of shell patterns; this simple double crochet shell looks lovely in feminine garments or as a simple edging.

The Pattern

The foundation chain for this pattern consists of a multiple of 6, plus 1 for the turning chain (for example 4 x 6 = 24 + 1 = 25).

Row 1: SC into 2nd ch from hook. SC into each ch across, ch 1, and turn.

Shell of 5 DL

SC

Skipped SCS

Row 2: SC into 1st st. * Skip 2 sts. 5 DC into next st, skip 2 sts, and SC into next st. Rep from * to end of row (a). Ch 3 and turn.

Row 3: The turning ch counts as 1 DC. 2 DC into 1st st (b). * 1 SC into middle DC of shell from prev row, 5 DC into next SC. Rep from * to last st. Work 3 DC in last st, ch 1, and turn.

Rep rows 2 and 3.

a

b

Lacy and open, this stitch pattern uses V-stitches to create a variation on the basic shell pattern. Use it in similar projects, or experiment with new uses.

Combinations Used in This Pattern

V-stitch: Work [1 double crochet, chain 2, 1 double crochet] into the same stitch (a).

Odd V-stitch: Work [2 double crochets, chain 2, 1 double crochet] into the same stitch (b).

a

b

The Pattern

The foundation chain for this pattern consists of a multiple of 8 plus 2, plus 1 for the turning chain (for example, 24 + 2 + 1 = 27).

Row 1: SC into 2nd ch from hook. SC into each ch across. Ch 3 and turn.

Row 2: * V-st into 2nd st, skip 2 sts, and work 1 odd V-st into next st. Rep from * to last 3 sts. Skip 2 sts and DC into last st. Ch 3 and turn.

Row 3: * 1 odd V-st into ch-2 space, and 1 V-st into next ch-2 space. Rep from * to end of row. DC into space between turning ch and DC of prev row. Ch 3 and turn.

Row 4: * 1 V-st into ch-2 space. Work 1 odd V-st into next ch-2 space. Rep from * to end of row. DC into space between turning ch and DC of prev row. Ch 3 and turn.

Rep rows 3 and 4.

Popcorn Dance Pattern

A popcorn stitch is worked into this lively variation of the odd shells pattern. This pattern creates open fabric with excellent drape, or a great edging.

Combinations Used in This Pattern

V-stitch: Work 1 double crochet, chain 2, and 1 double crochet all into the same stitch (a).

Popcorn stitch: Work 4 double crochets into the same stitch. Join through the top and chain 1 (b). (See the section "Popcorns" on page 96.)

Popcorn V-stitch: Work 1 double crochet, chain 2, and work 1 popcorn stitch all into the same stitch.

The Pattern

The foundation chain for this pattern consists of a multiple of 8 plus 2, plus 1 for the turning chain (for example, 24 + 2 + 1 = 27).

Row 1: SC into 2nd ch from hook. SC into each ch across. Ch 1 and turn.

Row 2: * 1 popcorn V-st into 2nd st, skip 2 sts, and 1 V-st into next st. Rep from * to last 3 sts. Skip 2 sts and DC into last st. Ch 3 and turn.

Row 3: * 1 popcorn V-st into ch-2 space and 1 V-st into next ch-2 space. Rep from * to end of row. 1 DC into space between turning ch and DC of prev row. Ch 3 and turn.

Row 4: * 1 V-st into ch-2 space; work 1 popcorn V-st into next ch-2 space. Rep from * to end of row. 1 DC into space between turning ch and DC of prev row. Ch 3 and turn.

Rep rows 3 and 4.

Follow a Diagram

Following a diagram of crochet symbols is easy once you get the hang of it. Look closely at the chart of symbols and you'll find that the symbols represent the stitches well. Once you are used to diagrams, it's easy to follow one at a glance.

Each crochet stitch is represented by a symbol, as shown below. In a diagram, the symbols are laid out to represent a piece of crocheted fabric, showing you which stitches to work and where to work them.

You can practice crocheting with diagrams only using the stitch patterns on pages 127–131. Each of the patterns begins with a row of chain stitches. To follow the pattern, refer to the symbols chart on this page, start at the first arrow, and work through the diagram stitch by stitch.

Crochet Symbols

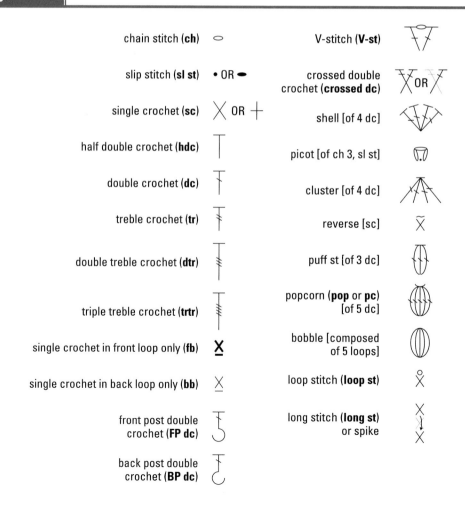

chain stitch (**ch**)

slip stitch (**sl st**)

single crochet (**sc**)

half double crochet (**hdc**)

double crochet (**dc**)

treble crochet (**tr**)

double treble crochet (**dtr**)

triple treble crochet (**trtr**)

single crochet in front loop only (**fb**)

single crochet in back loop only (**bb**)

front post double crochet (**FP dc**)

back post double crochet (**BP dc**)

V-stitch (**V-st**)

crossed double crochet (**crossed dc**)

shell [of 4 dc]

picot [of ch 3, sl st]

cluster [of 4 dc]

reverse [sc]

puff st [of 3 dc]

popcorn (**pop** or **pc**) [of 5 dc]

bobble [composed of 5 loops]

loop stitch (**loop st**)

long stitch (**long st**) or spike

CHAPTER 8

More Techniques

Working in multiple colors and lace patterns, making knit-like stitches with Tunisian crochet, and crocheting with beads and other materials are just a few of the fascinating variations on crochet that can add an enormous amount of interest to your work.

Changing yarn color between rows is an easy way to give your crochet a variety of personalities, even if you're just working a simple stitch. Chapter 3 introduced the technique of adding a new ball of yarn to change color; you can use that technique here to easily crochet an infinite variety of striped patterns.

Choose several colors and work each row in a different color (see top-left photo).

Changing yarn color after several rows creates wider stripes (see top-right photo).

Alternate thick and thin stripes by varying the number of rows between color changes (see bottom-left photo).

For a heathered look, work with two yarns held together for several rows, and then switch out one color for a new one. One color is a consistent base, while the other colors create subtle stripes (see bottom-right photo).

Working with color designs is exciting. You can bring the simplest stitches to life just by changing color in prescribed spots to create a design. Here you will follow a charted design to produce a stunning piece of work.

Understand Stranding

RIGHT SIDE AND WRONG SIDE

When the spaces between color changes are small, you can carry both colors across the row, working one color and carrying the other loosely across the wrong side of the piece. This kind of color work creates a *right side* (the side that shows the design; see the top photo) and a *wrong side* (the side where the strands can be hidden; see the bottom photo). The stranded yarn is always carried on the wrong side. Be careful of this as you turn your work with each row.

SECURE THE STRANDED YARN

To secure the stranded yarn, catch the stranded yarn every few stitches. To do so, allow the stranded yarn to be looped over by the stitch being worked (see bottom photo).

If you catch the yarn securely enough, you can snip the strands and weave them in later to allow for better drape in your fabric.

Follow a Charted Pattern

Crochet patterns that involve color work often include charts. Each square in the chart represents one stitch. For this pattern, you use only single crochet (see Chapter 2).

1. Your pattern will tell you how long your foundation chain needs to be. For this pattern, start with a foundation chain that is a multiple of 20.

2. Begin working from the bottom-right corner of the chart. Here, you are to work 1 single crochet for each block in row 1.

3. Read row 2 and all the even rows from left to right.

4. Read row 3 and all the odd rows from right to left.

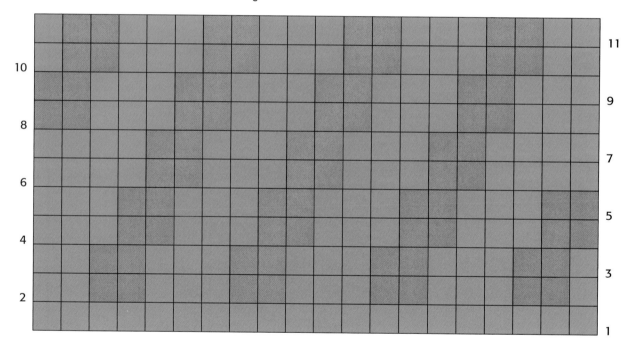

$\mathbf{I}$ ntarsia is used for color patterns when the spaces between color changes are too large for stranding to be practical or when more than two yarns are in use. Instead of stranding the unused yarn across the work, you simply drop it and let it hang until you need it again.

Work Intarsia

Dropping one color and picking up another is simple. Using the old color, work the last stitch to the final step. Pick up the new color and yarn over with both yarns held together to complete the stitch. Drop the old yarn and continue with the new yarn.

There is little difference between the front and back sides when a color pattern is worked with intarsia. The first photo (a) shows the front side of an intarsia swatch. The second photo (b) shows the unworked yarn dangling from the back of the intarsia swatch.

Many patterns list the precise amount of each color of yarn required; this is so you can make small balls or bobbins of each color (b). Keeping the colors tidy prevents confusion and tangles as you work.

a

b

Follow a Charted Pattern

Each square in the chart represents one stitch. For this pattern, you use only single crochet (see Chapter 2).

1. Start with a foundation chain of 15.

2. Begin working from the bottom-right corner of the chart and work row 1 from right to left.

3. Work the even rows from left to right.

4. Work the odd rows from right to left.

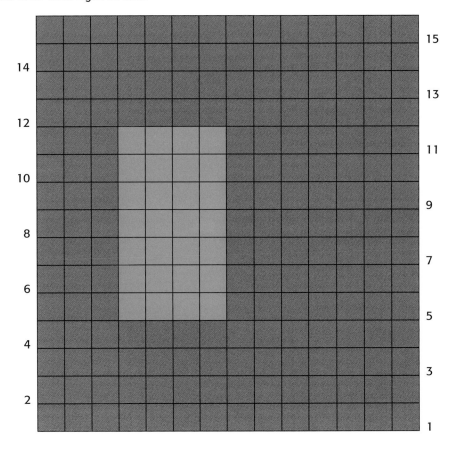

Tapestry crochet is used to create pieces with intricate color-work designs and motifs. This method is worked at a tight gauge and creates a stiff fabric, perfect for baskets and bags.

Work Tapestry Crochet

Tapestry crochet designs and motifs are depicted in charts like this one. This seven-stitch pattern can be repeated many times to create a motif like the example shown above.

Tapestry crochet is often worked in rounds without turning, meaning that the texture of the front and back sides of the rows doesn't alternate. This keeps the stitches slanting in the same direction and helps create a clear motif on the side facing you as you work—the "right side." The charted design is made with this in mind. To read the chart, read every row from right to left instead of alternating directions with each row.

NOTE: If you wish to work a motif in flat rows that was designed for a project in the round, you may need to make adjustments to the motif to account for the alternating slant of the stitches created by turning each row.

The method for switching colors used in tapestry crochet is slightly different from the method for switching colors described in Chapter 3. When you reach the last stitch of a section of color in the pattern, work the last stitch to the final step. Pick up the next color in the pattern and yarn over with only this yarn to complete the stitch (see photo). The completed stitch will look a bit funny, with the top half of the stitch in the new color and the bottom half in the previous color.

Tunisian Simple Stitch

It has been said that Tunisian crochet—also known as Afghan stitch—is like a cross between knitting and crocheting. This is because you make each row in two steps using a long Tunisian (or Afghan) hook. First you pick up all the stitches (forward pass), and then you bind them off (return pass). To get started, you make a foundation forward pass.

Tunisian crochet creates a fabric that is flat and has a unique texture.

Pattern abbreviation: Tss.

Foundation Forward Pass

The foundation row is the same for any variation of Tunisian crochet.

1. Make a chain equal to the number of stitches you require.

2. Insert your hook into the second chain. Yarn over and draw up a loop.

   There are now 2 loops on the hook.

3. Insert the hook into the next chain, yarn over, and draw up a loop.

   There are now 3 loops on the hook.

4. Repeat step 3 until you reach the end of the row. Do not turn your work.

   You now have 1 loop on your hook for each chain.

Foundation Return Pass

In the return pass, you essentially bind off each stitch that you picked up in the forward pass. You work the foundation return pass with the right side of the work facing you. Do not turn the work.

1 Yarn over and draw the yarn through 1 loop on the hook.

2 Yarn over and draw the yarn through 2 loops on the hook.

You are essentially binding off each stitch that you picked up in the forward row.

3 Repeat step 2 until you reach the last 2 stitches of the return row. Yarn over and draw through the final 2 stitches.

At the end of the row, 1 loop remains on the hook.

Forward Pass

Once you've worked the foundation
rows, continue to alternate working
forward and return passes.

1 Skip the first vertical bar from the
previous row. Insert your hook
behind the next vertical bar.

NOTE: Each vertical bar corresponds to
1 Tunisian simple stitch.

2 Yarn over and draw up a loop.

There are now 2 loops on the hook.

3 Insert the hook behind the next vertical bar. Yarn
over and draw up a loop.

4 Repeat step 3 until 1 stitch remains.

5 For the last stitch in the forward pass, insert the
hook into both vertical bars at the end of the row.
Yarn over and draw up a loop.

You now have as many loops on your hook as there
are stitches in the previous row.

Return Pass

You work the Tunisian simple stitch return pass with the right side of the work facing you. Do not turn the work.

① Yarn over and draw the yarn through 1 loop on the hook.

② Yarn over and draw the yarn through 2 loops on the hook.

③ Repeat step 2 until you reach the end of the return row. One loop remains on the hook.

Tunisian Knit Stitch

The Tunisian knit stitch creates a fabric that looks much like the right side of knitted stockinette stitch.

Pattern abbreviation: Tks.

Forward Pass

1. Work a foundation pass as you would for Tunisian simple stitch on page 140.

2. Skip the first stitch from the previous row. Working between 2 vertical bars, insert your hook from front to back under both horizontal strands.

3. Yarn over and draw the yarn through.

   There are now 2 loops on the hook.

4. Insert the hook from front to back under the next pair of horizontal strands. Yarn over and draw the yarn through.

5. Repeat steps 3 and 4 until you have completed the forward row.

Return Pass

You work the Tunisian knit stitch return pass with the right side of the work facing you. Do not turn the work.

1 Yarn over and draw the yarn through 1 loop on the hook.

2 Yarn over and draw the yarn through 2 loops on the hook.

3 Repeat step 2 until you reach the end of the return row.

One loop remains on the hook.

Tunisian Purl Stitch

The Tunisian purl stitch creates a fabric that looks much like the wrong side of knitted stockinette stitch.

Pattern abbreviation: Tps.

Foundation Forward Pass

1. Make a chain equal to the number of stitches you require.

2. Holding the yarn in front of your work, insert the hook into the second chain (a). Yarn over and draw the yarn through (b).

   There are now 2 loops on the hook.

2a

2b

3. Holding the yarn in front of your work, insert the hook into the next chain and draw the yarn through.

   There are now 3 loops on the hook.

4. Repeat step 3 until you reach the end of the row. Do not turn your work.

   You now have 1 loop on your hook for each chain. There is a little purl bump for each loop.

3

4

Foundation Return Pass

Work the foundation return row as you would for
Tunisian simple stitch on page 141.

Forward and Return Pass

1. Skip the first stitch from the previous row. Hold your hook with the yarn in front of the work (see photo) and insert it behind the next vertical bar, as you would if you were working Tunisian simple stitch.

2. Yarn over and draw the yarn through.

   There are now 2 loops on the hook.

3. Insert the hook behind the next vertical bar. Yarn over and draw the yarn through. Repeat until 1 stitch remains.

4. For the last stitch in the forward row, insert the hook into both vertical bars at the end of the row.

5. Yarn over and draw the yarn through.

6. Work the return row as you would for Tunisian simple stitch.

1

2

4

5

Increase in Tunisian Crochet

There are two different ways to shape your Tunisian crochet work. You can increase at the end of a forward or return pass or between stitches in a forward pass.

Increase

INCREASE WITHIN A FORWARD PASS

To increase within a forward pass, pick up extra loops by working into both a horizontal and a vertical strand of the same stitch.

① Insert your hook into the next horizontal strand. Yarn over and draw the yarn through.

② Insert the hook into the next vertical bar. Yarn over and draw the yarn through.

You have picked up 2 loops from the same stitch, resulting in an increase of 1 stitch.

INCREASE AT THE END OF A FORWARD PASS

① When you have reached the end of a forward pass, loosely make 1 chain for each stitch you need to increase by, plus 1.

② Remove the hook from the last chain, drawing the loop long to hold your place.

3 Insert the hook into the back loop of the first chain. Keep this loop on your hook.

4 Pick up the back loop of each remaining chain.

5 Return the last loop to your hook, pulling it tighter to fit snugly.

6 Work the return pass as usual.

INCREASE AT THE END OF A RETURN ROW

1 Work the return pass to the end. One loop remains on the hook. Make 1 chain for each stitch you need to increase by.

2 On the next forward pass, skip the first chain. Insert the hook into the second chain, yarn over, and draw up a loop. Repeat for each chain.

3 Pick up a loop in the first vertical bar. (You skip this bar on non-increase rows.) Continue to work a forward pass as usual.

Decrease in Tunisian Crochet

When you shape your Tunisian crochet work, you make decreases in the forward pass by working two stitches together.

Decrease

1. Insert your hook behind the next 2 vertical bars.
2. Yarn over and draw the yarn through both bars.

   You now have only 1 loop to work in the return pass, thus decreasing by 1 stitch.

3. Work the return pass as usual.

The final row of Tunisian crochet is worked differently from the rest of the piece. You work only a forward pass, and you bind off as you go, resulting in a neat, finished edge.

Bind Off

1 At the beginning of a forward pass, insert your hook behind the second vertical bar. Yarn over and draw the yarn through.

There are now 2 loops on your hook.

2 Yarn over and draw the yarn through both loops on the hook.

There is now 1 loop on your hook. You have bound off 1 stitch.

3 * Insert your hook behind the next vertical bar. Yarn over and draw the yarn through. Yarn over and draw the yarn through both loops on the hook (see photo). Repeat from * until the end of the row.

There is now 1 loop remaining on your hook.

4 Cut the yarn, leaving a 6-inch tail. Draw the yarn through the loop to fasten off.

3

4

Free-form Crochet

Free-form is to crochet what jamming is to music. Combining the crochet skills you already have with a variety of stitches, colors, and yarns, you can create truly unique, stunning pieces of art.

Free-Form

TO START

Free-form crochet is made without a pattern or guidelines. Making free-form pieces is a great way to use up small amounts of yarn and leftovers from completed projects, and to play with new stitches and patterns as you learn. Just gather several yarns that complement each other and start crocheting!

Use the stitch of your choice to create a shape of any sort. It can be a perfect circle (a), square, or rectangle, or it can be an amorphous blob (b).

ALTERNATIVE 1: MAKE SEVERAL PIECES

1 Make several more shapes out of different yarns.

2 Lay out the pieces and rearrange them until you like the way the configuration looks.

③ Attach the pieces together by using slip stitch or any stitch you prefer. (See the "Seam Pieces Together" sections on pages 191 and 194.)

ALTERNATIVE 2: JOIN YARN

① Use the stitch of your choice to create a shape of any sort. It can be a perfect circle, square, or rectangle, or it can be an amorphous blob.

② Instead of crocheting several separate pieces, you can build upon your initial piece by joining new yarns and crocheting shapes as you go. (See the section "Join New Yarn" on page 62.)

TIP

Use yarns from a similar color family to unite your work into a harmonious piece of art.

Chain a 12-inch cord and attach it in two places to your free-form creation. Use the cord to hang your piece on the wall.

You can make bags, hats, and garments out of free-form pieces. Experiment!

Felt/Full a Crocheted Item

Untreated wool and other animal fibers mat and shrink when agitated. This results in a fuzzy, dense fabric that is strong and extremely durable. Fulling pieces such as bags, slippers, and hats creates uniquely textured and durable products.

Felting refers to the process of agitating raw fibers in water until they bind together; **fulling** refers to agitating stitched fibers (including crocheted fibers) until they bind together. Although fulling is technically the correct term for doing this with crochet, felting has become the popular way to refer to all methods that deal with agitating and matting wool.

How to Felt

Before crocheting an entire project for felting, felt some swatches made with the same yarn and stitch so you can determine how severely the fabric felts and how much it shrinks lengthwise and widthwise. If you're following a pattern, this is the same as working up a gauge swatch. You can compare your results to the dimensions specified in the pattern and make adjustments if needed.

1 Crochet the piece you intend to felt. It's generally best to use a hook that is larger than recommended for your yarn. Be sure your crocheted piece is larger than you want the felted product to be in order to accommodate the shrinkage that results from felting, and that your stitches are looser than normal.

NOTE: You might want to experiment with hook size and with which stitch you use, as different stitches produce different felted fabrics.

② Place your crocheted piece in a mesh bag, zippered laundry bag, or pillowcase. Doing so will keep the piece from becoming pulled out of shape during agitation.

③ Set your washing machine to a warm or hot wash and add a small amount of mild detergent. Place the mesh bag and one or two pairs of jeans in the machine. The jeans will help with agitation.

2

④ Once the agitation cycle starts, check on your piece every 5 minutes. If it hasn't yet shrunk to the desired size, return it to the machine for more agitation. Continue to check it every 5 minutes until it is the desired size. You may have to run the machine through several agitation cycles for adequate felting.

NOTE: Avoid the spin cycle; it may stretch and warp the piece.

⑤ Rinse the felted piece gently. Without wringing, wrap it in a towel or two and press to remove any excess water.

5

⑥ Block your piece. (See page 203 in Chapter 10.) If you're blocking a 3-D item such as a bag or a hat, fill it with rolled towels or plastic bags until it is the proper shape. Let it dry. Drying may take a day or two.

TIP

Read yarn labels carefully to make sure your yarn is suited for felting or fulling. Wool that has been treated to make it machine washable (marked "superwash") will not felt or full when agitated.

Using bleaches and dyes, and blending other fibers with the wool can affect a yarn's reaction to agitation. Some won't felt or full at all, and others might felt only a little.

6

Crochet with Beads

Beads can add a playful or elegant element to crochet work. Experiment with beads of different sizes, shapes, and textures. Here are the basics you need to start your adventures with beads and crochet. You're bound to create some masterpieces along the way.

Using Beads

THREAD THE BEADS ONTO THE YARN

Patterns calling for bead crochet will specify the quantity and size of beads required. Thread all the beads you need onto the yarn before you begin to crochet.

1. Fold a piece of thread over the yarn tail.

   This folded piece of thread works as a flexible needle. Think of the ends of the thread as the point of a needle.

2. Slide beads onto the thread "needle" and then onto the yarn.

WORK BEADS INTO A CROCHET STITCH

1. Before completing the final step of any stitch, slide a bead close to your hook. (The example in the photo uses single crochet.)

2 Yarn over and pull through to complete the stitch. This step secures a bead in the stitch. The bead sits on the side of the fabric facing away from you as you work the row.

EXPERIMENT WITH OTHER STITCHES

Beads can be worked into any crochet stitch. Here is an example of working beads into a double crochet stitch.

Slip a bead into the final step of a lover's knot (see page 165). This might sound tricky, but it's the same as working simpler stitches. Give it a try!

Crochet with Different Materials

Once you have the crochet bug, it's hard to resist trying to wrap all sorts of materials around your hook. Have fun trying out these suggestions.

Materials to Try

TWINE AND ROPE

Twine and rope offer an alternative to regular yarn. They are best used for a project that calls for a sturdy, stiff "yarn." The rough fibers offer a great texture, too. You may want to wear protective gloves while working with rough fibers.

CASSETTE TAPE

The ribbon from an old cassette tape is a perfect example that there are many recyclable "yarns" to try. To use cassette tape for crocheting, cut the ribbon at the beginning of `the tape and pull the tape out of the cassette as you work.

HANDMADE RAG YARN

Turn your favorite old T-shirts or a tired bed sheet into yarn. This kind of "yarn" is perfect for making rugs and baskets.

Make Rag Yarn

STRIP METHOD

1 Cut or tear strips of fabric.

2 Tie or sew the strip ends together.

SPIRAL METHOD

1 Starting at an outer edge, cut a spiral from the outside in.

2 As you wind the ball, allow the strip to fold or twist in on itself. This method works best with lightweight fabric.

3 Tie or sew the strip ends together.

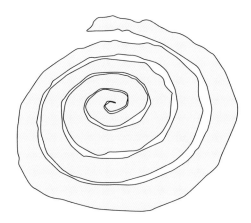

ZIGZAG METHOD

1 Cut the fabric approximately 1 inch from edge A. Don't cut all the way; stop approximately 1 inch from the edge.

2 Starting from edge B, cut approximately 1 inch from the last strip that you cut, stopping approximately 1 inch from the edge.

3 Continue to follow steps 1 and 2 across the fabric.

4 Tie or sew the strip ends together.

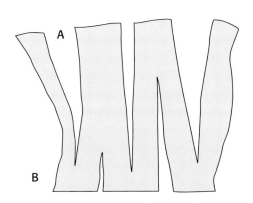

Make Broomstick Loops

You make broomstick loops by slipping long loops onto any rod that has a wider diameter than the hook you're using. An actual broomstick is not necessary; large knitting needles work well for this stitch. The larger the "broomstick," the larger the loops.

Broomstick Loops

You can work these loops into any stitch. Start with a chain or row of any length.

Right-handed (a): Work from left to right, with the hook in your right hand and the broomstick in your left hand.

Left-handed (b): Work from right to left, with the hook in your left hand and the broomstick in your right hand.

a

b

❶ Row 1: Without turning your work, insert the hook into the next stitch from the previous row, yarn over, and draw up a loop, lengthening the loop so that you can place it on the broomstick (a). Leave the loop on the broomstick. Repeat across the row (b).

NOTE: At the end of a row of broomstick loops, the loops are still on the broomstick. The next row locks these loops in place so they don't unravel.

1a

1b

2 Row 2: Slip 1 loop off the broomstick and onto the hook.

3 Yarn over and draw the yarn through both loops on the hook. Chain 1.

4 Slip the next loop off the broomstick and onto the hook.

5 Yarn over and draw the yarn through both loops on the hook. Chain 1.

6 Repeat steps 4 and 5, working into every loop across the row.

7 Repeat rows 1 and 2.

Make a Broomstick Loop Ruffle

You can add this ruffle to any crocheted fabric for a loopy, ruffled edging.

Broomstick Loop Ruffle

Begin with a completed crocheted fabric.

1 Row 1: Work 2 single crochets into each stitch across. Chain 1 and turn.

2 Row 2: Work 1 broomstick loop into each single crochet across the row.

3 Row 3: * Slip 1 loop off the broomstick and onto the hook. Yarn over and draw the yarn through both loops on the hook. Chain 1. Repeat from *, working into every loop across the row.

4 Row 4: * Work 1 broomstick loop into the top of the broomstick loop from the previous row. Work 1 broomstick loop into the next chain stitch. Repeat from *, working into each stitch across the row.

5 Repeat rows 3 and 4.

Broomstick loops are often worked together to create a traditional broomstick lace pattern as shown here.

Traditional Broomstick Lace

The foundation chain for this pattern consists of a multiple of 4, plus 1 for the turning chain.

1 Row 1: Work 1 broomstick loop into each chain across. (Refer to the section "Make Broomstick Loops" on pages 160 and 161.)

2 Row 2: * Slip 4 loops onto the hook, yarn over, and draw the yarn through all 4 loops to join them together. Chain 1. Work 4 single crochets into the center of the 4 loops you just joined. Repeat from * to complete the row.

4 single crochets

3 Row 3: Work 1 broomstick loop into each single crochet from the previous round.

4 Repeat rows 2 and 3.

Make a Lover's Knot Trellis

You make this stitch, also known as a *Solomon's knot,* by drawing up a long loop and then locking it with a stitch at the top of the loop. You can change the look of the stitch simply by changing the size of the loop. In this section, you will learn how to make a lover's knot and then how to make a trellis by using this stitch.

Lover's Knot

① Chain 1 and lengthen the loop on the hook (a).

1a

NOTE: It is important that the length of each loop is the same so that the stitches match. A great way to keep track is to compare the loop to a given part of your finger. Knuckles make great guideposts. Here, the loop is being measured to the second knuckle of a finger (b).

b

2 Yarn over and draw the yarn through the long loop.

3 Insert your hook between the long loop and the strand from the yarn over. Yarn over and draw the yarn through this space.

4 Yarn over (a) and draw the yarn through both loops remaining on the hook (b).

4a   4b

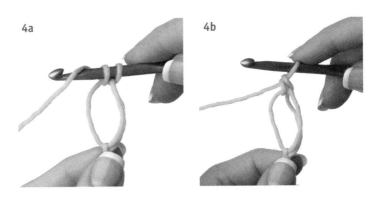

Trellis

The foundation row for this pattern consists of a multiple of 8 lover's knots.

1 Row 1: Work 1 single crochet into the fifth lover's knot from the hook (a). * Work 2 lover's knots, skip 1 lover's knot from the previous row, and work 1 single crochet into the next lover's knot (b). Repeat from * to complete the row. Work 3 lover's knots and turn.

2 Row 2: In the previous row, you created an arch with a lover's knot in the middle. Work 1 single crochet into the middle knot. * Work 2 lover's knots. Work 1 single crochet into the knot at the middle of the next arch (see photo). Repeat from * to complete the row.

Make a Clones Knot Mesh

The Clones knot is fun to make once you get into the swing of it. Once you learn how to make a Clones knot, you can use it to add attitude to any simple mesh pattern.

Knot

You work a Clones knot over the 3 chains closest to the hook.

1 Chain 3. Yarn over and wrap the yarn around the chain 3 as follows: Swing the hook from the front under the chain and to the back (a). Yarn over and swing back under the chain to the front (b).

2 Repeat step 1 four times.

There are now 11 loops on the hook.

NOTE: As you work the yarn overs, you are working over and covering 3 chains. If you have covered more than that, simply push the loops together.

3 Yarn over and draw the yarn through all 11 loops.

4 Slip stitch into the third chain to complete the Clones knot.

1a

1b

3

4

Mesh

The foundation row consists of a multiple of 8 of the following combination:

* Work 1 Clones knot and chain 6.

① Row 1: Work 1 single crochet into the fourth Clones knot from the hook. * Chain 6, work 1 Clones knot, and chain 6. Skip 1 Clones knot from the foundation row and work 1 single crochet into the next Clones knot. Repeat from * to the end of the row.

② Row 2: Chain 6, work 1 Clones knot, chain 6, work 1 Clones knot, and chain 6. Work 1 single crochet into the first Clones knot from the previous row. * Chain 6, work 1 Clones knot, chain 6, and work 1 single crochet into the next Clones knot from the previous row. Repeat from * to finish the row.

③ Repeat row 2 to the desired length.

Filet Crochet

Filet crochet is a simple form of crochet that depicts shapes and pictures in thread. This style of crochet is popular for use in home décor as curtains, tablecloths, edgings, and more. Explore the potential of filet crochet to make modern and interesting pieces.

How Filet Crochet Works

COLORS AND GRIDS

Filet crochet is traditionally made with cotton thread and a steel crochet hook. Traditionally only white thread was used, but experimenting with colors is certainly acceptable. Designs are based on a grid. The grid usually consists of double crochet stitches and chains that combine to create a mesh of squares.

FILET CROCHET CHARTS

Filet crochet designs are depicted in charts, in which each box represents one square of the grid. Read the chart beginning from the bottom right. You read odd-numbered rows from right to left, and even-numbered rows from left to right.

There is an abundance of books and Web sites that offer filet crochet charts.

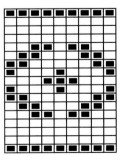

Make Filet Crochet

Filet crochet utilizes a grid base and positive and negative space to create shapes and pictures. Using a steel hook and cotton crochet thread, you can follow a chart to create delicate edgings and home décor pieces and garments.

WORK AN OPEN BLOCK

An open block consists of [chain 2, 1 double crochet] over 3 stitches (or the foundation chain) from the previous row.

1 Where you want the block to begin, chain 2. Skip 2 stitches. Work 1 double crochet into the next double crochet.

2 Repeat step 1 until a filled block is required.

WORK A FILLED BLOCK

A filled block consists of 3 double crochets over 3 stitches (or the foundation chain) from the previous row.

If you're working into an open block from the previous row:

1 Work 2 double crochets into the next chain-2 space. Work 1 double crochet into the next double crochet.

2 Repeat step 1 until an open block is required.

If you're working into a filled block from the previous row:

1 Work 1 double crochet into each of the next 3 double crochets.

2 Repeat step 1 until an open block is required.

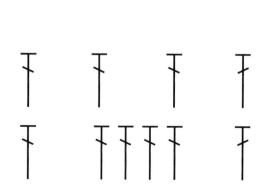

Make Hairpin Lace

Hairpin lace uses single crochet stitches to secure loops of yarn around a loom consisting of two prongs attached at the top and bottom. You make strips of hairpin lace and then attach the strips into unique-looking garments and other items.

SET UP THE LOOM AND GET STARTED

Set the prongs of the loom to the desired width. Before placing the bottom on the loom, use a loose slip knot to attach yarn to one of the prongs. Leaving the loop loose, center the knot in the loom.

You will continue to use one hand to hold the hook and one to control the yarn. Start with the slip knot on the prong on the yarn-hand side of the loom. This example features the left hand as the yarn hand and the right hand as the hook hand.

Guideline

TIP

To manage the strip as it goes, tie on a guideline. With a piece of yarn twice the length you plan the strip to be, tie the yarn at the top of the loom; run it alongside the prong, through the slip knot loop, across the bottom of the loom, and back up the other prong; and then tie the end to the top of the loom (see the above illustration). If you're planning a long strip, the guideline will hang past the loom; wrap the excess guideline on itself until needed.

WORK THE FIRST STITCH

1 Wrap the yarn across the front of the loom (over, not behind, the opposite prong) and to the back, with the yarn hanging in the back middle. Insert the hook up through the slip knot loop, grab the yarn with the hook, and draw a loop through the slip knot loop. Chain 1. To keep track of the start stitch, mark this stitch.

FLIP THE LOOM

2 Do not remove the hook from the loop. Rotate the hook, parallel with the prongs, with the hook pointing down and the handle pointing up. Tilt the handle through the loop and grab it from the back of the loom.

3 Flip the loom toward your yarn hand, allowing the yarn to wrap around. The marked prong is now on the opposite side, the hook is in position, and the yarn is in the yarn hand at the back of the loom.

SINGLE CROCHET

4 Insert the hook into the loop space closest to the top of the loom, grab the yarn with the hook, and draw a loop through the loop space. Yarn over and pull through 2 loops to make 1 single crochet.

5 Continue to work, repeating the steps to flip the loom and work a single crochet.

NOTE: Keep the work pushed down on the loom to give yourself room to maneuver the hook. When the loom is too full for comfort, remove the bottom of the loom and slide all but the newest loops off the loom. Replace the bottom and roll up the loose hairpin lace. You can use a rubber band or stitch holders to secure the rolled lace.

6 To fasten off, cut the yarn, leaving a tail, and draw through the last loop. Leave the guideline in the hairpin loops as you remove the lace from the loom. Use the guideline to keep the strips organized until you are ready to attach them.

TIP

There are many different ways to join strips of hairpin lace; if you're working with a pattern, it should provide those instructions. Here is a simple way that is similar to working a crochet seam (see page 195): Align 2 strips of hairpin lace with the beginning of each strip to the left side. Lay 1 strip on top of the other with loops from each strip lined up with each other. Work a single crochet 2 loops together by inserting the hook through the first loop of each strip. Continue to work single crochet through the loops across the 2 strips.

173

CHAPTER 9

Troubleshooting

Oops! Something doesn't look right and you can't figure out where you went wrong? In this chapter, you'll learn how to diagnose where things went wrong, how to correct mistakes, and how to avoid them in the future.

Pink cardigan   4/13

Diagnose Mistakes

Sometimes things go awry. Before you throw your crochet project across the room or rip it out entirely, take a look and figure out what went wrong. You'll learn from your mistakes and may be able to correct them easily.

Catch Common Mistakes

If your piece is getting narrower or wider where it's not supposed to, count the number of stitches in the row and compare that number to:

- The number of stitches the pattern says you should have in the row.
- The number of stitches in each of the past several rows.

You might find that you accidentally increased or decreased all at once or over several rows.

The best way to prevent accidental increases and decreases is to keep track of how many stitches you're working in each row. By doing so, you'll be able to catch mistakes before you've worked too far.

ACCIDENTALLY DECREASE?

Look for accidental decreases by

- Holding the piece up to a light or a window and looking for holes caused by skipped stitches.

- Examining your piece to see if you skipped any stitches mid-row or mid-round.

SKIP THE FINAL STITCH?

Did you accidentally omit the final stitch in the previous row? This is a common mistake when you're making taller stitches because the turning chain that counts as a stitch can be easy to overlook. Take care to ensure that you don't miss it.

ACCIDENTALLY INCREASE?

Look for accidental increases. Did you work more than one stitch into the same stitch when you weren't supposed to?

WORK IN THE TURNING CHAIN?

Did you accidentally work into a chain from the turning chain as if it were the first stitch of the row?

Fix Mistakes

Once you have identified a mistake, choose the best way to fix it. Remember that even experts make mistakes; don't be discouraged!

RIP BACK

In crochet, it's easy to rip back to a mistake. If you choose to rip back, simply tug gently on your working yarn to unravel the stitches to the error. Then pick up at that point in the pattern.

DO A SNEAKY FIX

Sometimes the mistake is as minimal as one decrease or increase, and it won't look terrible to simply compensate for it instead of ripping out the rows you worked so hard on. Fix the problem by following these steps:

Decrease: 2 DC TOG to connect increase

Accidental increase

1 Diagnose the cause of the decrease or increase so that you don't repeat it.

2 Work an increase to correct an accidental decrease or a decrease to correct an accidental increase. Choose a place in the row where this correction will disappear as much as possible.

TIP

Read through your pattern carefully, making notes to help you through tricky spots.

If Something Still Seems Wrong

If things just don't seem right with your project, take a closer look to make sure you're doing what the pattern tells you to.

CHECK YOUR PATTERN

Take a close look at the pattern's directions. Are you using the right stitch? Are you working the stitches into the correct place? Does the pattern have specific instructions to work a spike stitch, into only one loop, or around the post? Make sure you haven't overlooked a special instruction.

Did you make big changes to the type or weight of yarn suggested? If the yarn is very different from the kind used in the original pattern, be prepared for your finished product to look different.

If your work doesn't match the picture or things don't add up right, compare your work to the instructions step by step. If there is a mistake in the pattern, look online to see if the publisher provides a correction. If not, you may be left to your own ability to improvise. Trust your instinct or ask another crocheter for help.

CHECK WHERE YOUR PATTERN WAS PUBLISHED

If you're using a pattern published in another country, remember that they may use stitch terms differently from the way the terms are used in your own country. For example, the British and Australian *double crochet* stitch is known as a *single crochet* stitch in the United States.

U.S.	UK
slip stitch	slip stitch
single crochet	double crochet
half double crochet	half treble crochet
double crochet	treble crochet
treble crochet	double treble crochet

If a step in a pattern has you stumped, try asking for help in an online message board (for a list of online resources, see page 6). Also, check the publication's Web site to see if any corrections (known as *errata*) to the pattern have been posted.

Use Stitch Markers

If you find yourself getting lost in your work or you're doing complicated pattern repeats, or if you're constantly having to recount the number of stitches in a row or round, use stitch markers as guideposts. Also, if your crochet time is interrupted a lot, marked stitches will help you dive right back in where you left off.

MARK PROGRESS IN A ROW

Use stitch markers to mark your progress in long rows. For example, in a row of 100 stitches, you could mark the 20th, 40th, 60th, and 80th stitches. Not only will this make keeping track of the number of stitches easier and faster, but it will also make finding accidental increases and decreases easier.

MARK REPEATS

- For a pattern that uses repeats of a complicated stitch pattern within a row, mark the end of each repeat to keep track of how many repeats you've made.

- For a pattern that repeats over a number of rows, mark the first row of the repeat sequence you are working.

NOTE: You may want to make notes about what a particular stitch marker means. Clearly marking important information in your work can ease your fretting so you can get back to enjoying the project.

Some plied yarns, as lovely as they are, can be prone to splitting while you work. Here are some tips to control this problem.

- Be gentle with your yarn. Yarn can become strained and worse for the wear if worked too tightly or handled roughly.

- Store and carry yarn in a bag to protect it from getting knocked around.

- Ripping back a project can leave yarn kinked and split; work carefully and rip back gently.

- Working tight stitches with a small hook strains the yarn. Creating loose stitches reduces the chance that you'll stab through the yarn with the hook.

TIP

It may seem that pulling a misbehaving yarn tight would be the best way to control it as you work, but pulling tight can actually cause loosely plied yarn to split.

Smooth Uneven Sides

If the sides of your work look uneven, wobbly, or squished, the problem is likely related to turning chains. (See page 34 for more information on turning chains.)

If you make tight chains, your turning chain may not be tall enough. You might try increasing your turning chain by one chain. This only works with a very tight turning chain.

Treating a turning chain like an actual stitch can leave a gap between the turning chain and the rest of the row.

To remove this gap, work a turning chain that is one chain shorter than is usually called for. Do not skip a space; instead, work into the first stitch of the previous row. In this case, the turning chain doesn't count as a stitch. Experiment to see what works best for your project.

TURNING CHAIN: TO TWIST OR NOT TO TWIST

If you turn your work with the hook in the turning chain, the chain is twisted.

If you remove the hook before turning and then reinsert it, the chain is not twisted.

Each method creates a subtle difference in the sides of your work. Experiment to see which works best for you.

TIP

Remember, you can always use a simple edging to even out the sides. See Chapter 13 for more information on edgings.

Loosen Up a Tight Foundation Chain

It's important that your foundation chain isn't too tight. If it is too tight, you will have difficulty working into it. If you continue to have trouble with making loose chain stitches, try using a hook one or two sizes larger than the project calls for (remember to check your gauge on a trial swatch).

A tight foundation chain can restrict the drape and give of your fabric. If you find that your fabric needs an edge with a little extra give, try adding some extra chains throughout the foundation chain. This technique works best with mesh or lace patterns that don't use all the chains in the foundation chain. As an example, for a crocheted mesh, with 30 arches add 30 chains to the foundation chain, and skip one additional chain between each arch when working the first row. Alternatively, you can use foundation stitches, which produce a much stretchier foundation than a chain (see the section "Make a Foundation Chain" on page 32).

Arch mesh swatch with tight foundation chain

Mesh swatch with loose foundation chain

As you crochet, use stitch markers to mark any increases and decreases used to shape a garment. This will help you to see where the shaping occurs so you can decide how to fix an ill-fitting garment.

If there are any areas that are simply too baggy, pinch the fabric to "take up" the excess stitches. If you pinched four stitches, try decreasing the number of stitches in that area by four.

If the shaping stitches seem out of place, you can try moving the shaping sequence over a few stitches in one direction or try starting the sequence in a different row.

You might find from a pattern's schematic that a medium bust size will fit you well, but the waist shaping of a large will make a garment that better fits your body. Do some sleuthing in the pattern to see how you might make the section of the pattern with waist shaping for the large size while working with the rest of the medium instructions.

CHAPTER 10

Final Details and Finishing

You've completed crocheting a project. Congratulations! But chances are you're not done yet. This chapter covers the final steps to finishing a project and presents some basic embellishments to add as final touches.

Make a Buttonhole

Buttons are functional and decorative additions to crocheted garments and accessories. They come in all shapes, sizes, colors, and textures, and it's simple to incorporate them into your work. Here are two basic methods for making a buttonhole to fit any button.

Within a Row

Use this technique to make a horizontal buttonhole within a row of crochet.

1 Work to the point where you will insert a button-hole. Chain 3, skip 3 stitches (see photo), and con-tinue in pattern to the end of the row. Make a turning chain and turn.

We used a 3-stitch buttonhole for this example. Depending on the size of your button, you may need to make your buttonhole larger or smaller. Simply compare the button to the buttonhole to make sure that it's a perfect fit. Adjust the number of skipped stitches and chains as needed so that the button-hole is slightly smaller than the button.

2 Work the next row according to the pattern, working 3 stitches as called for into the chain-3 space (a).

You've made a horizontal buttonhole (b).

Across Rows

Use this technique to make a vertical buttonhole over 2 or more rows of crochet.

1. Work to the point where you will insert a button-hole. Make a turning chain and turn.

2. Work back to the beginning of your work. Make a turning chain and turn.

3. Work to the end of the short row and fasten off.

4. Join the yarn 1 stitch from the end of the first short row. * Work in pattern to the end of the short row. Make a turning chain and turn.

5. Repeat from * twice.

6 Work in pattern to the end of the short row. Chain 1 (a). Work the next stitch into the last stitch from step 3. Continue to the end of the row, work a turning chain, and turn.

6a

You've made a vertical buttonhole (b).

6b

Inevitably, some of the projects you crochet will need to be assembled in the end. Seaming might seem tedious, but the thrill of putting on a completed sweater for the first time can't be matched. You can use one of several sewing techniques to sew crocheted pieces together.

WHIPSTITCH SEAM

A whipstitch seam is perhaps the easiest seam to sew. It works best along straight edges.

1 Hold the 2 pieces to be seamed with right sides together and with stitches or rows matched up.

NOTE: The right side is the side that shows when the garment is worn. The wrong side is the side worn against the skin, or the side where the ends are woven in. When right sides are held facing each other for seaming, the piece will later be turned right side out, hiding the seam on the inside.

2 Using matching yarn or thread and a yarn needle, begin on the right by inserting the needle from back to front through the first stitch or row of each piece, leaving a 6-inch tail.

3 Bringing the needle over the top of the work, insert it from back to front through the next pair of stitches to the left.

4 Repeat step 3 to the end of the seam. Fasten off and weave in the yarn tails.

1

2

3

BACKSTITCH SEAM

Backstitch creates a sturdy seam and is suited for use on curved or angled edges.

1. Hold the 2 pieces to be seamed with right sides together and with stitches or rows matched up.

2. Using matching yarn or thread and a yarn needle, begin on the right by inserting the needle from front to back through the first stitch or row of each piece.

3. Insert the needle from back to front through the next pair of stitches to the left.

4. Insert the needle from front to back through the first pair of stitches again.

5. Skipping the next pair of stitches to the left, insert the needle from back to front through the next pair of stitches to the left.

6. Insert the needle from front to back into the pair of stitches to the right.

7. Skipping 1 pair of stitches, insert the needle from back to front into the next pair of stitches to the left.

2

3

4

8 Repeat steps 6 and 7 to the end of the seam. Fasten off and weave in the yarn tails.

8

WOVEN SEAM

A woven seam (also referred to as *mattress stitch*) is suitable for use only when seaming stitches to stitches (not stitches to row ends or row ends to row ends). It is popular for joining motifs because it is an invisible seam.

1 Hold together the two pieces to be seamed with their right sides together and with stitches matched up. Using matching yarn or thread and a yarn needle, insert the needle into the center of the top of the first stitch or row of one piece and pull the yarn through.

2 Insert the needle into the center of the top of the first stitch on the other piece and pull the yarn through loosely.

3 Continue to alternate from one piece to the other, tightening the seam every few inches.

Seam Pieces Together by Crocheting

As an alternative to sewing pieces together, you can use slip stitch or single crochet to create a seam. Slip stitching creates a simple seam and is suited for use on irregularly shaped edges. Single crochet creates a bulky seam that is decorative if worked on the outside of a piece. These techniques are quick and create sturdy and optionally decorative seams.

Create a Slip-Stitch Seam

1 Hold the 2 pieces to be seamed with right sides together and with stitches or rows matched up.

NOTE: The right side is the side that shows when the garment is worn. The wrong side is the side worn against the skin, or the side where your ends are woven in. When right sides are held facing each other for seaming, the piece will later be turned right side out, hiding the seam on the inside.

2 Using matching yarn and an appropriately sized crochet hook, begin on the right by inserting the hook from front to back through both loops of each of the first pair of stitches, or through each of the first pair of rows.

NOTE: If your pieces are made from bulky yarn, you may choose to create your seam through only 1 loop of each stitch to keep the seam flat and neat.

3 Yarn over and draw the yarn through both stitches and through the loop on the hook, creating 1 slip stitch.

4 Repeat steps 2 and 3 to the end of the seam, working into the next pair of stitches or rows to the left. Fasten off and weave in the yarn tails.

Create a Single-Crochet Seam

1 Hold the 2 pieces to be seamed with right sides together and with stitches or rows matched up (as shown in the photo on the previous page).

Alternatively, you can work this seam with the *wrong sides* together, to have the seam show on the right side.

2 Using matching yarn and an appropriately sized crochet hook, begin on the right by inserting the hook from front to back through both loops of each of the first pair of stitches, or through each of the first pair of rows.

3 Yarn over and draw the yarn through both stitches. Yarn over again and draw the yarn through both loops on the hook, creating 1 single crochet.

4 Repeat steps 2 and 3 to the end of the seam, working into the next pair of stitches or rows to the left. Tie off and weave in the yarn tails.

NOTE: Take care not to work your stitches too tightly. Staying loose keeps your seams flexible and maintains the drape of your garment.

Sewing in a zipper, by hand or by machine, is an excellent skill to have. Use a zipper appropriate for the size of the opening in your project. If your piece features open lace, work rows of solid crochet where the zipper will be attached. If you're sewing a zipper into a bag or other item that will be seamed closed on three sides, attach the zipper before seaming.

Zippers

1. With wrong sides facing and using a contrasting-color yarn, baste the crocheted edges closed using a whipstitch (see the section "Whipstitch Seam" on page 191) so that they lie flat and do not overlap.

2. Lay the right side of the zipper face-down on top of the wrong side of the basted opening, aligning the center of the zipper with the opening. Pin the zipper in place using straight pins, or baste it in place using sewing thread in a contrasting color.

3 If you're using a sewing machine (do so only if the project can lie flat), sew the zipper to the garment. If you're sewing by hand (required for projects that are already closed on 2 or more sides), use a running stitch or backstitch to sew the zipper to the garment.

4 Remove the pins or basting thread. On the wrong side, whipstitch the flat sides of the zipper to the crocheted fabric so they lie flat. Turn the project right side out.

TIP

Be careful if you use a sewing machine to sew your zipper. Bulky fabric can cause trouble for a machine, and a sewing machine may damage your crocheted fabric. Sewing a zipper by hand doesn't take too long.

197

Make Pompoms

Pompoms add a playful embellishment to crocheted items, especially for kids' garments.
Place them on top of hats, at the ends of
cords, or in any other spot that could use a
little pizzazz.

Pompoms

1. Cut 2 pieces of cardboard into circles the same size
   you want your pompom to be. Cut a pie piece out of
   each circle; then cut a circle out of the center of
   each of the circles. The 2 pieces should be identical.

2. Lay a piece of yarn in a full circle over 1 of the cardboard circles. Lay the second cardboard circle over
   this yarn, sandwiching the yarn between the 2
   pieces of cardboard.

③ Hold the 2 circles together. Wrap the yarn around the circle about 50 times—or more if you want a really fluffy pompom.

④ Tie the yarn sandwiched between the 2 cardboard circles into a very tight knot; this will secure the pompom and cause the ends to flare out.

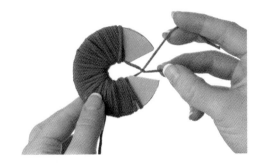

⑤ Using sharp scissors, cut the yarn between the 2 circles.

⑥ Trim the ends of the pompom so that they are uniform and neat.

Make Fringe

Fringe is most often used to adorn afghans and scarves, but you can use fringe creatively to add a playful or elegant detail to hats, shawls, belts, and more.

Fringe

CUT FRINGE

1. Cut a piece of cardboard that is slightly longer than the fringe you want to make, or use a CD jewel case as shown in the photo. The piece of cardboard should be at least 3 or 4 inches wide.

2. Wrap the yarn lengthwise around the cardboard or jewel case. This ensures that all the pieces of fringe are the same length without having to measure each strand.

3. Secure a rubber band around the yarn. After you've cut the fringe, this rubber band will keep the pieces under control until you're ready to use them. Cut the yarn along the bottom of the cardboard or jewel case. Keep the yarn folded in half.

ATTACH FRINGE

1. Insert a large crochet hook from back to front through the edge stitch to which you want to attach the fringe. Grab the middle of the folded fringe yarn with the hook and bring about 1 inch of the middle of the fringe through the stitch.

② Keeping the hook inserted through the center of the fringe, use it to grab the entire bunch of fringe.

③ Draw the fringe through the loop and tighten.

④ Trim the ends of the fringe so that they're even.

There are limitless ways to add flair with fringe. For full, thick fringe, attach several strands of fringe to the fabric in groups instead of individual strands. Consider combining different colors and textures for a lush fringe.

Patch Pockets

atch pockets are simple to crochet and simple to add to any project. They're also functional and decorative.

1. Crochet a square, semicircle, or rectangle to serve as the pocket.

2. On the garment or accessory, use a pin or stitch marker to mark the placement of the pocket. If you're working on a garment, you might want to try it on to ensure proper placement.

3. Sew the left, right, and bottom sides of the pocket to the right side of the project with a whipstitch, being sure to secure the top corners to prevent separation during wear and use.

Crocheted pieces made from natural fibers like cotton, wool, and silk look their best after they have been blocked to the proper shape and dimensions. Blocking also helps make stitches look uniform and even.

If you're constructing an item from several crocheted pieces, it is generally recommended that you block the pieces separately before assembling them.

Spray and Steam Blocking

You need a firm, flat surface to serve as a blocking board on which to pin your pieces. You can use a bed, lay several towels on a table or carpet, or use a large Styrofoam board.

1 Lay your crocheted pieces out on your blocking board as shown in the photo. Using your pattern as a guide, pin the pieces to the required shape and dimensions.

NOTE: Be sure to use rustproof pins.

2 **Spray blocking:** Use a spray bottle to wet the pieces thoroughly, but not to the point of saturation, with tepid water.

Steam blocking: As an alternative to spraying, you can steam your pieces to block them. Use the steam from an iron or steamer held several inches above the pieces.

3 Allow the pieces to dry.

Block Your Finished Project *(continued)*

Wet Blocking

1. Gently submerge your crocheted piece(s) in cool water, adding mild soap or detergent to clean them, if desired. Do not agitate. Allow the piece(s) to soak for 10–15 minutes.

2. Drain the water from the sink and gently squeeze the excess water from the piece(s).

3. Roll the piece(s) gently in a towel to remove more water, as shown in the photo.

4. Lay the piece(s) out on your blocking board as directed in step 1 on the previous page.

5. Allow the piece(s) to dry completely.

> **TIP**
>
> Unless your pattern specifically calls for it, do not iron your crocheted pieces under any circumstances.

After you devote so much time, energy, and love to making crocheted items, it's important to care for them properly so that they remain in excellent condition for as long as possible.

Maintain Your Crocheted Items

FOLLOW CARE INSTRUCTIONS FOR WASHING CROCHETED ITEMS

All yarns are not created equal. Some are extremely delicate, and others are so durable you'd think they were made of steel.

When it comes to washing your crocheted items, be sure to follow the care instructions on the yarn label (see the section "Yarn Weight and Care Symbols" on page 16).

If you're giving an item as a gift, include a tag with care instructions and fiber information so the recipient knows how to wash the item correctly.

Made for you by Pam with lots of love!

This sweater is 100% wool. Either dry clean it or hand wash it in warm water with a mild detergent. Rinse it in warm water and lie out flat to dry.

STORE CROCHETED ITEMS

Store crocheted items in a clean, dry place away from pets. If the items are made of natural fibers, be sure to include cedar or lavender to repel moths and other pests that can wreak havoc.

CHAPTER 11

Flowers, Shapes, and Creatures

The fun flowers and shapes presented in this chapter are a great way to practice reading patterns. Use these motifs alone or combine them for projects of your own invention.

The examples in this chapter were made with DK-weight yarn and a 4.5mm hook. You can use any yarn to make your own flowers, shapes, and creatures; choose a hook size appropriate for the yarn you've selected.

Loopy Chain Flower

This quick and funky flower is made using loops of chain stitches worked into a round of single crochet.

Techniques Used

Ch   Chain stitch

Sl st   Slip stitch

SC   Single crochet

Work in the round (see Chapter 3)

Loopy Chain Flower Pattern

1 Ch 2. Work 4 SC in 2nd ch from hook (see photo). Join with a Sl st. Gently pull tail to tighten ring.

This round of SC creates a base for the petals. Each petal is made with a loop of chain stitches worked into a SC from this round.

② Ch 8. Sl st into 1st SC.

③ * Ch 8. Sl st into next SC, ch 8, and then Sl st into the same SC.

④ Rep from * to create a total of 8 loopy petals. Sl st to join at base of 1st petal.

Simple Daisy

Easy to crochet, this simple daisy makes a sweet addition to any project. Use it as an appliqué, make it into a pin, or even use it to patch up a pair of old jeans.

Techniques Used

Ch   Chain stitch

Sl st Slip stitch

SC   Single crochet

DC   Double crochet

Work in the round (see Chapter 3)

Simple Daisy Pattern

FOUNDATION ROUND

1. Ch 2. Work 5 SC into 2nd ch from hook. Join with a Sl st. Gently pull tail to tighten ring.

PETAL ROUND

Each petal is made by using a combination of stitches
worked into 1 SC.

1 Starting in 1st SC from prev round, [ch 2, 3 DC, ch 2,
Sl st]—1 petal made.

2 * Sl st into next SC (a). Work 1
petal [ch 2, 3 DC, ch 2, Sl st] into
this SC (b).

2a   2b

3 Rep from * to create a total of 5 petals. Sl st to join
at base of 1st petal.

4 Fasten off and weave in ends.

NOTE: Instead of weaving in the yarn tails, you can use
them to sew the daisy onto a crocheted project or tie it
onto a pin.

Add Layers to the Simple Daisy

Adding another layer of petals to the simple daisy is easy. Work one layer into the front loop and one into the back loop of the same round to create a flower with layers.

Techniques Used

Ch	Chain stitch	DC	Double crochet
Sl st	Slip stitch	FLO	Work in the front loop only (see Chapter 4)
SC	Single crochet	BLO	Work in the back loop only (see Chapter 4)

Simple Daisy Layers

FOUNDATION ROUND

① Ch 2. Work 5 SC into 2nd ch from hook. Join with a Sl st into 1st SC.

② Gently pull on tail to tighten ring.

PETAL ROUND 1

1 Starting with 1st SC from foundation round, work 1 petal [ch 2, 3 DC, ch 2, Sl st] into FLO.

2 * Sl st into next SC. Work 1 petal [ch 2, 3 DC, ch 2, Sl st] into FLO of this SC.

1

3 Rep from * to create a petal in FLO of each SC from foundation round. Join with a Sl st at base of 1st petal of round.

PETAL ROUND 2

1 Sl st into BLO of 1st SC from foundation round.

2 Work 1st petal [ch 2, 3 DC, ch 2, Sl st] into BLO of this SC.

3 * Sl st into BLO of next SC. Work 1 petal [ch 2, 3 DC, ch 2, Sl st] into back loop of this SC.

4 Rep from * to create a petal in BLO of each SC from the foundation round.

2

213

⑤ Join with a Sl st at base of 1st petal of round.
Fasten off.

Flower Projects

You can use your crocheted flowers to improvise fun projects. Here are a few ideas.

- **Make a flower ring:** Once the flower is made, chain a ring to fit your finger and slip stitch to the back of the flower to close the ring. (See the photo.)

- **Make a scarf:** Simply sew or crochet the flowers together however you like.

- **Make a bouquet:** Attach floral wire to the back of each flower.

Rosette

Unlike the previous flowers, this rosette is worked in a corkscrew and rolled up to create a layered flower that is easy to make.

Techniques Used

Ch   Chain stitch

TR   Treble stitch

Rosette Pattern

① Ch any number—the longer the chain, the larger the rosette.

② Work 4 TR into 4th ch from hook. * Work 5 TR into next ch.

③ Rep from *, working into each ch across. Fasten off.

④ Tuck in one end of the row and roll it into a spiral. Sew the bottom of the rosette using the tail from the beginning to fasten the layers at the base.

2

4

Corkscrew

Increasing by too many stitches in each row creates a ruffle. Increasing by far too many stitches causes the work to turn in on itself, resulting in a corkscrew that makes a playful fringe or ornament.

Techniques Used

Ch   Chain stitch

Sl st   Slip stitch

SC   Single crochet

Corkscrew Pattern

1. Ch any number—the longer the chain, the longer the corkscrew.

2. Sl st into 2nd ch from hook. * Work 4 SC into next ch. (see photo).

3. Rep from *, working into each ch across. Fasten off.

Mathematician Daina Taimina uses crochet to demonstrate a hyperbolic plane (a plane that curves away from itself at every point). Crochet is a unique fit for modeling this geometric concept that mirrors natural wonders like the growth of a coral reef. On top of all that, this hyperbolic ruffle is fun and easy to make.

Techniques Used

Ch   Chain stitch

SC   Single crochet

Hyperbolic Ruffle Pattern

1. Ch any number, plus 1 for the turning ch.

2. Row 1: Work 2 SC into 2nd ch from hook. * Work 1 SC into next 3 sts, work 2 SC into next st. Rep from * to finish the row, ch 1, and turn.

3. Rep row 1 as many times as you like.

TIP

The only rule for making a hyperbolic ruffle is to keep increasing at regular intervals. Try changing the number of stitches between increases for a different ruffle shape. You can also experiment with different stitches like double crochet.

Triangles Using Increases or Decreases

Use simple shaping techniques to create a triangle. Start with a point and increase as you go, or start with a long row and decrease to a point.

Techniques Used

Ch	Chain stitch	SC	Single crochet
Sl st	Slip stitch	SC TOG	Single crochet together (see Chapter 3)

TIP

Triangles have lots of uses. Appliqué triangles to completed projects for a playful look, especially for children's items like the owl on page 223. Or consider making a large triangle to use as a head scarf, dish rag, or face cloth.

Decrease Triangle

1. Ch any number, plus 1 for the turning chain.

2. Row 1: Work 1 SC into 2nd loop from hook. Work 1 SC into each ch across. Ch 1 and turn.

3. Row 2: Work SC2TOG over next 2 sts from prev row. Work 1 SC into each st across to finish the row. Ch 1 and turn.

4. Rep row 2 to decrease 1 st per row until only 3 sts are left.

5. Final row: SC3TOG to complete the triangle. Fasten off.

Increase Triangle

1. Ch 2.

2. Row 1: Work 3 SC into 2nd ch from hook. Ch 1 and turn.

3. Row 2: Work 2 SC into 1st st of prev row. Work 1 SC in each st across to finish the row. Ch 1 and turn.

4. Rep row 2 until triangle is the desired size.

Shapes in the Round

Follow this pattern to make a triangle, or alter it to make a square, a pentagon, a hexagon, or even an octagon.

Techniques Used

Ch   Chain stitch

Sl st   Slip stitch

DC   Double crochet

Create a ring using a loop (see Chapter 3)

Triangle Pattern

1. Round 1: Use a loop to form a ring ch 3 and work 2 DC into the ring. * Ch 2, work 3 DC into the ring. Rep from *. Ch 2, Sl st in 3rd ch of ch-3 at beg of round to join. Pull on tail of loop to tighten center.

2. Round 2: Ch 3; this chain counts as 1 DC. Skip 1st DC from prev round. Work 1 DC into each DC from prev round until you reach 1st ch space. Work [1 DC, ch 2, 1 DC] into ch space. * Work 1 DC into each DC, work [1 DC, ch 2, 1 DC] into ch space. Rep from * to complete round. Sl st in 3rd ch of ch-3 at beg of round.

3 Rep round 2 until triangle is the desired size. Fasten off.

TO MAKE A SQUARE
Change the number of repeats in the pattern to 2.

TO MAKE A PENTAGON
Change the number of repeats in the pattern to 3.

TO MAKE A HEXAGON
Change the number of repeats in the pattern to 4.

Make Creatures Using 2-D Shapes

Have fun turning flat crocheted shapes into whatever you imagine.

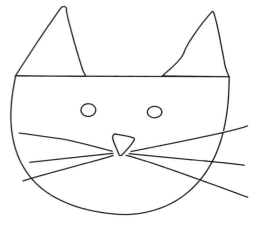

MAKE AN OWL

Seam two triangles together. Fold down the top point and attach it to the body. Attach crochet circles for the eyes. (See next page.)

MAKE A CAT'S FACE

Fold a circle in half and seam the edges. Attach triangles for the ears and embroider the eyes, nose, and whiskers.

MAKE A CREATURE

Seam two rectangles together. Add odd shapes for the ears, arms, or legs. Attach crochet circles for the eyes.

MAKE A HOUSE

Seam two rectangles and two triangles together. Attach crochet shapes for a door, chimney, or window.

Make an Owl

H ere's a close-up look at how to make the owl from the previous page.

Techniques Used

Ch	Chain stitch	Crocheting triangles (see page 218)
SC	Single crochet	Seaming (see pages 191 and 194)

Owl Pattern

1. Crochet 2 triangles.
2. Seam them together.
3. Fold and attach the point to create a beak.
4. Crochet two circles to make the wings. Fold each wing over the sides of the owl and attach.
5. Crochet and attach circles for the eyes.

Crochet a Ball

This simple ball pattern can be put to many creative uses, which includes using for the head of the amigurumi creature on page 227.

Techniques Used

Ch	Chain stitch	SC	Single crochet
Sl st	Slip stitch	SC TOG	Single crochet together (see Chapter 3)

Ball Pattern

This pattern is worked in the round. Do not turn your work at the end of a round.

1. Round 1: Use a loop to form a ring, ch 1. Work 7 SC into ring. Sl st into 1st SC to join (7 SC total).

2. Round 2: Ch 1. Work 2 SC into 1st st and into each st from prev round (14 SC total).

③ Round 3: Work 1 SC into each st from prev round (14 SC total).

④ Continue to work increase rounds until the ball is the width you want.

⑤ Work several rounds without increases to shape the ball. Use the number of rounds necessary to shape the ball.

⑥ Decrease rounds: * Work SC2TOG over the next 2 sts and 1 SC in each of the next 3 sts. Rep from * until 10 sts rem. Fasten off, leaving a long tail.

⑦ Use just enough stuffing to shape the ball, but don't over stuff. Overstuffing can stretch the stitches and create telltale gaps.

⑧ Weave tail through last 10 sts and pull gently to close ball.

TIP

Making balls of different sizes is simple. Follow this pattern and add more increase rounds, or consult the section "Shapes in the Round" on page 220 for more ideas.

Form a Tube

This simple tube pattern can be put to many creative uses, including an amigurumi creature on the next page.

Techniques Used

Ch   Chain stitch

Sl st   Slip stitch

SC   Single crochet

Tube Pattern

This pattern is worked in the round. Do not turn your work at the end of a round.

1. Ch 8. Sl st to join 1st ch to the last for working in the round.

2. Round 1: Ch 1. Work 8 SC into ch.

3. Round 2: Work 1 SC into each stitch of prev round.

4. Rep round 2 until tube is the desired size.

Known as amigurumi, these 3-D creatures made of balls and tubes are fun to crochet. Follow these simple tips to make up your own lovable creatures.

MAKE THE HEAD
Crochet a ball, leaving the bottom open.

MAKE THE BODY
Start with the ball pattern, but increase the number of even rounds before decreasing. Leave the top open and keep a long tail for seaming.

ASSEMBLE THE CREATURE
Stuff the head and body. Line up the openings at the head and the body. Use a long tail to whipstitch the head and body together. Consider adding tubes for arms or legs.

ADD PERSONALITY TO YOUR CREATURE
In this example the face is simply sewn on. There are many ways to give your amigurumi a personality. Consider using buttons and other notions to add features.

CHAPTER 12

Blocks and Motifs

Blocks and motifs are not only fun to make. They're portable, too—it's easy to carry the yarn and hook in your bag wherever you go. They also offer a lot of versatility; the sky is the limit for how to use them. You can combine different types, or stick with one to make a variety of things: bags, pillows, blankets, potholder covers, scarves—the list goes on!

The examples in this chapter were made with medium-weight yarn and a 5.0mm hook. You can use any yarn to make your own motifs; choose a hook size appropriate for the yarn you've selected.

A square worked in the round has a different look and texture than a square worked in rows.

Techniques Used

Ch   Chain stitch

Sl st   Slip stitch

SC   Single crochet

Square in the Round Pattern

① Ch 5, Sl st to 5th ch from hook to form a ring.

② Round 1: Ch 1, 12 SC into ring, Sl st to 1st SC of round.

③ Round 2: Ch 1, SC in 1st SC, * 3 SC in next SC, SC in each of the next 2 SC, rep from * twice, 3 SC in next SC, SC in last SC, Sl st to 1st SC of round.

4 Round 3: Ch 1, SC in each of the next 2 SC, * 3 SC in next SC, SC in each of the next 4 SC, rep from * twice, 3 SC in next SC, 2 SC, Sl st to 1st SC of round.

5 Round 4: Ch 1, SC in each of the next 3 SC, * 3 SC in next SC, SC in each of the next 6 SC, rep from * twice, 3 SC in next SC, 3 SC, Sl st to 1st SC of round.

6 To continue working rounds, rep round 4, adding 2 more SC to each side with each round.

TIP

You can make two different variations on this square: 1) work it in one solid color or 2) change colors per round or several rounds to create a stripe effect.

You create a mitered square when you make a 90-degree bend by decreasing in the middle of each row. This is a fun way to make a square with an interesting look.

Mitered Square Pattern

Create a foundation chain that is an odd number, plus 1 for the turning chain.

① Row 1: SC in 2nd ch and each ch across. Ch 1 and turn. Place marker in st at center of row.

2 Row 2: SC in each st across to st before marker. Remove marker. Work SC3TOG over center 3 sts. SC into each st across to end of row, ch 1, and turn. Place marker in st at center of row.

3 Rep row 2 until 3 sts remain in the row.

4 Final row: Work SC3TOG. Fasten off and weave in ends.

This pattern looks great with stripes of color, as shown here. You can join mitered squares together to make interesting and intricate patterns.

Use the squares as building blocks to create larger designs. Changing colors and using stripes are key in making these kinds of combinations. For a simple but different approach to making a blanket, consider working one blanket-sized mitered square.

Diagonal Square

This square starts with only three stitches, can be worked as wide as you like, and ends again with three stitches. Change yarn colors to accentuate the diagonal rows.

Techniques Used

Ch   Chain stitch

SC   Single crochet

SC2TOG   2 single crochet worked together (see Chapter 3)

SC3TOG   3 single crochet worked together (see Chapter 3)

Diagonal Square Pattern

1. Ch 2.

2. Row 1: 3 SC in 2nd ch from hook, ch 1, and turn.

3. Row 2: 2 SC in 1st SC, SC in next SC, 2 SC in last SC, ch 1, and turn.

4. Row 3: 2 SC in 1st SC, SC in each SC across row to last SC, 2 SC in last SC, ch 1, and turn.

5. Rows 4 and 5: Rep row 3.

6. Row 6: SC in each SC across row.

7 Rep rows 3–6 several times. The number of repeats you use will determine the size of your square.

8 Next row: SC in each SC across row. Ch 1 and turn.

NOTE: This row falls in the middle of the square; next you will work decreases.

9 Decrease rows: Skip 1st SC, SC in each SC across row to last 2 SC, skip 1 SC, SC in last stitch, ch 1, and turn.

10 Rep decrease row until 3 SC remain.

11 Last row: Work SC3TOG.

TIP

Draw diagonal lines on many pieces of square paper to plan out a project using this square: Arrange them in different ways to create different patterns. You will find that you can create many different effects depending on how you orient each individual square. This is a really useful method for planning most projects.

The traditional granny square has survived the decades because it's fun to make and easy to modify to suit your preferences. Granny squares make excellent building blocks for pieces like the purse on page 292 and for afghans.

Techniques Used

Ch	Chain stitch		Granny cluster	3 DC in ch 1-space
Sl st	Slip stitch		Corner set	[3 DC, ch 2, 3 DC] in ch-2 space
DC	Double crochet		Create a ring using a loop (see Chapter 3)	

Granny Square Pattern

1. Round 1: Using a loop for a ring, ch 3 and work 2 DC into ring. * Ch 2, 3 DC into ring. Rep from * twice to create 2 more granny clusters. Ch 2 Sl st in 3rd ch of ch-3 at beg of round. Fasten off. Tighten the ring.

2 Round 2: Join yarn in next ch-2 space. Work [ch 3, 2 DC, ch 2, 3 DC] into ch-2 space. * Ch 1. In next ch space, work a corner set [ch 2, 3 DC, ch 2, 3 DC]. Rep from * to work a corner set into each ch-2 space. Sl st in 3rd ch of ch-3 at beg of round. Fasten off.

NOTE: See the section "Join New Yarn" on page 62 for information on how to join yarn.

3 Round 3: Join yarn in next corner ch-2 space. Work [ch 3, 2 DC, ch 2, 3 DC] into ch space.

4 * Ch 1. Work 1 granny cluster into each ch-1 space, ch 1. In next ch-2 space, work a corner set [3 DC, ch 2, 3 DC].

5 Rep from * to work into each ch space. Sl st into 3rd ch of ch-3 at beg of round. Fasten off.

NOTE: From here, the number of granny clusters worked into chain spaces between corner sets increases with each round.

A ll these shapes are a twist on the basic granny square.

Techniques Used

Ch	Chain stitch		Granny cluster	3 DC in ch-1 space
Sl st	Slip stitch		Corner set	[Ch 2, 3 DC, ch 2, 3 DC] in ch-2 space
DC	Double crochet			

Create a ring using a loop (see Chapter 3)

Triangle Granny

1. Round 1: Using a loop for a ring, ch 3 (counts as 1 DC) and work 2 DC into ring. * Ch 3, 3 DC into ring; rep from * once, ch 3, Sl st to top of the ch-3 at beg of round. Fasten off.

2. Round 2: Join yarn in a ch-3 space. [Ch 3, 2 DC, ch 3, 3 DC] into same ch-3 space. * Ch 3, work [3 DC, ch 3, 3 DC] into next ch-3 space; rep from * once, ch 3, Sl st to top of ch-3 at beg of round. Fasten off.

③ Round 3: Join yarn in a corner ch-3 space. [Ch 3, 2 DC, ch 3, 3 DC] into same ch-3 space. Ch 3, work 3 DC in next ch-3 space, * ch 3, [3 DC, ch 3, DC] into next corner ch-3 space, ch 3, 3 DC into next ch-3 space; rep from * once. Sl st to top of the ch-3 at beg of round. Fasten off.

④ Rep round 3, increasing number of 3 DC between corners with each round until granny triangle is desired size.

Round Granny

① Round 1: Using a loop for a ring, ch 3 (counts as 1 DC) and work 1 DC into ring. * Ch 2, 2 DC into ring; rep from * 6 times, Sl st to top of ch-3 at beg of round. Fasten off.

② Round 2: Join yarn in a ch-2 space. Ch 3 (counts as 1 DC) and work 2 DC into same ch-2 space, ch 2, * 3 DC into next ch-2 space, ch 2; rep from * 6 times, Sl st to top of ch-3 at beg of round. Fasten off.

③ Round 3: Join yarn in a ch-2 space. Ch 3 (counts as 1 DC) and work 2 DC into same ch-2 space, ch 2. * Work 3 DC into next ch-2 space, ch 2; rep from * until round is finished, Sl st to top of ch-3 at beg of round. Fasten off.

④ Rep round 3 until circle is the size you want.

Granny Pentagon

1 Round 1: Using a loop for a ring, ch 3 (counts as 1 DC) and work 2 DC into ring. * Ch 2, 3 DC into ring; rep from * 3 times, ch 2, Sl st to top of ch-3 at beg of round. Fasten off.

2 Round 2: Join yarn in a ch-2 space. [Ch 3, 2 DC, ch 1, 3 DC] into same ch-2 space. * Ch 2, work [3 DC, ch 1, 3 DC] into next ch-2 space, rep from * 3 times, ch 2, Sl st to top of ch-3 at beg of round. Fasten off.

3 Round 3: Join yarn in a ch-2 space. [Ch 3, 2 DC, ch 2, 3 DC] into same ch-2 space, ch 1, work 3 DC into next ch-1 space, ch 1, * [3 DC, ch 2, 3 DC] into next ch-2 space, ch 1, 3 DC into next ch-1 space, rep from * 3 times, ch 1. Sl st to top of ch-3 at beg of round. Fasten off.

4 Round 4: Join yarn in a ch-1 space. Ch 3 (counts as 1 DC), work 2 DC into same ch-1 space, ch 1, * [3 DC, ch 2, 3 DC] into next ch-2 space, ch 1, 3 DC into next ch-1 space, ch 1; rep from * 4 times, [3 DC, ch 2, 3 DC] into next ch-2 space, ch 1, Sl st to top of ch-3 at beg of round. Fasten off.

The log cabin is a popular quilt motif. Try this crochet version for the same patchwork effect.

Techniques Used

Ch	Chain stitch
Sl st	Slip stitch

SC   Single crochet

Log Cabin Pattern

MAKE THE CENTER SQUARE

1 Ch 10 for the foundation chain.

2 Row 1: SC in 2nd ch from hook and each ch across, ch 1, and turn.

3 Row 2: SC in each SC across row.

4 Rep row 2, 9 times. Fasten off.

MAKE THE FIRST SIDE RECTANGLE OR SQUARE

1. Rotate the square so you can work into the side of the piece.

2. Join a new color to a corner on the side of the center square.

3. Row 1: Ch 1, SC in the side of 1st row and each row across, ch 1, and turn.

4. Rep row 1 until you have the size and shape you want.

MAKE ANOTHER RECTANGLE

1. Rotate the square. You will be working into the sides of the rows.

2. Join a new color to a corner on the side of the center square.

3. Row 1: Ch 1, SC in side of 1st row or stitch and each row or stitch across, ch 1, and turn.

4. Row 2: Rep row 1 until you have the size and shape you want.

To continue from here, keep rotating your work in the same direction, working another rectangle with each rotation until your block is the size and shape you want.

TIP

Your center square doesn't have to be perfect. You can work with a rectangle if you choose.

You can try using a different stitch with each block, too.

This motif starts with a circle and ends shaped like a square. Giving you another option when working with squares.

To accent the circles, try working the circles in a color that contrasts the outer square rounds. Use a matching color for the outer square rounds on each block. This will bring out the circles.

Techniques Used

Ch   Chain stitch

Sl st   Slip stitch

DC   Double crochet

Circle in a Square Pattern

1. Round 1: Using a loop for a ring, ch 3 (counts as 1 DC), 15 DC into ring, Sl st to top of ch-3.

2. Round 2: Ch 5. * DC in next DC, ch 2; rep from * 15 times, Sl st to 3rd ch at beg of round.

3. Round 3: Sl st in next ch stitch, ch 3 (counts as 1 DC), 2 DC in ch-2 space. * Ch 1, 3 DC into next ch-2 space; rep from * 14 times, Sl st to top of ch-3 at beg of round.

4. Round 4: Sl st in each of the next 2 DC, ch 1, work 1 SC into next ch-1 space. * Ch 7, SC into next ch-1 space, ch 5, SC into next ch-1 space; rep from * 3 times, Sl st to SC at beg of round.

5. Round 5: Sl st in each of the next 2 chs of ch-7 space, ch 3 (counts as 1 DC), [2 DC, ch 3, 3 DC] into same ch-7 space, 3 DC into each of the next 3 ch-5 spaces. * [3 DC, ch 3, 3 DC] into next ch-7 space, 3 DC into each of the next 3 ch-5 spaces; rep from * twice, Sl st to top of ch-3 at beg of round.

Simple openwork creates a cross pattern inside this square.

Because this block has open spaces, try backing it with a contrasting fabric. This idea could work for a pillow, a small bag, or even a book cover.

Techniques Used

Ch   Chain stitch

Sl st   Slip stitch

DC   Double crochet

Cross in a Square Pattern

1. Ch 6, Sl st to 6th ch from hook to form a ring.

2. Round 1: Ch 3 (counts as 1 DC), work 15 DC into ring. Sl st into top of ch-3 at beg of round.

3. Round 2: Ch 3 (counts as 1 DC), 2 DC in 1st DC, ch 2, skip 1 DC, DC in next DC, ch 2, skip 1 DC. * 3 DC in next DC, ch 2, skip 1 DC, DC in next stitch, ch 2, skip 1 DC; rep from * twice, Sl st to top of ch-3 from beg of round.

4. Round 3: Ch 3 (counts as 1 DC), 5 DC in next DC. * DC in next DC, [ch 2, DC in next DC] twice, 5 DC in next DC; rep from * twice, [DC in next DC, ch 2] twice, Sl st in top of ch-3 from beg of round.

5 Round 4: Ch 3, DC in each of the next 2 DC, 5 DC in next DC, * DC in each of the next 3 DC, ch 2, DC in next DC, ch 2, DC in each of the next 3 DC, 5 DC in next DC, rep from * twice, DC in each of the next 3 DC, ch 2, DC in next DC, ch 2; Sl st to top of ch-3 from beg of round.

6 Round 5: Ch 3 (counts as 1 DC), DC in each of the next 4 DC, 5 DC in next DC, DC in each of the next 5 DC, 2 DC into next ch-2 space, DC in next DC, 2 DC into next ch-2 space. * DC in each of the next 5 DC, 5 DC in next DC, DC in each of the next 5 DC, 2 DC into next ch-2 space, DC in next DC, 2 DC into next ch-2 space; rep from * twice, Sl st to top of ch-3 from beg of round.

T his pretty square has two layers of petals that stand out.

Techniques Used

Ch	Chain stitch	HDC	Half double crochet (see Chapter 3)
Sl st	Slip stitch	DC	Double crochet (see Chapter 3)
SC	Single crochet	TR	Treble crochet (see Chapter 3)

Flower in a Square Pattern

❶ Ch 6, Sl st to 6th ch from hook.

❷ Round 1: Ch 1, 16 SC into ring, Sl st to 1st SC of round.

❸ Round 2: Ch 6 (counts as 1 DC and 3 chains), skip 2 SC. * DC in next SC, ch 3, skip 1 SC; rep from * 7 times, Sl st to 3rd ch from beg of round.

❹ Round 3: Ch 1. Work * [SC, HDC, 5 DC, HDC, SC] into ch-3 arch to form a petal; rep from * 7 times, Sl st to 1st SC of round. Fasten off.

5 Round 4: Join between 2 petals. Ch 1, SC in same space between petals, ch 6. * SC in next space between petals, ch 6; rep from * 6 times. Sl st to 1st SC of round.

6 Round 5: Ch 1. Work * [SC, HDC, 6 DC, HDC, SC] to form a petal into ch-6 arch; rep from * 7 times, Sl st to 1st SC of round. Fasten off.

7 Round 6: Join to 2nd DC of a petal from round 5. Ch 1, SC in same DC, ch 6, skip 2 DC, SC in next DC. * Ch 6, SC in 2nd DC of next petal, ch 6, skip 2 DC, SC in next DC; rep from * 6 times, ch 3, DC in 1st SC of round. Sl st to 1st DC of round.

8 Round 7: Ch 3 (counts as 1 DC), 3 DC into ch space, ch 4, SC into next ch space. ch 6, SC into next ch space, ch 6, SC in next ch space, ch 3. * [4DC, ch 4, 4 DC] into next ch space, ch 3, SC into next ch space, ch 6, SC into next ch space, ch 6, SC into next ch space, ch 3; rep from * twice, 4 DC in next ch space, ch 4, Sl st to top of ch-3 from beg of round. Fasten off.

You can get creative with how you use this kind of motif. Join them close together or on a field of chain arches.

Techniques Used

Ch	Chain stitch		DTR	Double treble crochet (see Chapter 4)
Sl st	Slip stitch		Picot	Ch 4, Sl st to 4th ch from the hook
DC	Double crochet			

Ten Points Motif Pattern

1. Ch 12, Sl st to 12th ch from hook to form a ring.

2. Round 1: Ch 1, work 30 SC into ring, Sl st to 1st SC of round to join.

3. Round 2: Ch 5 (counts as DTR), DTR in next 2 SC, ch 3, * 3 DTR in next 3 SC, ch 3, rep from * 8 times, Sl st to top of ch-5.

4. Round 3: Ch 1, * SC in next DTR, 3 DC, picot, 3 DC in next ch-3 space, rep from * 9 times, Sl st to 1st SC. Fasten off.

Attach four of these small diamonds to make a larger square.

Techniques Used

Ch	Chain stitch	DC2TOG	2 DC worked together (see Chapter 4)
Sl st	Slip stitch	Picot	Ch 3, Sl st to 3rd ch from the hook
DC	Double crochet		

Diamond Motif Pattern

1 Ch 6, Sl st to 6th ch from hook to form a ring.

2 Round 1: Ch 1. * 3 SC, picot; rep from * 3 times. Sl st to 1st SC of round.

3 Round 2: Sl st in next SC from prev round, ch 2, DC in next st, ch 7, Sl st in 4th ch from hook, ch 3. * Skip [1 SC, 1 picot, 1 SC], DC2TOG in next SC, ch 7, Sl st in 4th ch from hook, ch 3; rep from * twice, Sl st to top of ch-2 from beg of round.

4 Round 3: Sl st into next ch space, * 5 SC into ch space, [2 SC, ch 2, 2 SC] into picot space, 5 SC into ch space, SC in next DC2TOG; rep from * 3 times, Sl st to 1st SC of round.

NOTE: You may have noticed that the directions to make a picot in this pattern differs from the picot directions in the Ten Points motif. Picots can be made with different numbers of chains to create a different look. Try making one with a lot of chains and compare the difference.

There are many different ways to join blocks and motifs. Each one creates a different look; it's up to you to decide what you want.

Join with Chain Arches

1. Join yarn to the first piece.
2. Ch 1, SC.
3. Ch 3.
4. SC into the second piece.
5. Ch 3.
6. SC into the first piece.
7. Rep steps 3–6.

These simple steps can easily be changed to fit the design you want. Experiment with chain lengths and taller stitches to get the look you're going for (see the two photos below for examples).

Sew the Pieces Together

Join the pieces with a slip stitch or single crochet. (See Chapter 2 for more on these stitches.) The seams create a solid fabric and leaves a ridge around each piece.

This photo shows the right side of the join.

Sew the pieces together using a whipstitch worked through the back loops only. (See the section "Seam Pieces Together by Sewing on page 191 for more information.) This kind of join creates a solid fabric. Sewing leaves very little trace, creating an invisible join if you use a matching color.

CHAPTER 13

Edgings

A crocheted edging can be the perfect finishing touch for your project.
An edging not only makes borders look neat, but it can also provide
an elegant design detail. This chapter shows you how to customize an
edging for your crocheted, knitted, or commercial fabric pieces.

Single Crochet Edging

Single crochet creates a neat, simple, tailored edging.

Make a Single Crochet Edging

1. Insert your hook anywhere along the edge of the piece to be edged and join yarn. See the section "Join New Yarn" on page 62.

2. Work 1 SC into each st across.

3. Work 2 or 3 SC into the corner st; experiment to create a corner you like.

4. Continue to work across the next side until you reach the corner. Rep the combination you used to turn your corner.

5. To work into the side, simply work into the side of a stitch from each row (shown on the right). To crochet into the bottom of the 1st row, work into unworked loop(s) remaining from your foundation chain.

6. Continue to work across edge of piece, working corners as needed. When you reach the end of the round, Sl st to 1st crochet of the round. Fasten off and weave in ends.

Picot edgings are an easy way to create an interesting edging. The size of the picot (see tip on the next page) determines whether your edging looks dainty, lacy, or even spiky.

Make a Picot Edging

1. Insert your hook anywhere along the edge of the piece to be edged and join yarn.

2. Work 1 SC into next st.

3. Ch 3 (a) and Sl st into 1st ch—1 picot made (b).

3a

3b

④ Skip 1 st; 1 SC into next st.

⑤ Rep steps 3 and 4 to create a picot edging.

⑥ Continue working the picot steps 3 and 4 across the piece. When you reach a corner, work 1 SC, 1 picot, and 1 SC into the corner space.

TIP

Work 5 chains to create a larger picot. You may need to skip 2 stitches before working the next single crochet to make the edging lay lie flat. Experiment!

Crab Stitch Edging

Crab stitch is most often used to create a simple and decorative border around a crocheted piece. You might see the stitch referred to as reverse single crochet (RSC).

As mentioned in the section "Make a Crab Stitch" on page 76, crab stitch is worked in reverse.

Make a Crab Stitch Border

1 Insert your hook anywhere along the edge of the piece to be edged. Join yarn and work a crab st into each st or space across the piece.

2 Work 2 crab sts into corner st to turn corner.

3 Work 1 crab st into each st or space along the side of your work.

4 When you reach the next corner, work 2 crab sts into corner st.

5 Repeat steps 3 and 4 until you reach the beginning of the edging round. Fasten off and weave in ends.

Single crochet stitches are often used to make a quick and simple edging. Tall stitches can be worked just as easily, but add a different look and feel. These edgings have just enough space between stitches to weave a ribbon through, which makes a lovely finish to your crochet work.

DOUBLE CROCHET EDGING

Ch 3, 1 DC into each st or st space around the piece, working [2 DC, ch 2, 2 DC] in each corner. When round is complete, Sl st to top of ch-3 from beg of round.

TREBLE CROCHET EDGING

Ch 4, 1 TR into each st or st space around the piece, working [2 TR, ch 2, 2 TR] in each corner. When round is complete, Sl st to top of ch-3 from beg of round.

FILET EDGING

Ch 3, 1 DC into next st, * ch 2, skip 2 sts or st spaces, 1 DC in each of next 2 sts or st spaces. Rep from * across, working [2 TR, ch 2, 2 TR] in each corner. When round is complete, Sl st to top of ch-3 from beg of round.

This section starts out with a simple arches edging that can stand on its own to give a piece a simple dainty look. You can add on to the basic arches edging to create more elaborate edgings.

ARCHES EDGING

① Join yarn to edge of piece.

② Round 1: Ch 1, 1 SC into each st or st space around the piece, Sl st to join last SC to 1st SC of round.

③ Round 2: Ch 1, * 1 SC in 1st st, ch 3, skip 1 SC, 1 SC in next st. Rep from * to complete round. Ch 3 and Sl st to 1st SC.

MESH EDGING

① Repeat steps 1–3 of the arches edging.

② Round 3: Sl st to ch-3 space, ch 1, * 1 SC into ch space, ch 3. Rep from * to complete round, Sl st to 1st SC.

③ Continue working Round 3 until the mesh edging is the desired size.

SCALLOP EDGING

① Follow steps 1–3 of the Arches Edging on the previous page.

② Follow step 2 of the Mesh Edging on the previous page.

③ Round 4: Sl st into ch space, ch 1, * 6 SC into ch space, rep from * to complete round, Sl st to 1st SC.

PICOT SCALLOP

① Follow steps 1–3 of the Mesh Edging on the previous page.

② Round 3: Sl st into ch space, ch 1, * 3 SC into ch space, ch 3, Sl st to 1st ch, 3 SC into ch space. Rep from * to complete round, Sl st to 1st SC.

TIP

Here are a couple of ways to experiment with the arched edgings:

- Change the number of chains in your arches and the number of spaces between arches.
- Work many rows of the mesh edging before adding one of the scalloped edgings.

Shell edgings are a classic finishing detail. A simple round of shells can transform the simplest piece into something pretty and charming.

SIMPLE SHELLS EDGING

① Round 1: Ch 1, SC into each st or st space around the piece, working [SC, ch 2, SC] in corner spaces, Sl st to join last SC to 1st SC.

② Round 2: Ch 1, * SC in next st, skip 2 sts, 5 DC in next st, skip 2 sts. Rep from *, continue to follow the order of the pattern in corner spaces as well, Sl st to 1st SC.

TREBLE CROCHET SHELLS

① Round 1: Ch 1, SC into each st or st space around the piece, working [SC, ch 2, SC] in corner spaces, Sl st to join last SC to 1st SC.

② Round 2: Ch 1, * SC in next st, ch 2, [2 TR TOG, ch 2] 3 times in next st. Rep from * across round, working a Sl st to 1st SC.

Now that you understand the basic idea, try creating shell combinations of your own.

Fancy Edgings

BLOCK EDGING

1. Round 1: Ch 1, 1 SC into each st or st space around the piece, Sl st to join last SC to 1st SC of round.

2. Round 2: Ch 3, skip 1st 3 SC, * 1 DC in next SC, ch 3 [1 DC around post of prev DC] 4 times, skip next 3 SC. Rep from * to complete round. Sl st to ch-3 from beg of round.

PETALS EDGING

1. Round 1: Ch 1, SC into each st or st space around the piece, working [SC, ch 2, SC] in corner spaces, Sl st to join last SC to 1st SC of round.

2. Round 2: Ch 1, * SC in next st or st space, ch 1, skip 1 st or st space, rep from *, working [SC, ch 1, SC] in each corner space. When round is complete, Sl st to ch 1 from beg of round.

3. Round 3: * Sl st into next ch space, [ch 2, 3 DC, ch 2, Sl st] into ch space, rep from * across round, continue to follow the order of the pattern in corner spaces as well. Sl st to Sl st from beg of round.

FANCY FANS EDGING

1 Round 1: Ch 1, SC into each st or st space around the piece, working [SC, ch 2, SC] in corner spaces, Sl st to join last SC to 1st SC of round.

2 Round 2: Ch 1, * SC in each of next 3 sts or st spaces, ch 3, rep from *, work [SC, ch 3, SC] in each corner space, when round is complete Sl st to ch 1 from beg of round.

3 Round 3: Ch 1, SC,* [DC, picot, ch 1] 5 times in ch-3 space, DC in same space, skip 1 SC, SC in next SC, rep from * across round, continue to follow the order of the pattern in corner spaces as well. Sl st to 1st SC of round.

DAISY CHAIN EDGING

1 Round 1: Ch 1, SC into each st or st space around the piece, working [SC, ch 2, SC] in corner spaces, Sl st to join last SC to 1st SC of round.

2 Round 2: Ch 1, SC, * ch 8, SC in 5th ch from hook, [ch 3, SC] 3 times into same ch space, ch 3, skip 3 SC from prev round, 1 SC in each of the next 3 SC from prev round. Rep from * across round, continue to follow the order of the pattern in corner spaces as well Sl st to 1st SC.

Edging Knit Fabric

Crochet edgings look great bordering hand-knitted fabric. It may take a little trial and error to figure out exactly where you want to insert the hook to work into the knitted piece.

Practice your crochet edging on the gauge swatch you knit for your project.

Use a hook equal to or smaller than the knitting needles used.

Try this stitch combination for your edging base. It will be forgiving of differences between the knitted fabric (including a stretchy rib) and the crochet edging:

Ch 1, SC in st space, ch 1, rep across round, working [SC, ch 1, SC] in corner spaces, Sl st to 1st SC.

Any trip through a thrift store will show you how popular crochet edgings once were. It used to be common to crochet a lovely border around every-day household objects like dish towels and handkerchiefs. Once you get the hang of it, customizing fabric with crochet is really easy and fun.

Consider the weight of your fabric when choosing your yarn. Most crocheted borders for fabric are done with thread or lace-weight yarn. If you want to use something thicker, test it out on a swatch of the fabric first to make sure it will work.

You will need to poke your own holes to work into. For this, you will need a craft awl and a ruler.

1. Use the awl to pierce the fabric at regular intervals. If the holes are too close together, the fabric may tear. Try ½ inch between each set of holes.

2. The holes are probably too far apart to work a continuous row of SC. Work a SC into each hole and chain 1 or 2 after each SC.

3. After this first round of edging, you can work any pattern you like.

CHAPTER 14

Patterns

The patterns in this chapter will help you explore the techniques and stitches you learned in previous chapters. Follow any pattern row by row, and you'll amaze yourself with what you can make!

Beanie Master Pattern

You can use this basic outline to make your own custom beanie. Try out different stitches and stitch patterns to create your own unique hats.

Work in the round (see Chapter 3)

Specifications

TECHNIQUES USED

Ch Chain

Sl st Slip stitch

Work in the round (see Chapter 3)

Beanie Master Pattern

1. Start with the ring or magic loop method of your choice.

2. Work 6, 7, or 8 sts into ring. The number of sts you choose depends on the yarn you use. Work the number of sts that best fits to make a neat 1st round. Sl st to 1st st of round and crochet a ch appropriate for the st you are using.

3. To make top of hat, work rounds of inc:

   Round 2: Work 2 sts in each st across, Sl st to 1st st of round, and ch the number appropriate for the st you are using.

Round 3: Work 2 sts in 1st st, 1 st in next st, rep across, Sl st to 1st st of round, and ch the number appropriate for the st you are using.

Round 4: Work 2 sts in 1st st, 1 st in each of the next 2 sts, rep across, Sl st to 1st st of round, and ch the number appropriate for the st you are using.

Continue inc rounds, adding 1 more st between each 2-st inc until rounds worked cover crown of head.

④ To shape crown, divide the number of sts in your last round by 4. For next round, work 4 inc spread out with that number of sts in between. Sl st to 1st st of round, and ch the number appropriate for the st you are using.

⑤ Work 1 st in each st across round. Sl st to 1st st of round, ch the number appropriate for the st you are using. Continue to work even rounds until hat is the size you want.

⑥ Turn and work another even round. This creates a subtle finish to the hat.

Basic Beanie

This version of the beanie pattern uses the extended single crochet stitch, giving it a yummy texture.

Specifications

MATERIALS

1 hank Fleece Artist *Kid Aran* (50% kid/50% wool, 410 yd./250g) in Mahogany

5.5mm hook

Stitch marker

TECHNIQUES USED

Ch   Chain

Sl st   Slip stitch

ESC   Extended single crochet (see Chapter 4)

Adjustable ring (see Chapter 3)

FINISHED SIZE

One size fits most adult heads. See pattern for advice on customizing the fit.

Circumference = 22 inches

GAUGE

12 stitches and 13 rows = 4 inches in ESC

Make the Beanie

1. Start with an adjustable ring.

2. Round 1: 8 SC into ring, Sl st into 1st SC to join round. Gently pull on tail to tighten ring. Mark 1st st with stitch marker and ch 2 (8 SC total).

3. Round 2: 1 ESC into same st the Sl st is worked into, * 2 ESC in next SC, rep from * until 1 st remains, remove marker, 1 ESC in same st the 1st ESC was worked into, Sl st in 1st ESC to join. Place marker in 1st st. Continue to move marker to indicate 1st st of every round. Ch 2 (16 ESC total).

4. Round 3: 1 ESC into same st the Sl st is worked into. Place marker in 1st st. Continue to move marker to indicate 1st st of every round. * 1 ESC into next st and 2 ESC into next st. Rep from * until 1 st remains. 1 ESC into next st. 1 ESC in same st the 1st ESC was worked into; Sl st into 1st ESC to join. Ch 1 (24 ESC total).

5. Round 4: Work 1 ESC into same st the Sl st is worked into. * Work 1 ESC in each of the next 2 sts. Work 2 ESC into next st. Rep from * until 1 st remains. Work 1 ESC into next st. Work 1 ESC into same st the 1st ESC was worked into. Sl st into 1st ESC to join. Ch 1 (32 ESC total).

6. Round 5: Work 1 ESC into same st the Sl st is worked into. * Work 1 ESC in each of the next 3 sts; work 2 ESC into next st. Rep from * until 1 st remains. Work 1 ESC into next st. Work 1 ESC into same st the 1st ESC was worked into. Sl st to 1st ESC to join. Ch 1 (40 ESC total).

NOTE: With each round, 1 more stitch is worked even between increases.

7. Round 6: Work 1 ESC into same st the Sl st is worked into. * Work 1 ESC into each of the next 4 sts; work 2 ESC into next st. Rep from * until 1 st remains. Work 1 ESC into next st. Work 1 ESC into same st the 1st ESC was worked into. Sl st to 1st ESC to join. Ch 1 (48 ESC total).

8. Round 7: Work 1 ESC into same st the Sl st is worked into. * Work 1 ESC into each of the next 5 sts; work 2 ESC into next st. Rep from * until 1 st remains. Work 1 ESC into next st. Work 1 ESC into same st the 1st ESC was worked into. Sl st to 1st ESC to join. Ch 1 (56 ESC total).

SHAPE THE CROWN

1 Round 8: Work 1 ESC into same st the Sl st is worked into. * Work 1 ESC into each of the next 14 sts; work 2 ESC into next st. Rep from * until 1 st remains. Work 1 ESC into next st. Work 1 ESC into same st the 1st ESC was worked into. Sl st into 1st ESC to join. Ch 1 (60 ESC total).

2 Round 9: Work 1 ESC into same st the Sl st is worked into. * Work 1 ESC into each of the next 15 sts; work 2 ESC into next st. Rep from * until 1 st remains. Work 1 ESC into next st. Work 1 ESC into same st the 1st ESC was worked into. Sl st into 1st ESC to join. Ch 1 (64 ESC total).

3 Rounds 10–19: Work 1 ESC into each st around. Sl st into 1st ESC to join. Ch 1 (64 ESC total).

TURN TO CREATE A SUBTLE BAND

1 Round 20: Turn. Work 1 ESC into each st around. Sl st into 1st ESC to join. Ch 1 (64 ESC total).

2 Rounds 21–22: Work 1 ESC into each st around. Sl st into 1st ESC to join.

3 Fasten off and weave in ends.

Add a feminine touch to the beanie pattern with this sweet edging.

Specifications

MATERIALS

1 hank Fleece Artist *Kid Silk* (70% kid/30% silk, 410 yd./250g) in Ruby Red

5.5mm hook

Stitch marker

TECHNIQUES USED

Ch   Chain

Sl st   Slip stitch

ESC   Extended single crochet (see Chapter 4)

Adjustable ring (see Chapter 3)

Popcorn Dance pattern (see Chapter 7)

V-stitch: Work [1 DC, ch 2, 1 DC] into the same st.

Popcorn stitch: Work 4 DCs into the same st. Join through the top and ch 1. (See the section "Popcorns" in Chapter 5.)

Popcorn V-stitch: Work [1 DC, ch 2, and 1 popcorn st] all into the same st.

FINISHED SIZE

One size fits most adult heads

Circumference = 22 inches

GAUGE

12 stitches and 13 rows = 4 inches in ESC

Make the Cloche

MAKE THE BODY

1 Rounds 1–8: Work beanie pattern through round 8 (60 ESC total).

2 Rounds 9–19: Work 1 ESC into each st around. Sl st into 1st ESC to join. Ch 1 (60 ESC total).

MAKE THE EDGING

1 Edging round 1: Ch 3. Starting in 2nd st of round, * work 1 popcorn V-st, skip 2 sts, and work 1 V-st. Rep from * around until 5 sts remain. Skip 2 sts and work [1 DC, ch 2] into next st. Sl st into top ch of the ch-3 at beg of round.

2 Edging round 2: Ch 3. * Work 1 V-st into next ch-2 space. Work 1 popcorn V-st into next ch-2 space. Rep from * around. Sl st into top ch of the ch-3 at beg of round.

3 Fasten off and weave in ends.

Baby Beanie

The simple stitch combination used in this version of the beanie creates a soft, springy texture.

Specifications

MATERIALS

1 skein Rowan *Cashsoft Baby DK* (57% extra fine merino/33% acrylic microfiber/10% cashmere, 140 yd./50g) in Cloud

4.5mm hook

TECHNIQUES USED

Ch   Chain

Sl st   Slip stitch

SC   Single crochet

DC   Double crochet

Adjustable ring (see Chapter 3)

FINISHED SIZE

Circumference = 16 inches

To make a smaller hat, work fewer increase rounds.

GAUGE

12 stitches and 14 rows = 4 inches

Make the Baby Beanie

① Start with an adjustable ring.

② Round 1: Work 6 SC into ring, Sl st in 1st SC to join round.

③ Round 2: * 1 SC and 1 DC in next SC, rep from * across round (12 sts total).

④ Round 3: * 2 SC in next st, 1 SC in next st, rep from * across round (18 sts total).

5 Round 4: * 1 SC and 1 DC in next st, 1 SC in next st, 1 DC in next st; rep from * across round (24 sts total).

6 Round 5: * 1 SC and 1 DC in next st, 1 SC in next st, 1 DC in next st, 1 SC in next st, 1 DC and 1 SC in next st, 1 DC in next st, 1 SC in next st, 1 DC in next st; rep from * across round (30 sts total).

7 Round 6: * 1 SC and 1 DC in next st, [1 SC in next st, 1 DC in next st] 2 times, rep from * across round (36 sts total).

8 Round 7: * 1 SC and 1 DC in next st, 1 SC in next st, 1 DC in next stitch, 1 SC in next st, 1 DC in next st, 1 SC in next st, 1 DC and 1 SC in next st, 1 DC in next st, 1 SC in next st, 1 DC in next st, 1 SC in next st, 1 DC in next st, rep from * 3 times across the round (42 sts total).

9 Round 8: * 1 SC and 1 DC in next st, [1 SC in next st, 1 DC in next st] 3 times, rep from * across round (48 sts total).

10 Round 9: * 1 SC and 1 DC in next st, [1 SC in next st, 1 DC in next st] 4 times, rep from * 4 times across the round, 1 SC in next st, 1 DC in next st, 1 SC and 1 DC in next st (54 sts total).

11 Round 10: * 1 SC in next st, 1 DC in next st, rep from * across round.

12 Rep round 10 until the hat is the size you want.

13 Fasten off and weave in ends.

Booties Master Pattern

Booties are quick and easy to crochet. Use the master pattern and then add a finishing touch to make a boot, Mary Jane, or crisscross-style bootie.

Specifications

MATERIALS
4mm hook

4 stitch markers

Pencil and paper to take notes

CRISSCROSS
1 skein Mission Falls *136 Merino Superwash* (100% wool, 136 yd./50g) in #028 Pistachio

3 yd. Mission Falls *136 Merino Superwash* (100% wool, 136 yd./50g) in #025 Mallow

4 buttons

MARY JANE
1 skein Mission Falls *136 Merino Superwash* (100% wool, 136 yd./50g) in #025 Mallow

2 buttons

BOOT
1 skein Mission Falls *136 Merino Superwash* (100% wool, 136 yd./50g) in #015 Putty

3 yd. Mission Falls *136 Merino Superwash* (100% wool, 136 yd./50g) in #025 Mallow

TECHNIQUES USED
Ch   Chain

Sl st   Slip stitch

SC   Single crochet

SC2TOG   2 single crochet worked together (see Chapter 3)

FINISHED SIZE
Custom fit

GAUGE
4 stitches = 1 inch

5 rows = 1 inch

Master Pattern for Bootie Sole

1 Make a chain the length of the ball of the foot to the inside of the heel. Ch 1.

2 Write down the number of chains used.

3 Row 1: SC in 2nd ch from hook and each ch across, ch 1 and turn.

4 Round 1: SC in each SC across row, ch 1, rotate, work 1 SC same space as last SC worked, ch 1, SC in same space as last SC, rotate, working into back side of foundation ch, SC across, ch 1, SC same space as last SC worked, ch 1, SC in same space as the last SC.

5 Round 2: 1 SC in 1st SC of round 1 (place marker here). * SC in each SC across to ch-1 space, 1 SC in ch-1 space, ch 1, 1 SC in next SC, ch 1, SC in next ch-1 space, rep from * to finish round.

NOTE: To keep track of the start of each round, move the marker at the beginning of each round.

6 Round 3: Rep round 2. Rep round 2 again for a wider bootie.

7 Write down how many times you repeat round 2.

8 Rounds 4–6: Work 1 SC in each SC across round.

9 Fold the sole lengthwise and place markers in the 4 sts where you will start your decreases. Space the decreases two on each side.

10 Round 7: * 1 SC in each SC across round to marked st, SC2TOG (move marker to new st), rep from *. 1 SC in each SC to finish round.

11 Round 8: Work 1 SC in each SC across round. (Move markers as you work.)

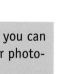

TIP

Aside from keeping notes on paper, you can try using sticky notes in the book or photocopy the pattern to write notes on.

⑫ Round 9: Rep round 7.

⑬ Use the instructions for one of the following bootie styles or work from here to design your own bootie.

CRISSCROSS

❶ Work Bootie master pattern to round 8.

❷ Fold bootie in half lengthwise. Place markers at the halfway point on both sides of the bootie.

❸ Sew buttons to each side of the bootie.

❹ Make the straps: 1 SC in each SC across round to marked st, * work a ch that reaches across to the button (mark the ch) plus enough chains to make a loop for your button, SC in the marked ch, continue to work SC in each ch * and SC across to next marked st.

To create the second strap, rep from * to * working in underside of ch, SC in marked ch and each ch across, Sl st to side of next SC. Fasten off.

❺ Trim the bootie: Join a contrasting color and work one Sl st in each st across the bootie and straps.

MARY JANE

❶ Work Bootie master pattern to round 8.

❷ Fold bootie in half lengthwise. Place markers at the halfway point on both sides of the bootie.

❸ Sew the button to the bootie.

❹ Strap row 1: 1 SC in each SC across round to marked st, work a ch that reaches across to the button (mark the ch) plus enough chains to make a loop for your button, SC in marked ch, continue to work SC in each ch and SC across to next marked st, ch 1, and turn.

❺ Strap row 2: 1 SC in each SC across row to ch loop. 5 SC in ch loop, working in underside of ch, Sl st in each ch across, Sl st to side of next SC. Fasten off.

TIP

Variations

Variation 1: Change to a new color at Strap row 1.

Variation 2: Join a new color and Sl st across.

279

BOOT

1 Work Bootie master pattern to round 9.

2 Fold bootie in half lengthwise. Place 3 markers 1 on each side at the halfway point and 1 at the back of the bootie.

3 Round 10: * 1 SC in each SC across round to marked st, SC2TOG in next SC, rep from * twice.

4 Continue to work 1 SC in each SC across rounds until boot is the desired height, Sl st in next SC. Fasten off.

Sock Master Pattern

Crochet stitches make comfy, springy socks. Use this master pattern to make your own custom fit socks.

Specifications

MATERIALS

2 hanks Shibui *Sock* (100% superwash merino, 191 yd./50g)

3.75mm hook

Approx. 6 stitch markers

Paper and pencil to take notes

TECHNIQUES USED

Ch   Chain

Sl st   Slip stitch

SC   Single crochet

BLO   Back loop only (see Chapter 4)

SC2TOG 2 single crochet worked together (see Chapter 3)

Adjustable ring (see Chapter 3)

FINISHED SIZE

Custom fit

GAUGE

5 stitches = 1 inch

6 rows = 1 inch

Make the Socks

NOTE: You will need to keep detailed notes as you work through the pattern. Use these notes to make the second socks. This also makes it easier to make corrections.

START THE TOE

1 Foundation Row: Working into the ridge on the back-side of the chain, Sl st in each ridge loop across the chain. The foundation row will have two sets of loops, one on the top (the slip stitches) and one on the bottom (the foundation chain).

2 Note the number of chains and number of stitches in your foundation row.

3 Round 1: Ch 1, * rotate 180 degrees, SC in each stitch across this side of the round (place marker in this SC), rep from * (place marker in last SC).

INCREASE ROUNDS

1 Round 2: * 2 SC in the next st, 1 SC in each SC across the round to marked SC, 2 SC in the SC before marked SC, 1 SC in marked SC (move marker to this stitch), rep from * to finish the round.

NOTE: Each marker should be in the SC between increases on each end of the round.

2 Note the number of stitches after the first increase round.

3 Repeat the increase round until the sock reaches the bottom of the toe when stretched a little. Each increase round adds 4 sts to the stitch count.

4 Note the number of increase rounds worked and the number in the stitch count of the last round.

EVEN ROUNDS

1 Round 1: SC in each st across the round (place a marker at the beginning of the round).

2 Rep round 1 until the sock foot reaches just past the middle of the arch of your foot.

3 Note the number of even rounds worked from the round with the stitch marker. Also note the total number of rounds worked from the foundation row.

MAKE THE HEEL

1 Fold the stocking foot flat so that it looks like the bottom of your foot, with the middle of the foundation row centered at the top. The open side of the folded stocking foot, with the end of your last round, is the bottom of the foot. Place a marker in the stitch on the right and left side of the bottom of the foot. To build a heel you will start to work from here in rows between the markers. It doesn't matter where the last round ended, simply work to the next marker.

2 Heel Row 1: SC in each SC across the row to the next marker, turn.

3 Heel Row 2: Ch 1, SC in each SC to the next marker, turn.

4 Heel Row 3: Ch 1, SC in each SC until the last st. Leave the last stitch unworked, turn.

5 Rep row 3 until the number of stitches in the row is equal to the number of stitches in the foundation chain (refer to your notes).

NOTE: You may wish to mark each skipped stitch.

6 Mark the last unworked SC.

7 Note the number of Heel Rows worked.

HEEL TURN ROWS

1 Heel Turn Row: Ch 1, SC in each SC across the row, 1 SC into the marked SC of the previous row, turn.

2 Rep the heel turn row until you meet up with the last round before the heel rows began.

3 Final Heel Row: Ch 1, SC in each SC across the round, mark the last SC (move this marker up with each round that follows).

4 Note the stitch count of the previous round.

SHAPE THE ANKLE

1 There will be a crook on each side of the sock where the ankle will be. Place 1 marker at each crook.

2 Ankle Round 1: SC in each SC across the round to the marked crook, SC2TOG in the next 2 SC, SC in each SC across the round to the next marked crook, SC2TOG in the next 2 SC, SC in each SC to the end of the round.

3 Ankle Round 2: Place markers 1 inch to either side of both ankle decreases. SC in each SC across the round, work 2 SC in each marked st.

4 Ankle Round 3: 1 SC in each SC across the round.

FINISH THE SOCK

From here you can continue to work 1 SC in each SC across the round until the sock is the height you want. Or you can explore using stitch patterns to add some personality to your sock. The example shown here uses a simple rib pattern.

① Rib Round 1: 1 SC in BLO of the next SC, 1 SC in FLO of the next SC, rep across to end of the round.

② Rep rib round 1 until the sock is the height you prefer.

③ Note how many rib rows are worked.

Problem Solving

You may need to experiment to get just the right fit.

- If the sock is too narrow, work another increase round after the first even round.
- If the sock is too wide, unravel to the increase rounds and remove an increase round.
- If the ankle is too big, pinch the fabric and count the number of stitches pinched. Unravel to the place where the fabric gapes, space out decreases equal to the number of stitches you pinched. Take notes on the changes made.
- If the sock is too tight at any point, unravel to that point and add increases. Take notes on the changes made.

Cozy, Webby Sweater

This sweater is as cozy as it is contemporary. You use a large hook with two strands of DK-weight yarn to make a simple, webby fabric. The body is worked in one piece, reducing the amount of seaming necessary. You add the collar along the front and neck after the body is complete. See the end of the pattern for ideas on how to alter this pattern to make other simple sweaters.

Specifications

MATERIALS

This example was made using: 10 (10, 12, 12) balls South West Trading Company *Optimum DK* (100% wool, 154 yd./50g) in Silver

This pattern can be made with any DK-weight yarn.

10mm hook

TECHNIQUES USED

Ch	Chain
SC	Single crochet
FLO	Front loop only (see Chapter 4)
SC2TOG	2 single crochet worked together (see Chapter 3)

Increasing and decreasing (see Chapter 3)

FINISHED SIZE

Bust/Chest circumference S (M, L, XL): 32–36 (38–42, 44–48, 50–54) inches

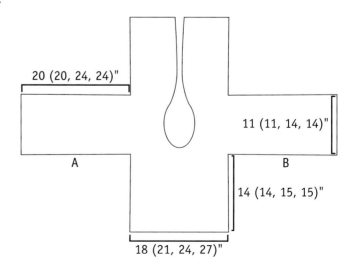

Make the Cozy, Webby Sweater

GET STARTED

You start this sweater at the bottom of the back and build out from there.

1 Ch 38 (44, 52, 58).

2 Row 1: Work 1 SC into 2nd ch from hook and each ch across. Ch 1 and turn.

3 Row 2: Work 1 SC into FLO of each st in prev row. Ch 1 and turn.

4 Rep row 2 through row 28 (28, 30, 30).

INCREASE TO ADD SLEEVES

1 Row 29 (29, 31, 31): Ch 39 (39, 45, 45).

This increase creates the left sleeve (A) of the sweater.

2 Row 30 (30, 32, 32): Work 1 SC into 2nd ch from hook and each ch across. Continue to work 1 SC into FLO of each st of prev row. Ch 39 (39, 45, 45) and turn.

This increase creates the right sleeve (B) of the sweater.

3 Row 31 (31, 33, 33): Work 1 SC into 2nd ch from hook and each ch across. Continue to work 1 SC into FLO of each st of prev row. Ch 1 and turn.

4 Row 32–35 (32–35, 34–39, 34–39): Work 1 SC into FLO of each st of prev row. Ch 1 and turn.

5 At row 35 (35, 39, 39): Place marker in st in middle of row.

WORK SIDE A

Row 36 (36, 40, 40): Work 1 SC into FLO of each st of prev row until you reach marker. Work 1 SC into this st. Ch 1 and turn.

SHAPE THE NECKLINE WITH DECREASES

1. Row 37 (37, 41, 41): Work 1 SC into FLO of 1st st and SC2TOG into FLO over next 2 sts. Continue across, working 1 SC into FLO of each st of prev row. Ch 1 and turn.

2. Row 38 (38, 42, 42): Work 1 SC into FLO of each st of prev row. Ch 1 and turn.

3. Row 39 (39, 43, 43): Work 1 SC into FLO of 1st st and SC2TOG into FLO over next 2 sts. Continue across, working 1 SC into FLO of each st of prev row. Ch 1 and turn.

4. Row 40 (40, 44, 44): Work 1 SC into FLO of each st of prev row. Ch 1 and turn.

5. **For small and medium sizes:**

   Row 41: Work 1 SC into FLO of each st of prev row. Ch 1 and turn.

   For large and extra-large sizes:

   Row 45: Work 1 SC into FLO of 1st st and SC2TOG into FLO over next 2 sts. Continue across, working 1 SC into FLO of each st of prev row. Ch 1 and turn.

6. Rows 42–48 (42–48, 46–50, 46–50): Work 1 SC into FLO of each st of prev row. Ch 1 and turn.

SHAPE THE NECKLINE WITH INCREASES

1. Row 49 (49, 51, 51): Work 1 SC into FLO of 1st st and 2 SC into FLO of 2nd st. Continue across, working 1 SC into FLO of each st of prev row. Ch 1 and turn.

2. Row 50 (50, 52, 52): Work 1 SC into FLO of each st of prev row. Ch 1 and turn.

3. Row 51 (51, 53, 53): Work 1 SC into FLO of 1st st and 2 SC into FLO of 2nd st. Continue across, working 1 SC into FLO of each st of prev row. Ch 1 and turn.

4. Row 52 (52, 54, 54): Work 1 SC into FLO of each st of prev row. Ch 1 and turn.

5. Row 53 (53, 55, 55): Work 1 SC into FLO of 1st st and 2 SC into FLO of 2nd st. Continue across, working 1 SC into FLO of each st of prev row. Ch 1 and turn.

6. Row 54 (54, 56, 56): Work 1 SC into FLO of each st of prev row. Ch 1 and turn.

7. **For small and medium sizes:**

   Place marker at 39th st in from end of sleeve.

   Row 55: Work 1 SC into FLO of 1st st and 2 SC into FLO of 2nd st. Continue across, working 1 SC into FLO of each st of prev row until marked st. Work 1 SC into this st. Ch 1 and turn.

   Rows 56–84: Work 1 SC into FLO of each st of prev row. Ch 1 and turn.

   For large and extra-large sizes:

   Row 57: Work 1 SC into FLO of 1st st and 2 SC into FLO of 2nd st. Continue across, working 1 SC into FLO of each st of prev row. Ch 1 and turn.

Row 58: Work 1 SC into FLO of each st of prev row. Ch 1 and turn.

Place marker at 44th st in from end of sleeve.

Row 59: Work 1 SC into FLO of 1st st and 2 SC into FLO of 2nd st. Continue across, working 1 SC into FLO of each st of prev row until marked st. Work 1 SC into this st. Ch 1 and turn.

Rows 60–90: Work 1 SC into FLO of each st of prev row. Ch 1 and turn.

WORK SIDE B

① Row 36 (36, 40, 40): Join yarn at marked st and work 1 SC into this st. Work 1 SC into FLO of each st of prev row. Ch 1 and turn.

② Row 37 (37, 41, 41): Work 1 SC into FLO of each st of prev row. Ch 1 and turn.

SHAPE THE NECKLINE WITH DECREASES

① Row 38 (38, 42, 42): Work 1 SC into FLO of 1st st and SC2TOG into FLO over next 2 sts. Continue across, working 1 SC into FLO of each st of prev row. Ch 1 and turn.

② Row 39 (39, 43, 43): Work 1 SC into FLO of each st of prev row. Ch 1 and turn.

③ Row 40 (40, 44, 44): Work 1 SC into FLO of 1st st and SC2TOG into FLO over next 2 sts. Continue across, working 1 SC into FLO of each st of prev row. Ch 1 and turn.

④ Row 41 (41, 43, 43): Work 1 SC into FLO of each st of prev row. Ch 1 and turn.

⑤ **For small and medium sizes:**

Row 42: Work 1 SC into FLO of each st of prev row. Ch 1 and turn.

For large and extra-large sizes:

Row 44: Work 1 SC into FLO of 1st st and SC2TOG into FLO over next 2 sts. Continue across, working 1 SC into FLO of each st of prev row. Ch 1 and turn.

⑥ Rows 43–47 (43–47, 45–49, 45–49): Work 1 SC into FLO of each st of prev row. Ch 1 and turn.

SHAPE THE NECKLINE WITH INCREASES

① Row 48 (48, 50, 50): Work 1 SC into FLO of 1st st and 2 SC into FLO of 2nd st. Continue across, working 1 SC into FLO of each st of prev row. Ch 1 and turn.

② Row 49 (49, 51, 51): Work 1 SC into FLO of each st of prev row. Ch 1 and turn.

③ Row 50 (50, 52, 52): Work 1 SC into FLO of 1st st and 2 SC into FLO of 2nd st. Continue across, working 1 SC into FLO of each st of prev row. Ch 1 and turn.

④ Row 51 (51, 53, 53): Work 1 SC into FLO of each st of prev row. Ch 1 and turn.

⑤ Row 52 (52, 54, 54): Work 1 SC into FLO of 1st st and 2 SC into FLO of 2nd st. Continue across, working 1 SC into FLO of each st of prev row. Ch 1 and turn.

⑥ Row 53 (53, 55, 55): Work 1 SC into FLO of each st of prev row. Ch 1 and turn.

⑦ **For small and medium sizes:**

Place marker at 39th st in from end of sleeve.

Row 54: Work 1 SC into FLO of 1st st and 2 SC into FLO of 2nd st. Continue across, working 1 SC into FLO of each st of prev row until marked st. Work 1 SC into this st. Ch 1 and turn.

Rows 55–84: Work 1 SC into FLO of each st of prev row. Ch 1 and turn.

For large and extra-large sizes:

Row 57: Work 1 SC into FLO of 1st st and 2 SC into FLO of 2nd st. Continue across, working 1 SC into FLO of each st of prev row. Ch 1 and turn.

Row 58: Work 1 SC into FLO of each st of prev row. Ch 1 and turn.

Place marker at 44th st in from end of sleeve.

Row 59: Work 1 SC into FLO of 1st st and 2 SC into FLO of 2nd st. Continue across, working 1 SC into FLO of each st of prev row until marked st. Work 1 SC into this st. Ch 1 and turn.

Rows 60–90: Work 1 SC into FLO of each st of prev row. Ch 1 and turn.

⑧ Fasten off and weave in ends.

FINISH THE SWEATER

① Fold sweater as shown.

② Use backstitch to seam from edge of sleeve across and down side of sweater.

③ Rep to seam other side of sweater.

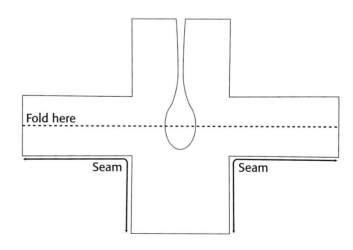

Fold here

Seam   Seam

CREATE THE COLLAR

1. Along front and neck, work shell pattern into sides of rows in body of sweater:

2. Join yarn into row space at front bottom edge. * Work [1 DC, ch 1, 1 TR, ch 1, 1 TR, ch 1 and 1 DC] into space. Skip 1 row space and work 1 SC into next row space. Skip 1 row space. Rep from * along front sides and neck of sweater.

ALTER THIS PATTERN TO MAKE A DOLL SWEATER

You can use the basic shape of this sweater to make any simple sweater in any yarn or stitch pattern you choose. Simply work in rows to create the shape like the illustration on the previous page, then follow the finishing directions.

The doll sweater shown here was made using the same basic pattern shape.

Sweet and Chic Granny Square Bag

Granny squares are easy, cheery, and quick to stitch. Combine a rich yarn, such as Crystal Palace Cotton Chenille, with sweet colors and a traditional navy to create a bag that is both old-fashioned and irresistibly chic.

Specifications

MATERIALS

Crystal Palace *Cotton Chenille* (100% cotton, 98 yd./50g):

- 2 skeins in #4272 Navy
- 1 skein in #7366 Rose
- 1 skein in #1015 Ecru
- 1 skein in #5638 Ice Blue
- 1 skein in #1240 Lime Green
- 1 skein in #2230 Pumpkin
- 1 skein in #7684 Antique Brown

5.5mm hook

Fabric for bag lining and matching thread

TECHNIQUES USED

SC	Single crochet
BLO	Back loop only (see Chapter 4)
FLO	Front loop only (see Chapter 4)

Granny Square pattern (see Chapter 12)

Seaming (see Chapter 10)

Adjustable ring (see Chapter 3)

FINISHED SIZE

21 inches wide x 7 inches tall x 3 inches deep

GAUGE

14 stitches = 4 inches

$13\frac{1}{2}$ rows = 4 inches

1 Granny Square without border = $5\frac{3}{4}$ inches

Make the Granny Square Bag

TO BEGIN

You will make 6 squares in total. Each square includes 3 rounds of the granny square pattern and a border. Make 2 squares in each color combination:

Square 1:

Round 1: Ice Blue
Round 2: Antique Brown
Round 3: Lime Green

Square 2:

Round 1: Ice Blue
Round 2: Antique Brown
Round 3: Lime Green

Square 3:

Round 1: Lime Green
Round 2: Ecru
Round 3: Rose

1 Round 1: Using an adjustable ring, ch 3. Work 2 DC into ring. * Ch 2 and work 3 DC into ring. Rep from * twice to create 2 more granny clusters. Ch 2, Sl st into 3rd ch of ch-3 at beg of round. Fasten off.

2 Round 2: Join yarn in next ch-2 space. Work [ch 3, 2 DC, ch 2, 3 DC] into ch space. * Ch 1. In next ch space, work a corner set [ch 2, 3 DC, ch 2, 3 DC]. Rep from * to work a corner set into each ch-2 space. Sl st into 3rd ch of ch-3 at beg of round. Fasten off.

3 Round 3: Join yarn in next corner ch space. Work [ch 3, 2 DC, ch 2, 3 DC] into ch space. * Ch 1. Work 1 granny cluster in next ch-1 space; ch 1. In next ch-2 space, work a corner set [ch 2, 3 DC, ch 2, 3 DC]. Rep from * twice to work into each ch space. Sl st in 3rd chain of ch-3 at beg of round.

4 Fasten off and weave in ends.

CROCHET A BORDER AROUND EACH SQUARE

1 Round 4: Join ice blue yarn, ch 3, and work 1 DC into each st and side space from prev round. Work [2 DC, ch 2, 2 DC] into corner spaces.

2 Round 5: Join navy yarn, ch 1, and work 1 SC into each st from prev round. Work [1 SC, ch 1, 1 SC] into each corner. Sl st to 1st st of round and ch 1.

3 Round 6: Rep round 5.

4 Fasten off and weave in ends.

MAKE THE BODY

1 Ch 10.

2 Row 1: Work 1 SC into each ch across. Ch 1 and turn.

3 Row 2: Work 1 SC into each st from prev row. Ch 1 and turn.

4 Rows 3–22: Rep row 2.

5 Row 23: Work 1 SC into FLO of each st from prev row. Ch 1 and turn.

6 Row 24: Place marker in this row. Work 1 SC into BLO of each st from prev row. Ch 1 and turn.

7 Row 25: Work 1 SC into FLO of each st from prev row. Ch 1 and turn.

8 Rows 26–89: Rep row 2.

9 Row 90: Work 1 SC into FLO of each st from prev row. Ch 1 and turn.

10 Row 91: Place marker in this row. Work 1 SC into BLO of each st from prev row. Ch 1 and turn.

11 Row 92: Work 1 SC into FLO of each st from prev row. Ch 1 and turn.

12 Rows 93–115: Rep row 2.

13 Fasten off and weave in ends.

MAKE THE HANDLES

Use leftover yarn from the squares to create striped handles, switching colors with each row.

1 Ch 41.

2 Row 1: Work 1 SC into each ch across. Ch 1 and turn.

3 Rows 2–5: Work 1 SC into each SC from prev row. Ch 1 and turn.

4 To shape handle, fold in half lengthwise. Seam 1st and last rows to each other using SC; join yarn at 10th st of rows. Work 20 SC across.

5 Fasten off and weave in ends, leaving a tail on each end for seaming.

FINISH THE BAG

Join the squares to create 2 side panels for the purse:

1 Whipstitch 3 squares together to create 1 side panel.

2 Whipstitch remaining 3 squares together to create other side panel.

Edge each panel with more SC:

3 Join navy yarn and ch 1. Work 1 SC into each st from prev round. Work [1 SC, ch 1, 1 SC] into each corner. Place marker in each ch-1 corner space. Sl st into 1st st of round.

Seam body to granny square panels:

4 With right sides facing outward, match marked corners of 1 panel with marked rows of body. Join navy yarn at 1 end and SC panel to body.

NOTE: This SC seam will be on the outside of the purse. This detail gives the purse a tailored look.

5 Rep with 2nd panel and other side of body strip.

6 Whipstitch handles to inside of panels.

MAKE THE BAG LINING

Because the granny squares create a fabric with open spaces, the lining is an important part of this bag's look and feel. Have fun choosing a fabric that reflects your own style.

1. Cut a piece of fabric that's 26 inches x 20 inches.

2. Cut fabric as shown to create a notch on each side.

3. Fold and iron creases to shape bottom of lining.

4. Fold and iron creases to shape each side of lining.

5. Sew each side.

6. Fold and iron creases to shape top of lining.

7. Place lining in bag. Pin lining into place, aligning corners and creases with corresponding parts of bag.

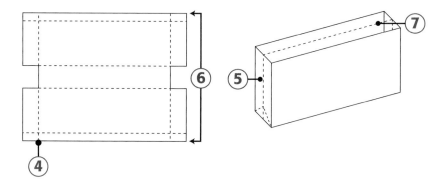

8. Sew lining into place. To keep stitches from showing through on the outside of the purse, sew halfway through each crocheted stitch.

HOW TO ALTER THIS PATTERN TO MAKE OTHER GRANNY SQUARE BAGS

The first step is to decide the size and shape you'd like for your bag. Then you should choose how many squares and rows of squares you want to use.

Next, choose a yarn that creates the gauge you prefer and matches your size requirements. For instance, you might decide to use a thinner yarn to make smaller squares.

Consider the Granny Squares to be building blocks and have fun designing your own bag.

Simple Sampler Scarf

Practice basic stitches with this sampler scarf. Make the scarf with the suggested hook for a dense fabric, or try a larger hook for a looser look. You can modify the width and length of your scarf so that it fits just right.

Specifications

MATERIALS

Lion Brand *Wool Ease Thick and Quick* (80% acrylic/ 20% wool, 106 yd./170g)

- 1 skein in Citron
- 1 skein in Lemongrass
- 1 skein in Navy
- 1 skein in Raspberry

15mm hook

TECHNIQUES USED

Ch	Chain
SC	Single crochet
HDC	Half double crochet
DC	Double crochet
TR	Treble crochet

FINISHED SIZE

Width: 12 inches. It's easy to change the width if you wish. Simply make a longer or shorter foundation chain.

Length: For a scarf that wraps once around your neck and stops at your hips, make a scarf as tall as your shoulders. To make a longer scarf, work until the length is equal to your height.

GAUGE

5 stitches = 4 inches

2 rows = 4 inches

Make the Simple Sampler Scarf

1 Ch 18.

2 Row 1: Work 1 TR into 5th ch from hook and into each ch across; ch 1 and turn.

3 Row 2: Work 1 SC into 1st st of row and into each st across; ch 3 and turn.

4 Row 3: The turning ch counts as a DC. Work 1 DC into 2nd st of row and into each ch across; ch 1 and turn.

5 Row 4: Work 1 SC into 1st st of row and into each st across; ch 2 and turn.

6 Row 5: Work 1 HDC into 1st st of row and into each st across; ch 1 and turn.

7 Rep rows 1–5 until scarf reaches the desired length.

8 Fasten off and weave in ends.

Handmade coasters add warmth and charm to your table.

Specifications

MATERIALS

Approx 12 yards Lion Brand *Lion Cotton* (100% cotton, 236 yd./140g) in Natural

Approx 12 yards Lion Brand *Cotton-Ease* (50% cotton/ 50% acrylic, 207 yd./100g) in Lake

5mm hook

TECHNIQUES USED

Ch   Chain

SC   Single crochet

Crab stitch (see Chapter 4)

FINISHED SIZE

Width = 4 inches

Circumference = 14 inches

GAUGE

Approx 4 stitches = 1 inch

Approx 4 rows = 1 inch

Make the Circular Coaster

You work this project in the round by using the spiral method to create quick, easy circles. Use one yarn color for yarn A or the main color and a second color as yarn B or the edging.

1. With yarn A, ch 2.

2. Round 1: Work 6 SC into 2nd ch from hook. Mark 1st st with stitch marker.

3 Round 2: Work 2 SC into each st from prev round. Continue to move marker to indicate 1st st of every round (12 SC total).

4 Round 3: * Work 2 SC into next st from prev round and 1 SC into next st. Rep from * across round (18 SC total).

5 Round 4: * Work 2 SC into next st from prev round and 1 SC into each of the next 2 sts. Rep from * across round (24 SC total).

6 Round 5: * Work 2 SC into next st from prev round and 1 SC into each of the next 3 sts. Rep from * across round (30 SC total).

7 Round 6: * Work 2 SC into next st from prev round and 1 SC into each of the next 4 sts. Rep from * across round (36 SC total).

8 Round 7: * Work 2 SC into next st from prev round and 1 SC into each of the next 5 sts. Rep from * across round (42 SC total).

ADD THE EDGING

1 Join yarn B and work 1 crab st into each st across round. Sl st to 1st st of round to join.

2 Fasten off and weave in ends.

TIP

Variations

1. To make a thicker coaster, make 2 coasters and work the edging through both.

2. To back your coaster with felt:

- Trace your coaster on the felt and cut out.
- You can either whipstitch the layers together or work the crochet edging. See Chapter 13 for more on crocheting into fabric.

3. Try using contrasting colors in your coasters.

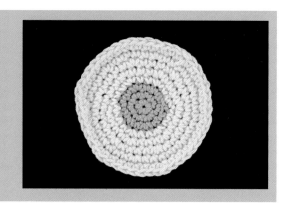

Trivet

This trivet is made with a pentagon granny, but you can try using any of the granny shapes. This example uses two strands of yarn at once to create a thicker Trivet.

Specifications

MATERIALS

1 skein Lion Brand *Cotton-Ease* (50% cotton/50% acrylic, 207 yd./100g) in Lake

NOTE: To work with two strands of yarn at once, prepare a new ball of yarn pulling from both ends of the skein at the same time.

6.5mm hook

TECHNIQUES USED

Ch   Chain

Sl st   Slip stitch

DC   Double crochet

Adjustable ring (see Chapter 3)

FINISHED SIZE

Circumference = 30 inches

GAUGE

1, 3 DC cluster = 1 inch tall and ¾-inch wide

Make the Trivet

1 Round 1: Using a loop for a ring, ch 3 (counts as 1 DC) and work 2 DC into ring. * Ch 2, 3 DC into ring; rep from * 3 times, ch 2, Sl st to top of ch 3 at beg of round. Fasten off.

2 Round 2: Join yarn in a ch-2 space. [Ch 3, 2 DC, ch 2, 3 DC] into same ch-2 space. * Ch 1, work [3 DC, ch 2, 3 DC] into next ch-2 space; rep from * 3 times, ch 1, Sl st to top of ch 3 at beg of round. Fasten off.

3 Round 3: Join yarn in a ch-2 space. [Ch 3, 2 DC, ch 2, 3 DC] into same ch-2 space * ch 1, work 3 DC into next ch-1 space, ch 1, [3 DC, ch 2, 3 DC] into next ch-2 space, rep from * 3 times, ch 1, work 3 DC into next ch-1 space, ch 1, Sl st to top of ch 3 at beg of round. Fasten off.

4 Round 4: Join yarn in a ch-2 space. [Ch 3, 2 DC, ch 2, 3 DC] into same ch-2 space * [ch 1, work 3 DC into next ch-1 space] 2 times, ch 1, [3 DC, ch 2, 3 DC] into next ch-2 space, rep from * 4 times, ch 1, Sl st to top of ch 3 at beg of round. Fasten off.

5 Round 5: Join yarn in a ch-2 space. [Ch 3, 2 DC, ch 2, 3 DC] into same ch-2 space * [ch 1, work 3 DC into next ch-1 space] 3 times, ch 1 [3 DC, ch 2, 3 DC] into next ch-2 space, rep from * 4 times, ch 1, Sl st to top of ch 3 at beg of round. Fasten off.

6 Round 6: Work a SC border: work 1 SC in each DC, [1 SC, ch 1, 1 SC] into each ch-2 corner space, and 1 SC into each ch-1 space. Sl st to top of ch 3 at beg of round. Fasten off.

Inspired by a lip balm tin, this little round box is perfect for keeping small secrets inside. This versatile pattern can be crocheted with any yarn to create boxes of different sizes.

Specifications

MATERIALS
1 skein Fonty *Majorque* (60% cotton/40% linen, 135 yd./50g) in #136 Pink

2.75mm hook

This pattern can be made using a wide variety of yarns. Consider using a bulky yarn to make a large box.

TECHNIQUES USED
Ch   Chain

Sl st Slip stitch

SC   Single crochet

FLO   Front loop only (see Chapter 4)

Adjustable ring (see Chapter 3)

Working rounds in rows (see Chapter 3)

FINISHED SIZE
Lid: 1¾ inches wide x ⅜ inch deep

Body: 1½ inches wide x ¾ inch deep

GAUGE
6 stitches = 1 inch

7 rows = 1 inch

Make the Round Box

MAKE THE BOTTOM
1. Start with an adjustable ring.

2. Round 1: Work 6 SC into ring. Sl st into 1st SC to join round. Gently pull on tail to tighten ring. Ch 1 and turn (6 SC total).

Round Box (continued)

3 Round 2: Work 2 SC into 1st SC. * Work 2 SC into next SC. Rep from * 4 times. Sl st into 1st SC to join. Ch 1 and turn (12 SC total).

4 Round 3: Work 2 SC into 1st SC and 1 SC into next SC. * Work 2 SC into next SC and 1 SC into next SC. Rep from * 4 times. Sl st into 1st SC to join. Ch 1 and turn (18 SC total).

5 Round 4: Work 2 SC into 1st SC and 1 SC into each of the next 2 SC. * Work 2 SC into next SC and 1 SC into each of the next 2 SC. Rep from * 4 times. Sl st into 1st SC to join. Ch 1 and turn (24 SC total).

6 Round 5: Work 1 SC into FLO of each st from prev round. Sl st into 1st SC to join. Ch 1 and turn (24 SC total).

NOTE: Working in the front loop only in this row creates a ridge to form the bend.

7 Round 6: Work 1 SC into each st from prev round. Sl st into 1st SC to join. Ch 1 and turn (24 SC total).

8 Round 7: Work 1 SC into each st from prev round. Sl st to 1st SC to join. Ch 1, but do not turn (24 SC total).

NOTE: Whether or not a round is turned affects the texture of the fabric. This effect is used to create a slight ridge that the lid rests on.

9 Round 8: Work 1 SC into each st from prev round. Sl st to 1st SC to join. Ch 1, but do not turn (24 SC total).

10 Round 9: Work 1 SC into each st from prev round. Sl st to 1st SC to join. Ch 1 and turn (24 SC total).

11 Fasten off and weave in ends.

MAKE THE LID

1 Work rounds 1–4 as you did for the body.

2 Round 5: Work 2 SC into 1st SC. Work 1 SC into each of the next 3 SC. * Work 2 SC into next SC and 1 SC into each of the next 3 SC. Rep from * 4 times. Sl st to 1st SC to join. Ch 1 and turn (30 SC total).

3 Round 6: Work 1 SC into FLO of each st from prev round. Sl st to 1st SC to join. Ch 1 and turn (30 SC total).

4 Round 7: Work 1 SC into each st from prev round. Sl st to 1st SC to join. Ch 1 and turn (30 SC total).

5 Round 8: Work 1 SC into each st from prev round. Sl st to 1st SC to join (30 SC total).

6 Fasten off and weave in ends.

Bold Bag

Certain circumstances call for a bold, sturdy bag. This bag is worked in one piece and doesn't require seaming or lining. Felting the completed bag adds structure, strength, and texture.

Specifications

MATERIALS

Yarn A: 4 skeins *Rio de la Plata Wool Solid* (100% wool, 140 yd./99g) in Sparkling Grape

Yarn B: 1 skein *Rio de la Plata Wool Solid* (100% wool, 140 yd./99g) in Natural White

8mm hook

Stitch marker

TECHNIQUES USED

Ch	Chain
Sl st	Slip stitch
SC	Single crochet
SC3TOG	3 single crochets worked together (see Chapter 3)

Working rounds in rows (see Chapter 3)

Join new yarn (see Chapter 8)

Fulling (see Chapter 8)

FINISHED SIZE

Before felting: 22 inches wide x 15 inches tall x 6 inches deep

After felting: 17 inches wide x 11 inches tall x 5 inches deep

Size after felting may vary.

GAUGE

10 single crochets and 12 rows = 4 inches before felting

Make the Bold Bag

MAKE THE BOTTOM OF THE BAG

1. With yarn A, ch 43.

2. Row 1: Work 1 SC into 2nd ch from hook and into each ch across. Ch 1 and turn.

3. Row 2: Work 1 SC into each st from prev row. Ch 1 and turn.

4. Rows 3–18: Rep row 2.

MAKE THE BODY

1. Round 1: Work 1 SC into each st from prev row. Work 3 SC into last st of row to create a corner, place marker in middle st of corner. Work 1 SC into each row along side of rectangle. Work 3 SC to create a corner, place marker in middle st of corner. Work 1 SC into each st from foundation row. Work 3 SC to create a corner, place marker in middle st of corner. Work 1 SC into each row along side of rectangle. Work 2 SC and Sl st to 1st SC of round to create a corner, place marker in middle st of corner. Ch 1.

2. Round 2: * Work 1 SC into each st from prev round. Work 3 SC into marked st. Rep from * to end of row. Ch 1.

3. Round 3: Work 1 SC into each st from prev round. Ch 1.

4. Rounds 4–38: Rep round 3.

5. Round 39: Work 1 SC into each st from prev round. Change to yarn B and ch 1.

6. Round 40: Work 1 SC into each st from prev round. Ch 1.

7. Round 41: Rep round 40.

MAKE THE HANDLES

1 Lay bag flat and place marker 8 inches in from the outside on each side of bag. Flip bag over and place marker 8 inches in from the outside on each side of bag.

2 Round 42: Work 1 SC into each st from prev round until you reach 1st marker. Ch 38 and work 1 SC into st after 2nd marker. Work 1 SC into each st from prev round, until you reach 3rd marker. Ch 38 and work 1 SC into st after 4th marker. Work 1 SC into each st from prev round. Ch 1.

3 Round 43: Work 1 SC into each SC from prev round; work 1 SC into each ch from handle sections as well. Change to yarn A and ch 1.

NOTE: See Chapter 3 for information about joining new yarns.

4 Rounds 44–45: Work 1 SC into each st from prev round. Ch 1.

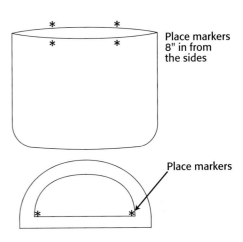

Place markers 8" in from the sides

Place markers

FINISH THE HANDLES

1 Place markers at inside corners of handles.

2 Handle round 1: Using yarn B, join into unworked side of handle ch. Work 1 SC into unworked side of each ch st until 1 st before marked corner. Work SC3TOG over next 3 sts. Work 1 SC into each st until 1 st before marked corner. Work SC3TOG over next 3 sts. Work 1 SC into each ch st to finish round, Sl st to 1st SC of round. Ch 1.

3 Handle round 2: Place markers at inside corners of handles. * Work 1 SC into each SC from prev round until 1 st before marked corner. Work SC3TOG over next 3 sts. Work 1 SC into each SC from prev round until 1 st before marked corner. Work SC3TOG over next 3 sts. Work 1 SC into each SC from prev round to finish round. Sl st into 1st SC of round. Change to yarn A and ch 1.

4 Handle rounds 3 and 4: Rep handle round 2.

5 Fasten off and weave in ends.

6 Follow directions for felting in Chapter 8.

Exquisite Washcloths

This is an excellent pattern for practicing new stitches. A hand-made washcloth is a true luxury, and this quick project makes a thoughtful gift, too.

Specifications

MATERIALS

1 skein Organic Cotton by Blue Sky Alpacas (100% cotton, 150 yd./100g) in Nut (yarn A)

Dyed Cotton by Blue Sky Alpacas (100% cotton, 150 yd./100g)

    1 skein in Shell (yarn B)

    1 skein in Thistle (yarn C)

1 skein Cotton Chenille by Crystal Palace Yarns (100% mercerized cotton, 98 yd./50g), in color #1015 (yarn D)

5.5mm hook

TECHNIQUES USED

Ch	Chain stitch
SC	Single crochet
TR	Treble crochet
HDC	Half double crochet

FLO	Front loop only (see Chapter 4)
BLO	Back loop only (see Chapter 4)

Crunchy Dots pattern (see Chapter 7)

Granite Stitch pattern (see Chapter 7)

FINISHED SIZE

Half Double Crochet: 7½ inches x 6¾ inches

Crunchy Dots: 8 inches x 7½ inches

Granite: 7 inches x 6½ inches

GAUGE

Half Double Crochet: 14 half double crochet and 8 rows = 4 inches

Crunchy Dots: 12 stitches and 10 rows = 4 inches

Granite Stitch: 15 stitches and 14 rows = 4 inches

Make the Washcloths

HALF DOUBLE CROCHET WASHCLOTH

1. Using yarn D, ch 24.

2. Row 1: Work 1 HDC into 3rd ch from hook and into every ch across; ch 2 and turn.

3. Row 2: Work 1 HDC in FLO of 1st st. * Work 1 HDC in BLO of next st. Work 1 HDC in FLO of next st. Rep from * across row. Ch 2 and turn.

4. Rep row 2 for 11 more rows or until washcloth is the desired size. Fasten off.

5. Join yarn B a few sts before a corner. * Work 1 SC in each st along row; work 2 SC to turn corner; work 1 SC into each space along side, and work 2 SC to turn corner. Rep from * to complete border.

CRUNCHY DOTS WASHCLOTH

1. Using yarn D, ch 25.

2. Row 1: Work 1 SC in 2nd ch from hook. * Work 1 SC in next ch; work 1 TR in next ch. Rep from * across to last ch. SC in last ch; ch 1 and turn.

3. Row 2: Work 1 SC in 1st st. * Work 1 SC in next st; work 1 TR in next st. Rep from * to last st of row; work 1 SC in last st. Ch 1 and turn.

4. Rep row 2 for 18 more rows or until washcloth is the desired size.

5. Join yarn B a few sts before a corner. * Work 1 SC in each st along row; work 2 SC to turn corner; work 1 SC into each space along side; and work 2 SC to turn corner. Rep from * to complete border.

GRANITE STITCH WASHCLOTH

1 Using yarn C, ch 24.

2 Row 1: Work 1 SC into 2nd ch from hook. * Work 1 SC into next ch, ch 1, and skip 1 ch. Rep from * until 2 chs remain. Ch 1, skip 1 ch, and work 1 SC into last ch. Ch 1 and turn.

3 Row 2: Work 1 SC into 1st st. * Work 1 SC into next ch space, ch 1, and skip 1 st. Rep from * to end of row. Work 1 SC into last st. Ch 1 and turn.

4 Rep row 2 for 18 more rows or until washcloth is the desired size.

5 Join yarn A a few sts before a corner. * Work 1 SC in each st along row; work 2 SC to turn corner; work 1 SC into each space along side; and work 2 to turn corner. Rep from * to complete border.

Cool Baby Hat

Practice your intarsia skills by adding simple color patterning to this hat. Just make a rectangle, fold it in half, seam the two sides, and find a baby to wear it.

Specifications

MATERIALS

HAT (ABOVE)

New Cotton by Lana Grossa (60% cotton/40% micro-fiber, 88 yd./50g)

    2 skeins in #12 mulberry
    1 skein in #2 orange

4.5mm hook

HAT (ON PAGE 312)

Lorna's Laces *Swirl DK* (85% merino wool/15% silk, 150 yd./100g)

    1 hank in Huron
    1 hank in Bittersweet

4.5mm hook

TECHNIQUES USED

Ch Chain

SC Single crochet

Join new yarn (see Chapter 3)

Intarsia (see Chapter 8)

FINISHED SIZE

Circumference = Approximately 20 inches

GAUGE

HAT (ABOVE)

14 single crochet and 18 rows = 4 inches

HAT (ON PAGE 312)

16 stitches = 2 inches

10 rows = 2 inches

Cool Baby Hat *(continued)*

Make the Cool Baby Hat

1 Create small balls of yarn to use as bobbins that can easily be left to hang as you switch between colors.

Yarn A	Work from the skein of Mulberry
Yarn B	9 feet of Orange
Yarn C	85 feet of Mulberry
Yarn D	23 feet of Orange
Yarn E	Work from the skein of Mulberry

2 Leaving a 12-inch tail (to be used later for seaming), ch 34 for the foundation ch.

3 Row 1: Using yarn A, work 1 SC into 2nd ch from hook. Work 1 SC into each ch across row, ch 1, and turn.

Follow the chart:

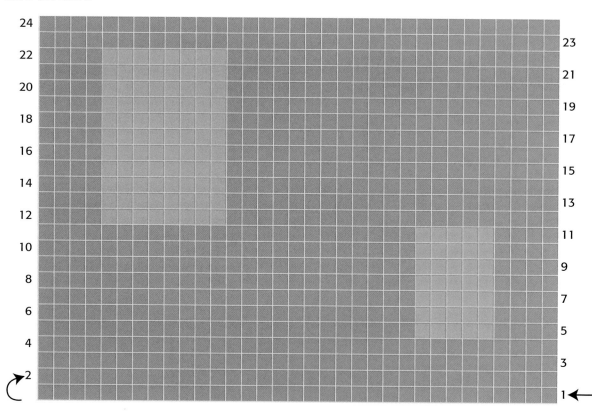

④ Rows 2–4: Work 1 SC into each st across row. Ch 1 and turn.

⑤ Row 5: Work 1 SC into each of the next 4 sts. Change to yarn B and work next 5 SC in yarn B. Change to yarn A and work 1 SC into each st to end of row. Ch 1 and turn.

⑥ Row 6: Work 1 SC into each of the next 24 sts. Change to yarn B and work next 5 SC in yarn B. Change to yarn A and work 1 SC into each st to end of row. Ch 1 and turn.

⑦ Rows 7–11: Continue to follow the chart.

⑧ Row 12: Work 1 SC into each of the next 4 sts. Change to yarn C and work 1 SC into each of the next 8 sts and work 1 SC in each st to end of row. Ch 1 and turn. Change to yarn D and work 1 SC into each of the next 4 sts. Ch 1 and turn.

⑨ Row 13: Work 1 SC into each of the next 21 sts. Change to yarn C and work 1 SC into each of the next 8 sts. Change to yarn A and work 1 SC into each st to end of row. Ch 1 and turn.

⑩ Row 14: Work 1 SC into each of the next 4 sts. Change to yarn C and work 1 SC into each of the next 8 sts. Change to yarn D and work 1 SC into each st to end of row. Ch 1 and turn.

⑪ Rows 15–22: Continue to follow the chart.

⑫ Row 23: Work 1 SC into each st across row. Ch 1 and turn. Tie off, leaving a 12-inch tail.

⑬ Rows 24–48: Work 1 SC into each st across row. Ch 1 and turn.

⑭ Fasten off, leaving a 12-inch tail.

⑮ Fold finished rectangle in half with crocheted rows running widthwise.

⑯ Use the tail from beg and end of rectangle to sew up each side.

NOTE: If the hat is too big, simply tuck the sides in from the seams and use a whipstitch to secure the tuck.

Magnificent Shawl

Long double treble stitches make this graceful shawl work up quickly. Shells are worked in the middle of each row to create the increases that form a triangular shape, making this deceptively simple shawl magnificent.

Specifications

MATERIALS

1–3 skeins South West Trading Company *Bamboo* (100% bamboo, 135 yd./50g) in Tequila

5mm hook

TECHNIQUES USED

Ch   Chain

SC   Single crochet

DTR   Double treble crochet (see Chapter 4)

FINISHED SIZE

One skein will make a scarf measuring 48 inches x 24 inches. For a longer scarf, add a second skein and keep working!

GAUGE

14 stitches and 4 rows = 4 inches

Make the Magnificent Shawl

1 Ch 18.

2 Row 1: Work 1 SC into 2nd ch from hook and into every ch across. Ch 5 and turn.

3 Row 2: Work 1 DTR into 1st st and each of the next 7 sts. Into next st: [Ch 1, 5 DTR, ch 1]. This shell creates the increases that shape the scarf. Work 1 DTR into each of the next 7 sts. Work 2 DTR into last st. Ch 5 and turn.

4 Row 3: Work 1 DTR into each DTR from prev row. Work 1 DTR into ch-1 space and 1 DTR into each of the next 2 DTR from prev row. Into next st: [Ch 1, 5 DTR, ch 1]. Work 1 DTR into each of the next 2 DTR from prev row and 1 DTR into ch-1 space. Work 1 DTR into each DTR from prev row until last st. Work 2 DTR into last st. Ch 5 and turn.

5 Rep row 3 until scarf reaches the desired size.

6 Fasten off and weave in ends.

Tunisian Tie

Have you ever felt like it's hard to find terrific projects to make for the men in your life? Polish your Tunisian crochet skills while you work up this simple necktie. The woven-like fabric makes for a unique and office-appropriate accessory.

Specifications

MATERIALS

1 hank KnitPicks *Sock Landscape* (100% merino wool, 192 yd./50g) in Yukon

4.5mm Tunisian crochet hook

TECHNIQUES USED

Ch Chain

Tss Tunisian simple stitch (see Chapter 8)

inc Increase (see Chapter 3)

dec Decrease (see Chapter 3)

FINISHED SIZE

One size fits most adults

GAUGE

24 stitches and 21 rows = 4 inches in Tss

Make the Tunisian Tie

BEGIN THE TUNISIAN TIE

1 Ch 19.

2 Foundation forward row: Pick up 1 loop in 2nd ch from hook. Pick up 1 loop in each ch across.

3 Foundation return row: Ch 1. * Yo and draw yarn through 2 loops on hook. Rep from * until 1 loop remains on hook at end of return row (18 Tss total).

4 Forward row: Pick up 1 loop in each vertical bar.

5 Return row: Ch 1. * Yo and draw yarn through 2 loops on hook. Rep from * until 1 loop remains on hook at end of return row.

6 Rep pairs of forward and return rows until tie measures 10 inches from beg.

DECREASE

1 On next forward row, dec 1 st on each end of row. Work return row as normal (16 Tss total).

2 Continue to dec 1 st on each end of forward rows every 22 rows until piece measures 26 inches (9 sts total). Work even for 30 inches until piece measures 56 inches.

WORK THE FINAL ROW

1 Work Tunisian bind-off row (see page 151). Fasten off and weave in ends.

2 Block to combat curl at either end (see page 203 or 204).

If your tie still curls, make a SC or Sl st border to add structure.

Spider Woman Belt

Spin your own web and wear it to show off your skills. This pattern takes what you already know about working in the round and making arches and turns it all into a web motif.

Specifications

MATERIALS

1 hank LanaKnits *All Hemp 6* (100% hemp, 150 yd./90g) in Sprout

5mm hook

Stitch markers

TECHNIQUES USED

Ch	Chain
SC	Single crochet
DC	Double crochet
TR	Treble crochet

Work in the round (see Chapter 3)

Mesh arches (see Chapter 3)

FINISHED SIZE

45½ inches plus 12 inch tassels

GAUGE

4 arches (3 chs and 1 SC) and 10 rows = 4 inches

Make the Belt

MAKE THE SPIDER WEB MOTIF
Use markers to help you keep your place as you follow this atypical pattern.

① Start with an adjustable ring.

② Round 1: Ch 4; this ch counts as 1 DC and 1 ch. Work * 1 DC, ch 1 into the ring. Rep from * 6 times and Sl st into top of 3rd ch to join (8 DC total).

③ Round 2: Ch 6, work 1 DC into 1st DC from prev round. Ch 3, * DC into next DC from prev round, ch 3, rep from * 5 times. Sl st over ch from beg of round.

④ Round 3: Ch 8 (place markers in 3rd and 6th chs), work 1 DC into next DC from prev round, ch 6, DC into next DC from prev round, * ch 5, DC into next DC from prev round. Rep from * 6 times.

⑤ Work 4 Sl st, 1 in each ch from marker to marker. Remove markers.

⑥ Ch 6 (place marker in 4th ch), DC into next DC from prev round, ch 7, DC into next DC from prev round, ch 7 (place marker in 4th ch), TR into next DC from prev round, ch 6, TR into next DC from prev round, place marker in this st), ch 5, DC into next DC from prev round. This is the end of this round.

⑦ Ch 6 and turn. Work 1 DTR into TR with marker and remove marker. Ch 6. Work 1 DTR into next DC from prev round. Ch 4. Work 1 DTR into ch with marker and then remove marker.

CREATE THE BODY
① Row 1: Ch 3, turn, SC in 1st ch space, ch 3, SC in next ch space, ch 3, SC in same ch space, ch 3, SC in same ch space, ch 3, SC in next ch space, ch 3, SC into DTR from prev row. Ch 3, SC in same ch space, ch 3, and turn.

② Row 2: Work 1 SC into 1st space created by chains from prev row. * Ch 3 and work 1 SC into next ch space. Rep from * until you have worked a SC into last ch space of row. Ch 3 and turn.

③ Rep row 2 to desired length.

CROCHET THE TAPERED ENDS
① Tapered row: Work 1 SC into 1st space created by chains from prev row. * Ch 3 and work 1 SC into next ch space. Rep from * until last ch space; leave this space unworked. Ch 3 and turn.

② Rep tapered row until 1 arch is left.

③ Fasten off and weave in ends.

④ Join yarn to other side of motif and work body pattern to same length.

⑤ Fasten off and weave in ends.

MAKE THE TASSELS

With your arm bent at a 90-degree angle, tuck the yarn between your thumb and forefinger and wrap the yarn around your elbow many times. Cut the tassels and tie them to the tapered ends of the piece.

Bunny Amigurumi

This cute bunny is a great example of what you can do with simple amigurumi shapes.

Specifications

MATERIALS

1 skein Lion Brand *Vanna's Choice* (100% acrylic, 145 yd./86g) in Silver Heather

4.5mm hook

1 stitch marker

Stuffing: Fiberfill, scrap yarn/fabric, etc.

TECHNIQUES USED

Ch   Chain

Sl st Slip stitch

SC   Single crochet

SC2TOG 2 single crochet worked together (see Chapter 3)

SC3TOG 3 single crochet worked together (see Chapter 3)

Adjustable ring (see Chapter 3)

FINISHED SIZE

Circumference = 12¼ inches

GAUGE

4 stitches = 1 inch

4 rows = 1 inch

Make the Bunny

MAKE THE BODY

1. Start with an adjustable ring.

2. Round 1: Work 7 SC into the ring. Place marker in 1st SC and move marker with each round.

3. Round 2: 2 SC in each SC across round (14 SC total).

4. Round 3: * 2 SC in next SC, 1 SC in next SC, rep from * across round (21 SC total).

5. Round 4: * 2 SC in next SC, 1 SC in each of the next 2 SC, rep from * across round (28 SC total).

6. Round 5: * 2 SC in next SC, 1 SC in each of the next 3 SC, rep from * across round (35 SC total).

7. Round 6: * 2 SC in next SC, 1 SC in each of the next 4 SC, rep from * across round (42 SC total).

8. Round 7: 1 SC in each of the next 3 SC, 2 SC in next SC, 1 SC in each of the next 14 SC, 2 SC in next SC, 1 SC in each of the next 4 SC, 2 SC in next SC, 1 SC in each of the next 14 SC, 2 SC in next SC, 1 SC in each SC to finish round (46 SC total).

9. Round 8: 1 SC in each of the next 4 SC, * 2 SC in next SC, 1 SC in each of the next 14 SC, 2 SC in next SC *, 1 SC in each of the next 6 SC, rep from * to *, 1 SC in each SC to finish round (50 SC total).

10. Round 9: 1 SC in each SC across round.

11. Rounds 10–21: Rep round 9.

⑫ Round 22: 1 SC in each of the next 4 SC, * SC2TOG over next 2 SC, 1 SC in each of the next 14 SC, SC2TOG over next 2 SC *, 1 SC in each of the next 6 SC, rep from * to *, 1 SC in each SC to finish round (46 SC total).

⑬ Round 23: 1 SC in each of the next 3 SC, * SC2TOG over next 2 SC, 1 SC in each of the next 146 SC, SC2TOG over next 2 SC *, 1 SC in each of the next 4 SC, rep from * to *, 1 SC in each SC to finish round (42 SC total).

⑭ Round 24: * SC2TOG over next 2 SC, 1 SC in each of the next 4 SC, rep from * across the round. (34 SC total).

⑮ Round 25: * SC2TOG over next 2 SC, 1 SC in each of the next 3 SC, rep from * across the round (28 SC total).

⑯ Add stuffing.

⑰ Round 26: * SC2TOG over next 2 SC, 1 SC in each of the next 2 SC, rep from * across the round (21 SC total).

⑱ Round 27: * SC2TOG over next 2 SC, 1 SC in next SC, rep from * across the round (14 SC total).

⑲ Round 28: * SC2TOG over next 2 SC, rep from * across the round (7 SC total).

⑳ Fasten off.

㉑ Lace the tail through the last round and draw closed.

MAKE THE EARS

1. Start with an adjustable ring.

2. Row 1: Work 3 SC into the ring, ch 1 and turn. Pull the ring tight.

3. Row 2: 2 SC in the 1st SC, 1 SC in the next SC, 2 SC in the last SC, ch 1 and turn (5 SC total).

4. Row 3–8: 1 SC in each SC across the row, ch 1 and turn.

5. Row 9: Skip the 1st SC, 1 SC in next 3 SC skip the last SC, ch 1 and turn (3 SC total).

6. Row 10: SC3TOG.

7. Edging: Work 1 Sl st into the side of each row, 1 Sl st across the first row, 1 Sl st into the side of each row, Sl st to join at the top of the leaf, fasten off and weave in the top tail. Leave the bottom tail to fasten the ear to the body.

8. Repeat Steps 1–7 to make a second ear.

TIP

You can change the ear's width by adding more stitches in a row. To make a longer ear, work more rows. The ears in the example shown are two different lengths.

MAKE A TAIL

1. Start with an adjustable ring.

2. Round 1: Work 6 SC into the ring.

3. Round 2: 2 SC in each SC across round (12 SC total).

4. Round 3: * 2 SC in next SC, 1 SC in next SC, rep from * across round (18 SC total).

5. Round 4: * 2 SC in next SC, 1 SC in each of the next 2 SC, rep from * across round (24 SC total).

6. Round 5: * 2 SC in next SC, 1 SC in each of the next 3 SC, rep from * across round (30 SC total).

7. Round 6: 1 SC in each SC across round.

8. Round 7: * SC2TOG over next 2 SC, 1 SC in each of the next 3 SC, rep from * across the round (24 SC total).

9. Round 8: * SC2TOG over next 2 SC, 1 SC in each of the next 2 SC, rep from * across the round (18 SC total).

10. Round 9: * SC2TOG over next 2 SC, 1 SC in next SC, rep from * across the round (12 SC total).

11. Add stuffing to the ball.

12. Round 10: * SC2TOG over next 2 SC, rep from * across the round (6 SC total).

13. Fasten off.

14. Lace the tail through the last round and draw closed. Use the yarn tail to sew the tail to the back of the bunny's body.

FINISHING

This is where you give your bunny a personality. There are a variety of ways to make a face. For this example some pink scrap yarn was "embroidered" into the stitches.

Consider using the tail pattern to create arms and legs.

Index